THE WIDE HORIZONS READERS

CURRICULUM FOUNDATION SERIES

REG. U.S. PAT. OFF.

WIDE HORIZONS

BOOK 5

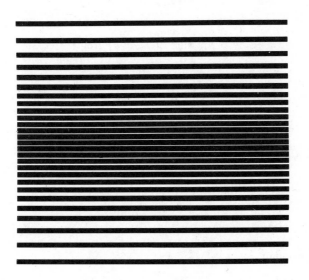

Helen M. Robinson
Marion Monroe
A. Sterl Artley
Charlotte S. Huck
William A. Jenkins
Ira E. Aaron

Scott, Foresman and Company

Acknowledgments

My Side of the Mountain
From the book *My Side of the Mountain,*
written and illustrated by Jean George.
Copyright © 1959 by Jean George.
Reprinted by permission of E. P. Dutton & Co., Inc.,
New York, and The Bodley Head, Ltd., London.

Mr. Mysterious & Company
From *Mr. Mysterious & Company* by Sid Fleischman.
Copyright © 1962 by Albert S. Fleischman.
Reprinted, with slight alterations, by permission of
Little, Brown and Co.—Atlantic Monthly Press, and
Willis Kingsley Wing Hutchinson & Company, Ltd.

The Wild Heart
From *The Wild Heart* by Helen Griffiths.
Copyright © 1963 by Helen Griffiths.
Reprinted by permission of Doubleday & Company, Inc.,
New York, and Hutchinson and Company (Publishers) Ltd.,
London.

Thomas Jefferson, His Many Talents
From Chapters One and Two of
Thomas Jefferson, His Many Talents
by Johanna Johnston. Illustrations by Richard Bergere.
Copyright © 1961 by Johanna Johnston.
Reprinted by permission of Dodd, Mead & Company, Inc.

Hakon of Rogen's Saga
From *Hakon of Rogen's Saga* by Erik Christian Haugaard.
Copyright © 1963 by Erik Christian Haugaard.
Illustrations by Leo and Diane Dillon.
Text and illustrations reprinted by permission of
the publishers, Houghton Mifflin Company.

Photograph
Jean George, page 14, by permission of Elan Young.

Preface

> Horizon, reach out!
> Catch at my hands, stretch me taut,
> Rim of the world:
> Widen my eyes by a thought.

These four lines from the poem "Measure Me, Sky," by Leonora Speyer, can be applied fittingly to The Wide Horizons Readers and expressed, very simply, in this way: *Wide Horizons,* make me use my mind to the best of my ability; broaden my interests, experiences, and outlooks to their very limits.

Wide Horizons, Book Five, has been given to you to read because you are one of those good readers who complete Basic Reading lessons quickly and capably and then seek to extend your reading horizons still further.

The selections in *Wide Horizons,* Book Five, are therefore more difficult than those in *Vistas,* but you will find within its covers everything you need to read and enjoy them by yourself. Each selection has the same theme as one of the groups of selections in *Vistas,* and the illustrations are from the original book. With each selection in *Wide Horizons,* Book Five, you will find material to add to your reading enjoyment. A photograph and a few interesting bits of information will introduce you to the author. There are questions and exercises to help you understand and appreciate the story. Poetry related to the material you have read comes next. Last, and perhaps best of all, is a list of briefly reviewed books for you to enjoy at your leisure.

You will not find a selection to accompany *The Helen Keller Story* in *Vistas*. While reading this biography, your extra time may be spent enjoying some of those books in the "More Books to Read" section mentioned above. It is hoped that you will keep a record of those books in a special notebook which you might label "My Wide Horizons Notebook." Other entries that you will want to make throughout the year will be the material you are asked to write about the books, your own ideas about the selections, and any other notes or related ideas that you would like to include.

Contents

Mr. Mysterious & Company
by SID FLEISCHMAN

The Wild Heart
by HELEN GRIFFITHS

Thomas Jefferson, His Many Talents
by JOHANNA JOHNSTON

Hakon of Rogen's Saga
by ERIK CHRISTIAN HAUGAARD

Up Periscopes!

Men aboard a submarine use its periscope to view the world above and around them. *Wide Horizons,* Book Five, can be that kind of an instrument for you. As you focus your attention on each selection in the book, you will find yourself taking a new look at the world above, around, and beyond you in time and space.

The Catskill Mountains in New York are the first sight to strike your lens. As you struggle with Sam Gribley to master the environment in which he chose to live for one year, you may find yourself saying, "I wouldn't have done that." But you cannot fail to be honestly awed and impressed by his determination and ingenuity. Through his account entitled *My Side of the Mountain,* you can experience with him the anxieties and delights that he came to know in his year of living entirely off the land. This selection is to be read as you get into *Vistas,* your Basic Reader, which opens with a group of stories about "thresholds"—beginnings, or points of entrance into new lives, new worlds, or new experiences. In *Wide Horizons,* the "threshold" is the new world Sam Gribley found and made for himself in the woods. *My Side of the Mountain* was written and illustrated by Jean George. It was a runner-up for the John Newbery Medal in 1960.

Periscopes west! Train them on a covered wagon, with a red canvas top and gold wheels, drawn by horses white as swans. Notice also the foot-high letters painted on the sides of the wagon that spell Mr. Mysterious &

Company. These words refer to Mr. Andrew Perkins Hackett, a traveling magician, and his family. As you follow the Hacketts from Texas to California, you will be entertained as all their audiences were with their feats of magic, skill, and legerdemain. But even more, Sid Fleischman, the author, also invites you to join the Hacketts between the acts—in all of the hilarious episodes that such a family of traveling magicians can conjure up as it heads west in 1884.

Shift your sights southward to Argentina. Into the view of your lens will come the vast treeless plains of South America called the pampas and a wild pony that gauchos have named La Bruja—The Witch. The story of her life is not a happy one, and the author, Helen Griffiths, has written realistically, in a manner that reaches out and draws each reader into the story.

Reading the first half of *The Wild Heart* will give you a clearer understanding of both human and animal life on these plains. It is a battle cry for freedom-loving creatures everywhere.

Twirl your lens to bring into view another time, and focus on a man. After reading the biography of Benjamin Franklin in *Wide Horizons*, Book Four, perhaps you decided that this man was our country's most gifted leader. Many, however, believe this honor belongs to Thomas Jefferson. At a dinner honoring all living Nobel Prize winners in the Western Hemisphere, the late President John F. Kennedy said, "I want to tell you how welcome you are to the White House. I think this is the most extraordinary collection of talent, of human knowledge,

10

Reprinted from *The Quotable Mr. Kennedy.* Edited by Gerald Gardner. By permission of Abelard-Schuman Ltd. All Rights Reserved. Copyright © 1962.

that has ever been gathered together at the White House, with the possible exception of when Thomas Jefferson dined alone." In the introduction of her book *Thomas Jefferson, His Many Talents,* Johanna Johnston refers to Thomas Jefferson as "one of the most versatile geniuses who ever lived." As young people growing up in the complex world of the twentieth century, you, too, can appreciate his genius. Moreover, you can identify with this man who always asked *why,* for countless occurrences in your own lives prompt you to pose the same question.

Jefferson's talents are not all explored in the section of the book used in *Wide Horizons.* To complete your picture of this great man, you will want to read all of Miss Johnston's book, as well as the series of books by Leonard Wibberly recommended in "More Books to Read" on page 419.

Your last view from your *Wide Horizons* periscope will be furthest away in time and space. *Hakon of Rogen's Saga,* by Erik Haugaard, takes you to an island in northern Norway at a time before the discovery of the New World. A saga is a tale or legend of heroic deeds. Sagas were first handed down through the centuries by word of mouth. Later, literary men saw the value of these tales and began to write them down.

Haugaard's exciting drama truly carries out the theme of "Kaleidoscope" in *Vistas.* Just as a design is formed by the bits of broken glass in a kaleidoscope, this story of men and gods has been skillfully shaped from fragments preserved by word of mouth, and facts gleaned from archaeological excavations. Although you "see"

Rogen through the eyes of a twentieth-century author, the view in your mind's eye extends far back into time, and far away into the wild North.

In the *Thorndike-Barnhart Dictionary* the definition of a poem reads: a composition in verse; an arrangement of words in lines with a regularly repeated accent; a composition showing great beauty of language or thought. In her verse entitled "Inside a Poem," Eve Merriam says:

It doesn't always have to rhyme,
but there's the repeat of a beat, somewhere
an inner chime that makes you want to
tap your feet or swerve in a curve;
a lilt, a leap, a lightning-split:—
thunderstruck the consonants jut,
while the vowels open wide as waves in the
    noon-blue sea.

You hear with your heels, your eyes feel
what they never touched before:
fins on a bird, feathers on a deer;
taste all colors, inhale
memory and tomorrow and always the tang is
    today.

Whether your appreciation of a poem stems from the perfection of its form, rhyme, or rhythm, or from the way it makes you feel, see, and hear things you have never felt, seen, or heard before, the poetry in *Wide Horizons* invites your response.

12

"Inside a Poem" from *It Doesn't Always Have to Rhyme* by Eve Merriam. Copyright © 1964 by Eve Merriam. By permission of Atheneum House, Inc.

For those of you who enjoy narrative poetry, "Robinson Crusoe's Story" follows *My Side of the Mountain.* If you enjoy the atmosphere of magic found throughout *Mr. Mysterious & Company*, you will enjoy the two poems that accompany it. They carry out this theme of magic and are entitled "Prologue for a Magician" and "Mr. Mistoffelees."

Images of La Bruja at different times in her life will be called forth as you read the poems that follow *The Wild Heart.* The sources of these poems are as varied as the horses that inspired the poets.

In the six lines entitled "Daily Life," Walt Whitman identifies those things in life that he held to be of greatest value. As you read the biography of Jefferson, consider why this poem was chosen to accompany it.

Some of the oldest poems ever written follow *Hakon of Rogen's Saga.* Taken from a collection of poetry called the *Elder Edda,* they date back almost one thousand years.

The brief notations that precede many of the poems will help you relate them to the books they accompany. If these poems lead you to seek out others that you enjoy, you may want to begin your own collection of favorites in a special poetry section of your notebook.

Jean George explains that *My Side of the Mountain* had its roots in her early life. As she writes: "When I was a child, my naturalist father took my brothers and me to the islands of the Potomac River and taught us how to make lunch and supper off the land. We often had turtle soup or cattail tubers, or he would bring us a dogtooth-violet bulb to try. It gave me a great sense of independence to think that I could live with nothing more than a penknife and fire."

Years later, with the help of college courses in writing and art, zoology, botany, and geology, Mrs. George helped her doctor-brothers prepare a survival manual for Navy pilots downed in the wilderness. She ate food her brothers brought in, slept in the lean-tos they constructed, and did illustrations for them.

In the years that followed, a story kept growing in her mind of a modern boy who could survive off the land. *My Side of the Mountain*, a runner-up for the Newbery Medal in 1960, is that story. Careful research made it a story that could have happened and might still happen. It is being made into a motion picture.

Mrs. George now lives in Chappaqua, New York, with her three children, Twig, Craig, and Luke.

MY SIDE OF THE MOUNTAIN

by Jean George

Illustrated by the author

Far back in the mind of many of us, and especially of boys, is a longing to live off the land as our forefathers did, to make a life with our own hands. *My Side of the Mountain* is the story of such an adventure. In this book the author has the main character, Sam Gribley, tell in his own words what he did, ate, observed, made, and felt in the months that he learned to survive alone on the land.

In the first section titled "In Which I Hole Up in a Snowstorm," Mrs. George has chosen an unusual way to introduce Sam Gribley. After meeting him you will be led to read on by a curiosity and a kind of admiration for this boy you hardly know.

MY SIDE OF
THE MOUNTAIN

Written and Illustrated by
JEAN GEORGE

E. P. DUTTON & COMPANY, INC.
New York

This book is dedicated to many people—

*to that gang of youngsters who
inhabited the trees and waters of
the Potomac River so many years
ago, and to the bit of Sam Gribley
in the children and adults around
me now.*

Contents

Gorge

tree

Mountain meadow

Gribley Beech

ol' apple tree

house site

walnut tree

cattail supply

My Side of the Mountain
signed S. Gribley

IN WHICH *I Hole Up in a Snowstorm*

I am on my mountain in a tree home that people have passed without ever knowing that I am here. The house is a hemlock tree six feet in diameter, and must be as old as the mountain itself. I came upon it last summer and dug and burned it out until I made a snug cave in the tree that I now call home.

My bed is on the right as you enter and is made of ash slats and covered with deerskin. On the left is a small fireplace about knee-high. It is of clay and stones. It has a chimney that leads the smoke out through a knothole. I chipped out three other knotholes to let fresh air in. The air coming in is bitter cold. It must be below zero outside, and yet I can sit here inside my tree and write with bare hands. The fire is small, too. It doesn't take much fire to warm this tree room.

It is the fourth of December, I think. It may be the fifth. I am not sure because I have not recently counted the notches in the aspen pole that is my calendar. I have been just too busy gathering nuts and berries, smoking venison, fish, and small game to keep up with the exact date.

The lamp I am writing by is deer fat poured into a turtle shell, with a strip of my old city trousers for a wick.

It snowed all day yesterday and today. I have not been outside since the storm began, and I am bored for the first time since I ran away from home eight months ago to live on the land.

I am well and healthy. The food is good. Sometimes I eat turtle soup, and I know how to make acorn pancakes. I keep my supplies in the wall of the tree in wooden pockets that I chopped myself.

Every time I have looked at those pockets during the last two days, I have felt just like a squirrel, which reminds me: I didn't see a squirrel one whole day before that storm began. I guess they are holed up and eating their stored nuts, too.

I wonder if The Baron—that's the wild weasel who lives behind the big boulder to the north of my tree—is also denned up. Well, anyway, I think the storm is dying down because the tree is not crying so much. When the wind really blows, the whole tree moans right down to the roots, which is where I am.

Tomorrow I hope The Baron and I can tunnel out into the sunlight. I wonder if I should dig the snow. But that would mean I would have to put it somewhere, and the only place to put it is in my nice, snug tree. Maybe I can pack it with my hands as I go. I've always dug into the snow from the top, never up from under.

The Baron must dig up from under the snow. I wonder where he puts what he digs. Well, I guess I'll know in the morning.

When I wrote that last winter, I was scared and thought maybe I'd never get out of my tree. I had been scared for two days—ever since the first blizzard hit the Catskill Mountains. When I came up to the sunlight, which I did by simply poking my head into the soft snow and standing up, I laughed at my dark fears.

Everything was white, clean, shining, and beautiful. The sky was blue, blue, blue. The hemlock grove was laced with snow, the meadow was smooth and white, and the gorge was sparkling with ice. It was so beautiful and peaceful that I laughed out loud. I guess I laughed because my first snowstorm was over and it had not been so terrible after all.

Then I shouted, "I did it!" My voice never got very far. It was hushed by the tons of snow.

I looked for signs from The Baron Weasel. His footsteps were all over the boulder, also slides where he had played. He must have been up for hours enjoying the new snow.

Inspired by his fun, I poked my head into my tree and whistled. Frightful, my trained falcon, flew to my fist, and we jumped and slid down the mountain, mak-

ing big holes and trenches as we went. It was good to
be whistling and carefree again, because I was sure
scared by the coming of that storm.

I had been working since May, learning how to make
a fire with flint and steel, finding what plants I could
eat, how to trap animals and catch fish—all this so

that when the curtain of blizzard struck the Catskills, I could crawl inside my tree and be comfortably warm and have plenty to eat.

During the summer and fall I had thought about the coming of winter. However, on that third day of December, when the sky blackened, the temperature dropped, and the first flakes swirled around me, I must admit that I wanted to run back to New York. Even the first night that I spent out in the woods, when I couldn't get the fire started, was not as frightening as the snowstorm that gathered behind the gorge and mushroomed up over my mountain.

I was smoking three trout. It was nine o'clock in the morning. I was busy keeping the flames low so they would not leap up and burn the fish. As I worked, it occurred to me that it was awfully dark for that hour of the morning. Frightful was leashed to her tree stub. She seemed restless and pulled at her tethers. Then I realized that the forest was dead quiet. Even the woodpeckers that had been tapping around me all morning were silent. The squirrels were nowhere to be seen. The juncos and chickadees and nuthatches were gone. I looked to see what The Baron Weasel was doing. He was not around. I looked up.

From my tree you can see the gorge beyond the meadow. White water pours between the black, wet boulders and cascades into the valley below. The water that day was as dark as the rocks. Only the sound told me it was still falling. Above the darkness stood another darkness. The clouds of winter, black and fearsome. They looked as wild as the winds that were bringing them. I grew sick with fright. I knew I had enough food. I knew everything was going to be perfectly all right. But knowing that didn't help. I was scared. I stamped out the fire and pocketed the fish.

I tried to whistle for Frightful but couldn't purse my shaking lips tight enough to get out anything but *pfffff*. So I grabbed her by the hide straps that are attached to her legs, and we dove through the deerskin door into my room in the tree.

I put Frightful on the bedpost and curled up in a ball on the bed. I thought about New York and the noise and the lights and how a snowstorm always seemed very friendly there. I thought about our apartment, too. At that moment it seemed bright and lighted and warm. I had to keep saying to myself: There were eleven of us in it! Dad, Mother, four sisters, four brothers, and me. And not one of us liked it except, perhaps, little Nina, who was too young to know. Dad didn't like it even a little bit. He had been a sailor once, but when I was born, he gave up the sea and worked on the docks in New York. Dad didn't like the land. He liked the sea, wet and big and endless.

Sometimes he would tell me about Great-grandfather Gribley, who owned land in the Catskill Mountains and felled the trees and built a home and plowed the land —only to discover that he wanted to be a sailor. The farm failed, and Great-grandfather Gribley went to sea.

As I lay with my face buried in the sweet, greasy smell of my deerskin, I could hear Dad's voice saying,

"That land is still in the family's name. Somewhere in the Catskills is an old beech with the name *Gribley* carved on it. It marks the northern boundary of Gribley's folly—the land is no place for a Gribley."

"The land is no place for a Gribley," I said. "The land is no place for a Gribley, and here I am, three hundred feet from the beech with *Gribley* carved on it."

I fell asleep at that point, and when I awoke, I was hungry. I cracked some walnuts, got down the acorn flour I had pounded, with a bit of ash to remove the bite, reached out the door for a little snow, and stirred up some acorn pancakes. I cooked them on a top of a tin can, and as I ate them, smothered with blueberry jam, I knew that the land was just the place for a Gribley.

IN WHICH *I Get Started on This Venture*

I left New York in May. I had a penknife, a ball of cord, an ax, and $40, which I had saved from selling magazine subscriptions. I also had some flint and steel, which I had bought at a Chinese store in the city. The man in the store had showed me how to use it. He had also given me a little purse to put it in, and some tinder to catch the sparks. He had told me that if I ran out of tinder, I should burn cloth and use the charred ashes.

I thanked him and said, "This is the kind of thing I am not going to forget."

On the train north to the Catskills I unwrapped my flint and steel and practiced hitting them together to make sparks. On the wrapping paper I made these notes:

A hard, brisk strike is best. Remember to hold the steel in the left hand and the flint in the right, and hit the steel with the flint.

The trouble is, the sparks go every which way.

And that *was* the trouble. I did not get a fire going that night, and, as I said, it was a scary experience.

I hitched rides into the Catskill Mountains. At about four o'clock a truck driver and I passed through a beautiful dark hemlock forest, and I said to him, "This is as far as I am going."

He looked all around and said, "You live here?"

"No," I said, "but I am running away from home, and this is just the kind of forest I have always dreamed I would run to. I think I'll camp here tonight." I hopped out of the cab.

"Hey, boy," the driver shouted. "Are you serious?"

"Sure," I said.

"Well, now, ain't that sumpin'? You know, when I was your age, I did the same thing. Only thing was, I was a farm boy and ran to the city, and you're a city boy running to the woods. I was scared of the city— do you think you'll be scared of the woods?"

"Heck, no!" I shouted loudly.

As I marched into the cool, shadowy woods, I heard the driver call to me, "I'll be back in the morning, if you want to ride home."

He laughed. Everybody laughed at me. When I had told Dad that I was going to run away to Great-grandfather Gribley's land, he had roared with laughter and told me about the time he had run away from home. He got on a boat headed for Singapore, but when the whistle blew for departure, he was down the gangplank and home in bed before anyone knew he was gone. Then he told me, "Sure, go try it. Every boy should try it."

I must have walked a mile into the woods until I found a stream. It was a clear, athletic stream that rushed and ran and jumped and splashed. Ferns grew along its bank, and its rocks were upholstered with moss.

I sat down, smelled the piney air, and took out my pen-knife. I cut off a green twig and began to whittle. I have always been good at whittling. I carved a ship once that my teacher exhibited for parents' night at school.

First I whittled an angle on one end of the twig. Then I cut a smaller twig and sharpened it to a point. I whittled an angle on that twig, and bound the two angles face to face with a strip of green bark. It was supposed to be a fishhook.

According to a book on how to survive on the land that I read in the New York Public Library, this was the way to make your own hooks. I then dug for worms. I had hardly chopped the moss away with my ax before I hit frost. It had not occurred to me that there would be frost in the ground in May, but then, I had not been on a mountain before.

This did worry me, because I was depending on fish to keep me alive until I got to my great-grand-father's mountain, where I was going to make traps and catch game.

wooden fish hook

sharpen

whittle angles

string

I looked into the stream to see what else I could eat, and as I did, my hand knocked a rotten log apart. I remembered about old logs and all the sleeping insects that are in them. I chopped until I found a white grub.

I swiftly tied a string to my hook, put the grub on, and walked up the stream looking for a good place to fish. All the manuals I had read were very emphatic about where fish lived, and so I had memorized this:

In streams, fish usually congregate in pools and deep, calm water. The heads of riffles, small rapids, the tail of a pool, eddies below rocks or logs, deep, undercut banks, in the shade of overhanging bushes—all are very likely places to fish.

This stream did not seem to have any calm water, and I must have walked a thousand miles before I found a pool by a deep, undercut bank in the shade of overhanging bushes. Actually, it wasn't that far; it just seemed that way because as I went looking and finding nothing, I was sure I was going to starve to death.

I squatted on this bank and dropped in my line. I did so want to catch a fish. One fish would set me upon my way, because I had read how much you can learn from one fish. By examining the contents of its stomach, you can find what the other fish are eating, or you can use the internal organs as bait.

The grub went down to the bottom of the stream. It swirled around and hung still. Suddenly the string came to life, and rode back and forth and around in a circle. I pulled with a powerful jerk. The hook came apart, and whatever I had went circling back to its bed.

Well, that almost made me cry. My bait was gone, my hook was broken, and I was getting cold, frightened, and mad. I whittled another hook, but this time I cheated and used string to wind it together instead of bark. I walked back to the log and luckily found another grub. I hurried to the pool, and I flipped a trout out of the water before I knew I had a bite.

The fish flopped, and I threw my whole body over it. I could not bear to think of it flopping itself back into the stream.

I cleaned it as I had seen the man at the fish market do, examined its stomach, and found it empty. This horrified me. What I didn't know was that an empty stomach means the fish are hungry and will eat about anything. However, I thought at the time that I was a goner. Sadly I put some of the internal organs on my hook, and before I could get my line to the bottom, I had another bite. I lost that one but got the next one. I stopped when I had five nice little trout and looked around for a place to build a camp and make a fire.

It wasn't hard to find a pretty spot along that stream. I selected a place beside a mossy rock in a circle of hemlocks.

I decided to make a bed before I cooked. I cut off some boughs for a mattress and then leaned some dead limbs against the boulder and covered them with hemlock limbs. This made a kind of tent. I crawled in, lay down, and felt alone and secret and very excited.

But, ah, the rest of this story! I was on the northeast side of the mountain. It grew dark and cold early. Seeing the shadows slide down on me, I frantically ran around gathering firewood. This is about the only thing I did right from that moment until dawn, because I remembered that the driest wood in a forest is the dead limbs that are still on the trees, and I gathered an enormous pile of them. That pile must still be there, for I never got a fire going.

I got sparks, sparks, sparks. I even hit the tinder with the sparks. The tinder burned all right, but that was as far as I got. I blew on it, I breathed on it, I cupped it in my hands, but no sooner did I add twigs than the whole thing went black.

Then it got too dark to see. I clicked steel and flint together, even though I couldn't see the tinder. Finally I gave up and crawled into my hemlock tent, hungry, cold, and miserable.

I can talk about that first night now, although it is still embarrassing to me, because I was so stupid and scared that I hate to admit it.

I had made my hemlock bed right in the stream valley, where the wind drained down from the cold mountaintop. It might have been all right if I had made

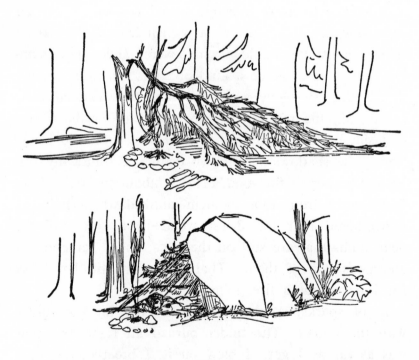

a couple of good shelters - make sure your fire is on scraped earth also be sure to put it out!

it on the other side of the boulder, but I didn't. I was right on the main highway of the cold winds as they tore down upon the valley below. I didn't have enough hemlock boughs under me, and before I had my head down, my stomach was cold and damp. I took some boughs off the roof and stuffed them under me, and then my shoulders were cold. I curled up in a ball and was almost asleep when a whippoorwill called. If you have ever been within forty feet of a whippoorwill, you will understand why I couldn't even shut my eyes. Its noise is deafening!

Well, anyway, the whole night went like that. I don't think I slept fifteen minutes, and I was so scared and tired that my throat was dry. I wanted a drink but didn't dare go near the stream for fear of making a misstep and falling in and getting wet. So I sat tight and shivered and shook, and—now I am able to say —I cried a little tiny bit.

Fortunately the sun has a wonderfully glorious habit of rising every morning. When the sky lightened, when the birds awoke, I knew I would never again see anything so splendid as the round red sun coming up over the earth.

I was immediately cheered and set out directly for the highway. Somehow I thought that if I was a little nearer the road, everything would be all right.

I climbed a hill and stopped. There was a house. A house warm and cozy, with smoke coming out the chimney and lights in the windows, and only a hundred feet from my torture camp.

Without considering my pride, I ran down the hill and banged on the door. A nice old man answered. I told him everything in one long sentence and then said, "And so, can I cook my fish here, because I haven't eaten in years."

He chuckled, stroked his whiskery face, and took the fish. He had them cooking in a pan before I knew what his name was.

When I asked him, he said Bill something, but I never heard his last name because I fell asleep in his rocking chair that was pulled up beside his big, hot, glorious wood stove in the kitchen.

I ate the fish some hours later, also some bread, jelly, oatmeal, and cream. Then he said to me, "Sam Gribley, if you are going to run off and live in the woods, you better learn how to make a fire. Come with me."

We spent the afternoon practicing. I penciled these notes on the back of a scrap of paper, so I wouldn't forget.

When the tinder glows, keep blowing and add fine, dry needles one by one—and keep blowing steadily, lightly, and evenly. Add one-inch dry twigs to the needles and then give her a big handful of small dry stuff. Keep blowing.

THE MANNER IN WHICH *I Find Gribley's Farm*

The next day I told Bill good-by, and as I strode, warm and fed, onto the road, he called to me, "I'll see you tonight. The back door will be open, if you want a roof over your head."

I said, "Okay," but I knew I wouldn't see Bill again. I knew how to make fire, and that was my weapon. With fire I could conquer the Catskills. I also knew how to fish. To fish and to make a fire. That was all I needed to know, I thought.

Three rides that morning took me to Delhi. Somewhere around here was Great-grandfather's beech tree with the name *Gribley* carved on it. This much I knew from Dad's stories.

By six o'clock I still had not found anyone who had even heard of the Gribleys, much less Gribley's beech, and so I slept on the porch of a schoolhouse and ate chocolate bars for supper. It was cold and hard, but I was so tired I could have slept in a wind tunnel.

At dawn I thought real hard: Where would I find out about the Gribley farm? Some old map. Where would I find an old map? The library? Maybe. I'd try it and see.

The librarian was very helpful. She was sort of young, had brown hair and brown eyes, and loved books as much as I did.

The library didn't open until ten-thirty. I got there at nine. After I had lolled and rolled and sat on the steps for fifteen or twenty minutes, the door whisked open, and this tall lady asked me to come on in.

All I said to her was that I wanted to find the old Gribley farm and that the Gribleys hadn't lived on it for maybe a hundred years, and she was off. I can still hear her heels click when I think of her scattering herself around those shelves finding me old maps, histories of the Catskills, and files of letters and deeds that must have come from attics around Delhi.

Miss Turner—that was her name—found it. She found Gribley's farm in an old book of Delaware County. Then she worked out the roads to it and drew me maps and everything. Finally she said, "What do you want to know for? Some school project?"

"Oh, no, Miss Turner, I want to go live there."

"But, Sam, it is all forest and trees now. The house is probably only a foundation covered with moss."

"That's just what I want. I am going to trap animals and eat nuts and bulbs and berries and make myself a house. You see, I am Sam Gribley, and I thought I would like to live on my great-grandfather's farm."

Miss Turner was the only person that believed me. She smiled, sat back in her chair, and said, "Well, I declare."

The library was just opening when I gathered the notes we had made and started off. As I pushed open the door, Miss Turner leaned over and said to me, "Sam, we have some very good books on plants and trees and animals, in case you get stuck."

I knew what she was thinking, and so I told her I would remember that.

With Miss Turner's map, I found the first stone wall that marked the farm. The old roads to it were all grown up and mostly gone, but by locating the stream at the bottom of the mountain, I was able to begin at the bridge and go north and up a mile and a half. There, caterpillaring around boulders, roller-coastering up ravines and down hills, was the mound of rocks that had once been Great-grandfather's boundary fence.

And then, do you know, I couldn't believe I was there. I sat on the old gray stones a long time, looking through the forest, up that steep mountain, and saying to myself, "It must be Sunday afternoon, and it's raining, and Dad is trying to keep us all quiet by telling us about Great-grandfather's farm, and he's telling it so real that I can see it."

And then I said, "No. I am here, because I was never this hungry before."

I wanted to run all the way back to the library and tell Miss Turner that I had found it. Partly because she would have liked to know and partly because Dad had said to me as I was leaving, "If you find the place, tell someone at Delhi. I may visit you someday." Of course he was kidding, because he thought I'd be home the next day, but after many weeks maybe he would think I meant what I said, and he might come see me.

However, I was too hungry to run back. I took my hook and line and went back down the mountain to the stream.

I caught a big old catfish. I climbed back to the stone wall in great spirits.

It was getting late, and so I didn't try to explore. I went right to work making a fire. I decided that even if I didn't have enough time to cut boughs for a bed, I was going to have cooked fish and a fire to huddle around during those cold night hours. May is not exactly warm in the Catskills.

By firelight that night I wrote this:

Dear Bill [that was the old man]:

After three tries I finally got a handful of dry grass on the glow in the tinder. Grass is even better than pine needles, and tomorrow I am going to try the outside bark of the river birch. I read somewhere that it has combustible oil in it that the Indians used to start fires. Anyway, I did just what you showed me and had cooked catfish for dinner. It was good.

Your friend,

Sam.

After I wrote that, I remembered I didn't know his last name, and so I stuffed the note in my pocket, made myself a bed of boughs and leaves in the shelter of the stone wall, and fell right to sleep.

I must say this now about that first fire. It was magic. Out of dead tinder and grass and sticks came a live, warm light. It cracked and snapped and smoked and filled the woods with brightness. It lighted the trees and made them warm and friendly. It stood tall and bright and held back the night. Oh, this was a different night from the first dark, frightful one. Also, I was stuffed on catfish. I have since learned to cook it more, but never have I enjoyed a meal as much as that one, and never have I felt so independent again.

IN WHICH *I Find Many Useful Plants*

The following morning I stood up, stretched, and looked about me. Birds, little birds, were singing and flying and pouring over the limbs of the trees.

"This must be the warbler migration," I said, and I laughed because there were so many birds. I had never seen so many. My big voice rolled through the woods, and their little voices seemed to rise and answer me.

They were eating. Three or four in a maple tree near me were darting along the limbs, pecking and snatching at something delicious on the trees. I wondered if there was anything there for a hungry boy. I pulled a limb down, and all I saw were leaves, twigs, and flowers. I ate a flower. It was not very good. One manual I had read said to watch what the birds and animals were eating in order to learn what is edible and nonedible in the forest. If the animal life can eat it, it is safe for humans. The book did suggest that a raccoon had tastes more nearly like ours. Certainly the birds were no example.

Then I wondered if they were not eating something I couldn't see—tiny insects, perhaps; well, anyway, whatever it was, I decided to fish. I took my line and hook and walked down to the stream.

I lay on a log and dangled my line in the bright water. The fish were not biting. That made me hungrier. My stomach pinched. You know, it really does hurt to be terribly hungry.

A stream is supposed to be full of food. It is the easiest place to get a lot of food in a hurry. I needed something in a hurry, but what? I looked through the clear water and saw the tracks of mussels in the mud. I ran along the log back to shore, took off my clothes, and plunged into that icy water.

I collected almost a peck of mussels in very little time at all, and began tying them in my sweater to carry them back to camp.

"But I don't have to carry them anywhere," I said to myself. "I have my fire in my pocket; I don't need a table. I can sit right here by the stream and eat." And so I did. I wrapped the mussels in leaves and sort of steamed them in coals. They are not quite as good as clams—a little stronger, I would say—but by the time I had eaten three, I had forgotten what clams tasted like and knew only how delicious fresh-water mussels were. I actually got full.

I wandered back to Great-grandfather's farm and began to explore. Most of the acreage was maple and beech, some pine, dogwoods, ash, and here and there a glorious hickory. I made a sketch of the farm on my road map, and put *x*'s where the hickories were. They were gold trees to me. I would have hickory nuts in the fall. I could also make salt from hickory limbs. I cut off one and chopped it into bits and scraps. I stuck them in my sweater.

The land was up and down and up and down, and I wondered how Great-grandfather ever cut it and plowed it. There was one stream running through it, which I was glad to see, for it meant I did not have to go all the way down the mountain to the big creek for fish and water.

Around noon I came upon what I was sure was the old foundation of the house. Miss Turner was right. It was ruins—a few stones in a square, a slight depression for the basement, and trees growing right up through what had once been the living room. I wandered around to see what was left of the Gribley home.

After a few looks I saw an apple tree. I rushed up to it, hoping to find an old apple. No apples beneath it. About forty feet away, however, I found a dried one in the crotch of a tree, stuck there by a squirrel and forgotten. I ate it. It was pretty bad—but nourishing, I hoped. There was another apple tree and three walnuts. I scribbled *x*'s. These were wonderful finds.

I poked around the foundations, hoping to uncover some old iron implements that I could use. I found nothing. Too many leaves had fallen and turned to loam; too many plants had grown up and died down over the old homesite. I decided to come back when I had made myself a shovel.

Whistling and looking for food and shelter, I went on up the mountain, following the stone walls, discovering many things about my property. I found a marsh. In it were cattails and arrowleaf—good starchy foods.

At high noon I stepped onto a mountain meadow. An enormous boulder rose up in the center of it. At the top of the meadow was a fringe of white birch. There were maples and oaks to the west and a hemlock forest to the right that pulled me right across the sweet grasses into it.

Never, never have I seen such trees. They were giants —old, old giants. They must have begun when the world began.

I started walking around them. I couldn't hear myself step, so dense and damp were the needles. Great boulders covered with ferns and moss stood among them. They looked like pebbles beneath those trees.

Standing before the biggest and the oldest and the most kinglike of them all, I suddenly had an idea.

THIS IS ABOUT *The Old, Old Tree*

I knew enough about the Catskill Mountains to know that when the summer came, they were covered with people. Although Great-grandfather's farm was somewhat remote, still, hikers and campers and hunters and fishermen were sure to wander across it.

Therefore, I wanted a house that could not be seen. People would want to take me back where I belonged if they found me.

I looked at that tree. Somehow I knew it was home, but I was not quite sure how it was home. The limbs were high and not right for a treehouse. I could build a back extension around it, but that would look silly. Slowly I circled the great trunk. Halfway around, the whole plan became perfectly obvious. To the west, between two of the flanges of the tree that spread out to be roots, was a cavity. The heart of the tree was rotting away. I scraped it with my hands; old, rotten, insect-ridden dust came tumbling out. I dug on and on, using my ax from time to time as my excitement grew.

With much of the old rot out, I could crawl in the tree and sit cross-legged. Inside I felt as cozy as a turtle in its shell. I chopped and chopped until I was hungry and exhausted. I was now in the hard, good wood, and chopping it out was work. I was afraid December would come before I got a hole big enough to lie in. So I sat down to think.

You know, those first days I just never planned right. I had the beginnings of a home but not a bite to eat, and I had worked so hard that I could hardly move forward to find that bite. Furthermore, it was discouraging to feed that body of mine. It was never satisfied, and gathering food for it took time and got it hungrier. Trying to get a place to rest it took time and got it more tired, and I felt I was going in circles and wondered how primitive man ever had enough time and energy to stop hunting food and start thinking about fire and tools.

I left the tree and went across the meadow looking for food. I plunged into the woods beyond, and there I discovered the gorge and the white cascade splashing down the black rocks into the pool below.

I was hot and dirty. I scrambled down the rocks and slipped into the pool. It was so cold I yelled. But when I came out on the bank and put on my two pairs of trousers and three sweaters, which I thought was a better way to carry clothes than in a pack, I tingled and burned and felt coltish. I leapt up the bank, slipped, and my face went down in a patch of dogtooth violets.

You would know them anywhere after a few looks at them at the Botanical Gardens and in colored flower books. They are little yellow lilies on long, slender stems with oval leaves dappled with gray. But that's not all. They have wonderfully tasty bulbs. I was filling my pockets before I got up from my fall.

"I'll have a salad-type lunch," I said as I moved up the steep side of the ravine. I discovered that as late as it was in the season, the spring beauties were still blooming in the cool pockets of the woods. They are all right raw—that is, if you are as hungry as I was. They taste a little like lima beans. I ate these as I went on hunting food, feeling better and better, until I worked my way back to the meadow, where the dandelions were blooming. Funny I hadn't noticed them earlier. Their greens are good, and so are their roots —a little strong and milky, but you get used to that.

A crow flew into the aspen grove without saying a word. The little I knew of crows from following them in Central Park, they always have something to say. But this bird was sneaking, obviously trying to be quiet. Birds are good food. Crow is certainly not the best, but I did not know that then, and I launched out to see where it was going. I had a vague plan to try to noose it. This is the kind of thing I wasted time on in those days when time was so important. However, this venture turned out all right because I did not have to noose that bird.

I stepped into the woods, looked around, could not see the crow, but noticed a big stick nest in a scrabbly pine. I started to climb the tree. Off flew the crow. What made me keep on climbing in face of such discouragement I don't know, but I did, and that noon I had crow eggs and wild salad for lunch.

At lunch I also solved the problem of carving out my tree. After a struggle I made a fire. Then I sewed a big skunk-cabbage leaf into a cup with grass strands. I had read that you can boil water in a leaf, and ever since then I had been very anxious to see if this was

good cooking fireplace with leaf bucket

true. It seems impossible, but it works. I boiled the eggs in a leaf. The water keeps the leaf wet, and although the top dries up and burns down to the water level, that's as far as the burning goes. I was pleased to see it work.

Then here's what happened. Naturally, all this took a lot of time, and I hadn't gotten very far on my tree, so I was fretting and stamping out the fire when I stopped with my foot in the air.

The fire! Indians made dugout canoes with fire. They burned them out, an easier and much faster way of getting results. I would try fire in the tree. If I was very careful, perhaps it would work. I ran into the hemlock forest with a burning stick and got a fire going inside the tree.

Thinking that I ought to have a bucket of water in case things got out of hand, I looked desperately around me. The water was far across the meadow and down the ravine. This would never do. I began to think the whole inspiration of a home in the tree was no good.

I really did have to live near water for cooking and drinking and comfort. I looked sadly at the magnificent hemlock and was about to put the fire out and desert it when I said something to myself. It must have come out of some book: "Hemlocks usually grow around mountain streams and springs."

I swirled on my heel. Nothing but boulders around me. But the air was damp. "Somewhere——" I said, and darted around the rocks, peering and looking and sniffing and going down into pockets and dales. No water. I was coming back, circling wide, when I almost fell in it. Two sentinel boulders, dripping wet, decorated with flowers, ferns, moss, weeds—everything that loved water—guarded a bathtub-sized spring.

"You pretty thing," I said, flopped on my stomach, and pushed my face into it to drink. I opened my eyes. The water was like glass, and in it were little insects with oars. They rowed away from me. Beetles skittered like bullets on the surface or carried a silver bubble of air with them to the bottom. Ha, then I saw a crayfish.

I jumped up, overturned rocks, and found many crayfish. At first I hesitated to grab them because they can pinch. I gritted my teeth, thought about how much more it hurts to be hungry, and came down upon them. I did get pinched, but I had my dinner. And that was the first time I had planned ahead! Any planning that I did in those early days was such a surprise to me and so successful that I was delighted with even a small plan. I wrapped the crayfish in leaves, stuffed them in my pockets, and went back to the burning tree.

Bucket of water, I thought. Bucket of water? Where was I going to get a bucket? How did I think, even if I found water, I could get it back to the tree? That's how citified I was in those days. I had never lived without a bucket before—scrub buckets, water buckets —and so when a water problem came up, I just thought I could run to the kitchen and get a bucket.

"Well, dirt is as good as water," I said as I ran back to my tree. "I can smother the fire with dirt."

Days passed—working, burning, cutting, gathering food—and each day I cut another notch on an aspen pole that I had stuck in the ground for a calendar.

IN WHICH *I Meet One of My Own Kind and Have a Terrible Time Getting Away*

Five notches into June, my house was done. I could stand in it, lie down in it, and there was room left over for a stump to sit on. On warm evenings I would lie on my stomach and look out the door, listen to the cicadas and crickets, and hope it would storm so that I could crawl into my tree and be dry. I had gotten soaked during a couple of May downpours, and now that my house was done, I wanted the chance to sit in my hemlock and watch a cloudburst wet everything but me. This opportunity didn't come for a long time. It was dry.

One morning I was at the edge of the meadow. I had cut down a small ash tree and was chopping it into lengths of about eighteen inches each. This was the beginning of my bed that I was planning to work on after supper every night.

With the golden summer upon me, food was much easier to get, and I actually had several hours of free time after supper for doing other things. I had been eating

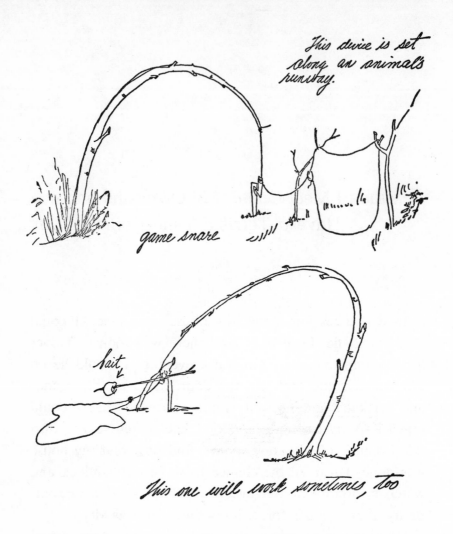

This device is set along an animal's runway.

game snare

bait

This one will work sometimes, too

frogs' legs, turtles, and, best of all, an occasional rabbit. My snares and traps were set now. Furthermore, I had a good supply of cattail roots I had dug in the marsh.

If you ever eat cattails, be sure to cook them well. Otherwise the fibers are tough, and they take more chewing to get the starchy food from them than they are worth. However, they taste just like potatoes after you've been eating them a couple of weeks and, to my way of thinking, are extremely good.

Well, anyway, that summer morning when I was gathering material for a bed, I was singing and chopping and playing a game with a raccoon I had come to know. He had just crawled in a hollow tree and had gone to bed for the day when I came to the meadow. From time to time I would tap on his tree with my ax. He would hang his sleepy head out, snarl at me, close his eyes, and slide out of sight.

The third time I did this, I knew something was happening in the forest. Instead of closing his eyes, he pricked up his ears and his face became drawn and tense. His eyes were focused on something down the mountain. I stood up and looked. I could see nothing. I squatted down and went back to work. The raccoon dove out of sight.

"Now what's got you all excited?" I said, and tried once more to see what he had seen.

I finished the posts for the bed and was looking around for a bigger ash to fell and make slats for the springs when I nearly jumped out of my shoes.

"Now what are you doing up here all alone?" It was a human voice. I swung around and stood face to face with a little old lady in a pale blue sunbonnet and a loose brown dress.

"Oh, gosh!" I said. "Don't scare me like that. Say one word at a time until I get used to a human voice." I must have looked frightened because she chuckled, smoothed the front of her dress, and whispered, "Are you lost?"

"Oh, no, ma'am," I stuttered.

"Then a little fellow like you should not be all alone way up here on this haunted mountain."

"Haunted?" said I.

"Yes, indeed. There's an old story says there are little men up here who play ninepins right down in that gorge in the twilight." She peered at me. "Are you one of them?"

"Oh, no, no, no," I said. "I read that story. It's just make-believe." I laughed, and she puckered her forehead.

"Well, come on," she said, "make some use of yourself and help me fill this basket with strawberries."

I hesitated—she meant *my* strawberry supply.

"Now, get on with you. A boy your age should be doing something worth while, 'stead of playing mumbly peg with sticks. Come on, young man." She jogged me out into the meadow.

We worked quite a while before we said any more. Frankly, I was wondering how to save my precious, precious strawberries, and I may say I picked slowly. Every time I dropped one in her basket, I thought how good it would taste.

"Where do ye live?"

I jumped. It is terribly odd to hear a voice after weeks of listening only to birds and crickets and raccoons, and what is more, to hear the voice ask a question like that.

"I live here," I said.

"Ye mean Delhi. Fine. You can walk me home."

Nothing I added did any good. She would not be shaken from her belief that I lived in Delhi. So I let it go.

We must have reaped every last strawberry before she stood up, put her arm in mine, and escorted me down the mountain. I certainly was not escorting her. Her wiry little arms were like crayfish pinchers. I couldn't have gotten away if I had tried. So I walked and listened.

She told me all the local and world news, and it was rather pleasant to hear about the National League, an atom-bomb test, and a Mr. Riley's three-legged dog that chased her chickens. In the middle of all this chatter she said, "That's the best strawberry patch in the entire Catskill range. I come up here every spring. For forty years I've come to that meadow for my strawberries. It gits harder every year, but there's no jam can beat the jam from that mountain. I know. I've been around here all my life." Then she went right into the New York Yanks without putting in a period.

As I helped her across the stream on big boulders, I heard a cry in the sky. I looked up. Swinging down the valley on long, pointed wings was a large bird. I was struck by the ease and swiftness of its flight.

"Duck hawk," she said. "Nest around here every year. My man used to shoot 'em. He said they killed chickens, but I don't believe it. The only thing that kills chickens is Mr. Riley's three-legged dog."

She tipped and teetered as she crossed the rocks, but kept right on talking and stepping as if she knew that, no matter what, she would get across.

I wasn't listening to her very much. I was thinking about the duck hawk. This bird, I was sure, was the peregrine falcon, the king's hunting bird.

"I will get one. I will train it to hunt for me," I said to myself.

Finally I got the little lady to her brown house at the edge of town.

She turned fiercely upon me. I started back.

"Where are you going, young man?"

I stopped. Now, I thought, she is going to march me into town. Into town? Well, that's where I'll go, then. And I turned on my heel, smiled at her, and replied, "To the library."

The King's Provider

Miss Turner was glad to see me. I told her I wanted some books on hawks and falcons, and she located a few, although there was not much to be had on the subject. We worked all afternoon, and I learned enough. I departed when the library closed. Miss Turner whispered to me as I left, "Sam, you need a haircut."

I hadn't seen myself in so long that this had not occurred to me. "Gee, I don't have any scissors."

She thought a minute, got out her library scissors, and sat me down on the back steps. She did a fine job, and I looked like any other boy who had played hard all day and who, with a little soap and water after supper, would be going off to bed in a regular house.

I didn't get back to my tree that night. The May apples were ripe, and I stuffed on those as I went through the woods. They taste like a very sweet banana, are earthy and a little slippery. But I liked them.

At the stream I caught a trout. Everybody thinks a trout is hard to catch because of all the fancy gear and flies and lines sold for trout fishing, but, honestly, they are easier to catch than any other fish. They have big mouths and snatch and swallow whole anything they see when they are hungry. With my wooden hook in its mouth, the trout was mine. The trouble is that trout are not hungry when most people have time to fish. I knew they were hungry that evening because the creek was swirling, and minnows and everything else were jumping out of the water. When you see that, go fish.

I made a fire on a flat boulder in the stream, and cooked the trout. I did this so I could watch the sky. I wanted to see the falcon again. I also put the trout head on the hook and dropped it in the pool. A snapping turtle would view a trout head with relish.

I waited for the falcon patiently. I didn't have to go anywhere. After an hour or so, I was rewarded. A slender speck came from the valley and glided up the stream. It was still far away when it folded its wings and bombed the earth. I watched. It arose, clumsy and big—carrying food—and winged back to the valley.

I sprinted down the stream and made myself a lean-to near some cliffs where I thought the bird had disappeared. Having learned that day that duck hawks prefer to nest on cliffs, I settled for this site.

Early the next morning I got up and dug the tubers of the arrowleaf that grew along the stream bank. I baked these and boiled mussels for breakfast; then I curled up behind a willow and watched the cliff.

The hawks came in from behind me and circled the stream. They had apparently been out hunting before I had gotten up, as they were returning with food. This was exciting news. They were feeding young, and I was somewhere near the nest.

I watched one of them swing in to the cliff and disappear. A few minutes later it winged out empty-footed. I marked the spot mentally and said, "Ha!"

After splashing across the stream in the shallows, I stood at the bottom of the cliff and wondered how on earth I was going to climb the sheer wall.

I wanted a falcon so badly, however, that I dug in with my toes and hands and started up. The first part was easy; it was not too steep. When I thought I was stuck, I found a little ledge and shinnied up to it.

I was high, and when I looked down, the stream spun. I decided not to look down any more. I edged up to another ledge and lay down on it to catch my breath. I was shaking from exertion, and I was tired.

I looked up to see how much higher I had to go when my hand touched something moist. I pulled it back and saw that it was white—bird droppings. Then I saw them. Almost where my hand had been sat three fuzzy whitish-gray birds. Their open mouths gave them a startled look.

"Oh, hello, hello," I said. "You are cute."

When I spoke, all three blinked at once. All three heads turned and followed my hand as I swung it up and toward them. All three watched my hand with opened mouths. They were marvelous. I chuckled. But I couldn't reach them.

I wormed forward, and *wham!*—something hit my shoulder. It pained. I turned my head to see the big female. She had bitten me. She winged out, banked, and started back for another strike.

Now I was scared, for I was sure she would cut me wide open. With sudden nerve I stood up, stepped forward, and picked up the biggest of the nestlings. The females are bigger than the males. They are the "falcons." They are the pride of kings. I tucked her in my sweater and leaned against the cliff, facing the bulletlike dive of the falcon. I threw out my foot as she struck, and the sole of my tennis shoe took the blow.

The female was now gathering speed for another attack, and when I say speed, I mean 50 to 60 miles an hour. I could see myself battered and torn, lying in the valley below, and I said to myself, "Sam Gribley, you had better get down from here like a rabbit."

I jumped to the ledge below, found it was really quite wide, slid on the seat of my pants to the next ledge, and stopped. The hawk apparently couldn't count. She did not know I had a youngster, for she checked her nest, saw the open mouths, and then forgot me.

I scrambled to the riverbed, being careful not to hurt the hot, fuzzy body that was against my own. However, Frightful, as I called her then and there because of the difficulties we had had in getting together, did not think so gently of me. She dug her talons into my skin to brace herself during the bumpy ride to the ground.

I stumbled to the stream, placed her in a nest of buttercups, and dropped beside her. I fell asleep.

62

When I awoke, my eyes opened on two gray eyes in a
white stroobly head. Small pinfeathers were sticking out
of the stroobly down, like feathers in an Indian quiver.
The big blue beak curled down in a snarl and up in a
smile.

"Oh, Frightful," I said, "you are a raving beauty."

Frightful fluffed her nubby feathers and shook. I
picked her up in the cup of my hands and held her under
my chin. I stuck my nose in the deep, warm fuzz. It
smelled dusty and sweet.

I liked that bird. Oh, how I liked that bird from that smelly minute. It was so pleasant to feel the beating life and see the funny little awkward movements of a young thing.

The legs pushed out between my fingers; I gathered them up, together with the thrashing wings, and tucked the bird in one piece under my chin. I rocked.

"Frightful," I said, "you will enjoy what we are going to do."

I washed my bleeding shoulder in the creek, tucked the torn threads of my sweater back into the hole they had come out of, and set out for my tree.

A BRIEF ACCOUNT OF *What I Did About the First Man Who Was after Me*

At the edge of the meadow I sensed all was not well at camp. How I knew there was a human being there was not clear to me then. I can only say that after living so long with the birds and animals, the movement of a human is like the difference between the explosion of a cap pistol and that of a cannon.

I wormed toward camp. When I could see the man I felt to be there, I stopped and looked. He was wearing a forester's uniform. Immediately I thought they had sent someone out to bring me in, and I began to shake. Then I realized that I didn't have to go back to meet the man at all. I was perfectly free and capable of settling down anywhere. My tree was just a pleasant habit.

I circled the meadow and went over to the gorge. On the way I checked a trap. It was a deadfall. A figure four under a big rock. The rock was down. The food was rabbit.

I picked a comfortable place just below the rim of the gorge where I could pop up every now and then and watch my tree. Here I dressed down the rabbit and fed Frightful some of the more savory bites from a young falcon's point of view: the liver, the heart, the brain. She ate in gulps. As I watched her swallow, I sensed a great pleasure. It is hard to explain my feelings at that moment. It seemed marvelous to see life pump through that strange little body of feathers, wordless noises, milk eyes —much as life pumped through me.

The food put the bird to sleep. I watched her eyelids close from the bottom up and her head quiver. The fuzzy body rocked, the tail spread to steady it, and the little duck hawk almost sighed as it sank into the leaves, sleeping.

I had lots of time. I was going to wait for the man to leave. So I stared at my bird, the beautiful details of the new feathers, the fernlike lashes along the lids, the saucy bristles at the base of the beak. Pleasant hours passed.

Frightful would awaken, I would feed her, she would fall back to sleep, and I would watch the breath rock her body ever so slightly. I was breathing the same way, only not so fast. Her heart beat much faster than mine. She was designed to her bones for a swifter life.

It finally occurred to me that I was very hungry. I stood up to see if the man was gone. He was yawning and pacing.

The sun was slanting on him now, and I could see him quite well. He was a fire warden. Of course, it has not rained, I told myself, for almost three weeks, and the fire planes have been circling the mountains and valleys, patrolling the mountains. Apparently the smoke from my fire was spotted, and a man was sent to check it. I recalled the bare, trampled ground around the tree, the fireplace of rocks filled with ashes, the wood chips from the making of my bed, and resolved hereafter to keep my yard clean.

So I made rabbit soup in a tin can I found at the bottom of the gorge. I seasoned it with wild garlic and jack-in-the-pulpit roots.

Jack-in-the-pulpits have three big leaves on a stalk and are easily recognized by the curly striped awning above a stiff, serious preacher named Jack. The jack-in-the-pulpits were acrid; they needed to be pounded to flour and allowed to stand to be really good. I had to eat them bitter.

The fire I made was of only the driest wood, and I made it right at the water's edge. I didn't want a smoky fire on this particular evening.

jack-in-the-pulpit

After supper I made a bough bed and stretched out with Frightful beside me. Apparently the more you stroke and handle a falcon, the easier it is to train.

I had all sorts of plans for hoods and jesses, as the straps on a falcon are called, and I soon forgot about the man.

Stretched on the boughs, I listened to the wood pewees calling their haunting good nights until I fell sound asleep.

IN WHICH *I Learn to Season My Food*

The fire warden made a fire sometime in the colder hours of the night. At dawn he was asleep beside white, smoldering ashes. I crawled back to the gorge, fed Frightful rabbit bites, and slipped back to the edge of the meadow to check a box trap I had set the day before. I made it by tying small sticks together like a log cabin. This trap was better than the snares or deadfalls. It had caught numerous rabbits, several squirrels, and a groundhog.

I saw, as I inched toward it, that it was closed. The sight of a closed trap excites me to this day. I still can't believe that animals don't understand why delicious food is in such a ridiculous spot.

Well, this morning I pulled the trap deep into the woods to open it. The trapped animal was light. I couldn't guess what it was. It was also active, flipping and darting from one corner to the next. I peeked in to locate it so that I could grab it quickly behind the head without getting bitten. I was not always successful at this and had scars to prove it.

I put my eye to the crack. A rumpus arose in the darkness. Two bright eyes shone, and out through that hole that was no wider than a string bean came a weasel. He flew right out at me, landed on my shoulder, gave me a lecture that I shall never forget, and vanished under the scant cover of trillium and bloodroot leaves.

He popped up about five feet away and stood on his hind feet to lecture me again. I said, "Scat!" so he darted right to my knee, put his broad, furry paws on my pants, and looked me in the face. I shall never forget the fear and wonder that I felt at the bravery of that weasel. He stood his ground and berated me. I could see by the flashing of his eyes and the curl of his lip that he was furious at me for trapping him. He couldn't talk, but I knew what he meant.

Wonder filled me as I realized he was absolutely unafraid. No other animal, and I knew quite a few by now, had been so brave in my presence. Screaming, he jumped on me. This surprised and scared me. He leapt from my lap to my head, took a mouthful of hair, and wrestled it. My goose bumps rose. I was too frightened to move. A good thing, too, because I guess he figured I was not going to fight back, and his scream of anger changed to a purr of peace. Still I couldn't move.

Presently down he climbed, as stately as royalty, and off he marched, never looking back. He sank beneath the leaves like a fish beneath the water. Not a stem rippled to mark his way.

70

And so The Baron and I met for the first time, and it was the beginning of a harassing but wonderful friendship.

Frightful had been watching all this. She was tense with fright. So young and inexperienced, but she knew an enemy when she saw one. I picked her up and whispered into her birdy-smelling neck feathers.

"You wild ones know."

Since I couldn't go home, I decided to spend the day in the marsh down the west side of the mountain. There were a lot of cattails and frogs there.

Frightful balanced on my fist as we walked. She had learned that in the short span of one afternoon and a night. She is a very bright bird.

On our way we scared up a deer. It was a doe. I watched her dart gracefully away, and said to Frightful, "That's what I want. I need a door for my house, tethers for you, and a blanket for me. How am I going to get a deer?"

This was not the first time I had said this. The forest was full of deer, and I already had drawn plans on a piece of birch bark for deadfalls, pit traps, and snares. None seemed workable.

The day passed. In the early evening we stole home, tree by tree, to find that the warden had gone. I cleaned up my front yard, scattered needles over the bare spots, and started a small fire with very dry wood that would not smoke much. No more wardens for me. I liked my tree, and although I could live somewhere else, I certainly did not want to.

Once home, I immediately started to work again. I had a device I wanted to try, and put some hickory sticks in a tin can and set it to boiling while I fixed dinner. Before going to bed, I noted this on a piece of birch bark:

> This night I am making salt. I know that people in the early days got along without it, but I think some of these wild foods would taste better with some flavoring. I understand that hickory sticks, boiled dry, leave a salty residue. I am trying it.

In the morning I added:

> It is quite true. The can is dry, and thick with a black substance. It is very salty, and I tried it on frogs' legs for breakfast. It is just what I have needed.

And so I went into salt production for several days, and chipped out a niche inside the tree in which to store it.

> June 19
> I finished my bed today. The ash slats work very well and are quite springy and comfortable. The bed just fits in the right-hand side of the tree. I have hemlock boughs on it now but hope to have deer hide soon. I am making a figure-four trap as tall as me, with a log on it that I

can barely lift. It doesn't look workable. I wish there were another way of getting a deer.

June 20

I decided today to dig a pit to trap a deer, so I am whittling a shovel out of a board I found in the stream this morning. That stream is very useful. It has given me tin cans for pots, and now an oaken board for a shovel.

Frightful will hop from the stump to my fist. She still can't fly. Her wing feathers are only about an inch long. I think she likes me.

bed made with ash slats—

How a Door Came to Me

One morning before the wood pewees were up, I was smoking a mess of fish I had caught in the stream. When I caught more than I could eat, I would bone them, put them on a rack of sticks, and slowly smoke them until they dried out. This is the best way to preserve extra food. However, if you try it, remember to use a hard wood—hickory is best. I tried pine on the first few fish, and ruined them with black, tarry smoke. Well, it was very silent—then came a scream. I jumped into my tree. Presently I had enough nerve to look out.

"Well, Baron Weasel!" I said in astonishment. I was sure it was the same weasel I had met in the trap. He was on the boulder in front of the hemlock, batting the ferns with his front feet and rearing and staring at me.

"Now, you stay right there," I said. Of course he flipped and came off the rock like a jet stream. He was at the door before I could stop him, and loping around my feet like a bouncing ball.

"You look glad all over, Baron. I hope all that frisking means joy," I said. He took my pants leg in his teeth, tugged it, and then rippled softly back to the boulder. He went down a small hole. He popped up again, bit a fern nearby, and ran around the boulder. I crept out to look for him—no weasel. I poked a stick in the hole at the base of the rock, trying to provoke him. I felt a little jumpy, so that when a shot rang out through the woods, I leapt a foot in the air and dove into my hole. A cricket chirped; a catbird scratched the leaves. I waited. One enormous minute later a dark form ran onto the meadow. It stumbled and fell to the ground.

I had the impression that it was a deer. Without waiting to consider what I might be running toward, I burst to the edge of the meadow.

No one was in sight; I ran into the grass. There lay a dead deer! With all my strength I dragged the heavy animal into the woods. I then hurried to my tree, gathered up the hemlock boughs on my bed, rushed back, and threw them over the carcass. I stuck a few ferns in them so they would look as if they were growing there and ran back to camp, breathless.

Hurriedly I put out the fire. covered it with dirt, hid my smoking rack in the spring, grabbed Frightful, and got in my tree.

Someone was poaching, and he might be along in a minute to collect his prize. The shot had come from the side of the mountain, and I figured I had about four minutes to clean up before the poacher arrived.

Then when I was hidden and ready, Frightful started her cry of hunger. I had not fed her yet that morning. Oh, how was I going to explain to her the awful need to be quiet? How did a mother falcon warn her young of danger? I took her in my hands and stroked her stomach. She fought me, and then she lay still in my hand, her feet up, her eyes bright. She stiffened and drooped. I kept on stroking her. She was hypnotized. I would stop for a few moments; she would lie still, then pop to her feet. I was sure this wasn't what her mother did to keep her quiet, but it worked.

Bushes cracked, leaves scuttled, and a man with a shotgun came into the meadow. I could just see his head and shoulders. He looked around and banged toward the hemlock forest. I crawled up on my bed and stroked the hungry Frightful.

I couldn't see the man from my bed, but I could hear him.

I heard him come to the tree. I could see his boots. He stopped by the ashes of the fire and then went on. I could see my heart lift my sweater. I was terrified.

I stayed on the bed all morning, telling the fierce little bundle of feathers in my hand that there was deer meat in store for her if she would just wait with me.

Way down the other side of the mountain, I heard another shot. I sure hoped that deer dropped on the poacher's toes and that he would now go home.

At noon I went to my prize. Frightful sat beside me as I skinned and quartered it. She ate deer until she was misshapen.

I didn't make any notes as to how long it took me to do all the work that was required to get the deer ready for smoking and the hide scraped and ready for tanning, but it was many, many days.

However, when I sat down to a venison steak, that was a meal! All it was, was venison. I wrote this on a piece of birch bark:

I think I grew an inch on venison!

Frightful and I went to the meadow when it was done, and I flopped in the grass. The stars came up, the ground smelled sweet, and I closed my eyes. I heard, *"Pip, pop, pop, pop."*

"Who's making that noise?" I said sleepily to Frightful. She ruffled her feathers.

I listened. *"Pop, pip."* I rolled over and stuck my face in the grass. Something gleamed beneath me, and in the fading light I could see an earthworm coming out of its hole.

Nearby another one arose, and there was a *pop.* Little bubbles of air snapped as these voiceless animals of the earth came to the surface. That got me to smiling. I was glad to know this about earthworms. I don't know why, but this seemed like one of the nicest things I had learned in the woods—that earthworms, lowly, confined to the darkness of the earth, could make just a little stir in the world.

IN WHICH *Frightful Learns Her ABC's*

Free time was spent scraping the fur off the deer hide to get it ready for tanning. This much I knew: in order to tan hide, it has to be steeped in tannic acid. There is tannic acid in the woods in oak trees, but it took me several weeks to figure out how to get it. You need a lot of oak chips in water. Water and oak give off tannic acid. My problem was not oak or water but getting a vessel big enough to put the deer hide in.

Coming home from the stream one night, I had an inspiration.

It had showered the day before, and as Frightful and I passed an old stump, I noticed that it had collected the rain. "A stump, an oak stump, would be perfect," I said right out loud to that pretty bird.

So I felled an oak over by the gorge, burned a hole in it, carried water to it, and put my deerskin in it. I let it steep, oh, maybe five days before I took it out and dried it. It dried stiff as a board, and I had to chew, rub, jump on it, and twist it to get it soft. When this was done, however, I had my door. I hung it on pegs inside my entrance, and because it was bigger than it had to be, I would cut off pieces now and then when I needed them. I cut off two thin strips to make jesses, or leg straps, for Frightful. All good falcons wear jesses and leashes so they can be tethered for their training.

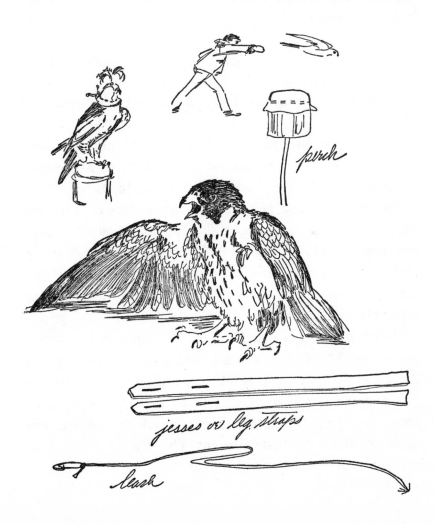

perch

jesses or leg straps

leash

I smoked the meat I couldn't eat and stored it. I used everything I could on that animal. I even used one of its bones for a spearhead. I was tired of catching frogs by the jump-and-miss system. I made two sharp points and strapped them to the end of a long stick, one on each side, to make a kind of fork. It worked beautifully. Frogs were one of my favorite meals, and I found I could fix them many ways; however, I got to like frog soup fixed in this way:

Clean, skin, and boil until tender. Add wild onions, also water-lily bulbs and wild carrots. Thicken with acorn flour. Serve in turtle shell.

By now my two pairs of pants were threadbare, and my three sweaters were frayed. I dreamed of a deerskin suit and watched my herd with clothes in mind.

The deer for my suit did not come easily. I rigged up a figure-four trap under the log and baited it with elderberries rolled into a ball. That just mushed up and didn't work. Then I remembered that deer like salt. I made a ball of hickory salt with turtle fat to hold it together.

Every evening Frightful and I, sometimes accompanied by The Baron Weasel, would go to the edge of the meadow and look toward the aspen grove to see if the great log had fallen. One night we saw three deer standing around it quietly, reaching toward the smell of salt. At that moment The Baron jumped at my pants leg, but got my ankle with an awful nip. I

guess I had grown some; my pants and socks did not meet any more. I screamed, and the deer fled.

I chased The Baron home. I had the uneasy feeling that he was laughing as he darted, flipped, buckled, and disappeared.

The Baron was hard to understand. What did he want from me? Occasionally I left him bites of turtle or venison, and although he smelled the offerings, he never ate them. The catbird would get them. Most animals stick around if you feed them. But The Baron did not eat anything. Yet he seemed to like me. Gradually it occurred to me that he didn't have a mate or a family. Could he be a lonely bachelor, taking up with odd company for lack of an ordinary life? Well, whatever, The Baron liked me for what I was, and I appreciated that. He was a personable little fellow.

Every day I worked to train Frightful. It was a long process. I would put her on her stump with a long leash and step back a few feet with some meat in my hand. Then I would whistle. The whistle was supposed eventually to mean food to her. So I would whistle, show her the meat, and after many false flaps she would finally fly to my hand. I would pet her and feed her. She could fly fairly well, so now I made sure that she never ate unless she flew to my fist.

One day at breakfast I whistled for Frightful. I had no food; she wasn't even hungry, but she came to me anyway. I was thrilled. She had learned a whistle meant "Come."

I looked into her steely eyes that morning and thought I saw a gentle recognition. She puffed up her feathers as she sat on my hand. I call this a "feather word." It means she is content.

Now each day I stepped farther and farther away from Frightful to make her fly greater and greater distances. One day she flew a good fifty feet, and we packed up and went gathering seeds, bark, and tubers to celebrate.

I used my oldest sweater for gathering things. It was not very convenient, and each time I filled it, I mentally designed bigger and better pockets on my deer-hide suit-to-be.

The summer was wonderful. There was food in abundance, and I gathered it most of the morning and stored it away in the afternoon. I could now see that my niches were not going to be big enough for the amount of food I would need for the winter, so I began burning out another tree. When the hickory nuts, walnuts, and acorns appeared, I was going to need a bin. You'd be surprised what a pile of nuts it takes to make one turtle shell full of nut meats—and not a snapping-turtle shell, either, just a box-turtle shell!

With the easy living of the summer also came a threat. Hikers and vacationers were in the woods, and more than once I pulled inside my tree, closed my deer-flap door, and hid while bouncing, noisy people crossed the meadow on their way to the gorge. Apparently the gorge was a sight for those who wanted a four-mile hike up the mountain.

One morning I heard a group arriving. I whistled for Frightful. She came promptly. We dove into the tree. It was dark in the tree with the flap closed, and I realized that I needed a candle. I planned a lamp of a turtle shell with a deer-hide wick, and as I was cutting off a piece of hide, I heard a shrill scream.

The voices of the hikers became louder. I wondered if one of them had fallen into the gorge. Then I said to Frightful, "That was no cry of a human, pretty bird. I'll bet you a rabbit for dinner that our deer trap worked. And here we are, stored in a tree like a nut and unable to claim our prize."

We waited and waited until I couldn't be patient any more, and I was about to put my head out the door when a man's voice said, "Look at these trees!"

A woman spoke. "Harold, they're huge. How old do you think they are?"

"Three hundred years old, maybe four hundred," said Harold.

They tramped around, actually sat on The Baron's boulder, and were apparently going to have lunch when things began to happen out there, and I almost gave myself away with hysterics.

"Harold, what's the matter with that weasel? It's running all over this rock." A scream! A scuttering and scraping of boots on the rocks.

"He's mad!" That was the woman.

"Watch it, Grace, he's coming at your feet." They ran.

By this time I had my hand over my mouth to keep back the laughter. I snorted and choked, but they never heard me. They were in the meadow—run right out of the forest by that fiery Baron Weasel.

I still laugh when I think of it.

It was not until dark that Frightful and I got to the deer, and a beauty it was.

The rest of June was spent smoking it, tanning it, and finally starting on my deerskin suit. I made a bone needle, cut out the pants by ripping up one pair

rack for smoking
fish and meat

of old city pants for a pattern. I saved my city pants and burned them bit by bit to make charred cloth for the flint and steel.

"Frightful," I said while sewing one afternoon. She was preening her now silver-gray, black, and white feathers. "There is no end to this. We need another deer. I can't make a blouse."

We didn't get another deer until fall, so with the scraps I made big square pockets for food gathering. One hung in front of me, and the other down my back. They were joined by straps. This device worked beautifully.

Sometime in July I finished my pants. They fit well, and were the best-looking pants I had ever seen. I was terribly proud of them.

With pockets and good tough pants I was willing to pack home many more new foods to try. Daisies, the bark of a poplar tree that I saw a squirrel eating, and puffballs. They are mushrooms, the only ones I felt were safe to eat, and even at that, I kept waiting to die the first night I ate them. I didn't, so I enjoyed them from that night on. They are wonderful. Mushrooms are dangerous, and I would not suggest that one eat them from the forest. The mushroom expert at the Botanical Gardens told me that. He said even he didn't eat wild ones.

The inner bark of the poplar tree tasted like wheat kernels, and so I dried as much as I could and powdered it into flour. It was tedious work, and in August, when the acorns were ready, I found that they made better flour and were much easier to handle.

I would bake the acorns in the fire and grind them between stones. This was tedious work, too, but now that I had a home and smoked venison and did not have to go hunting food every minute, I could do things like make flour. I would simply add spring water to the flour and bake this on a piece of tin. When done, I had the best pancakes ever. They were flat and hard, like I imagined Indian bread to be. I liked them and would carry the leftovers in my pockets for lunch.

On fine August evenings I would take Frightful to the meadow. I was training her to the lure. That is, I tied her meat on a piece of wood covered with hide and feathers. I would throw it in the air, and she would swoop out of the sky and catch it. She was absolutely free during these maneuvers and would fly high into the air and hover over me like a leaf. I made sure she was hungry before I turned her loose. I wanted her back.

After a few tries she never missed the lure. Such marksmanship thrilled me. Bird and lure would drop to the earth. I would run over, grab her jesses, and we would sit on the big boulder in the meadow while she ate. Those were nice evenings. The finest was the night I wrote this:

> Frightful caught her first prey. She is now a trained falcon. It was only a sparrow, but we are on our way. It happened unexpectedly. Frightful was climbing into the sky, circling and waiting for the lure, when I stepped forward and scared a sparrow.

The sparrow flew across the meadow. Out of the sky came a black streak—I've never seen anything drop so fast. With a great backwatering of wings, Frightful broke her fall and at the same time seized the sparrow. I took it away from her and gave her the lure. That sounds mean, but if she gets in the habit of eating what she catches, she will go wild.

IN WHICH *I Find a Real Live Man*

One of the gasping joys of summer was my daily bath in the spring. It was cold water; I never stayed in long, but it woke me up and started me into the day with a vengeance.

I would tether Frightful to a hemlock bough above me and splash her from time to time. She would suck in her chest, look startled, and then shake. While I bathed and washed, she preened. Huddled down in the water between the ferns and moss, I scrubbed myself with the bark of the slippery elm. It gets soapy when you rub it.

The frogs would hop out and let me in, and the wood thrush would come to the edge of the pool to see what was happening. We were a gay gathering—me shouting, Frightful preening, the wood thrush cocking its pretty head. Occasionally The Baron Weasel would pop up and glance furtively at us. He didn't care for water. How he stayed glossy and clean was a mystery to me

until he came to the boulder beside our bath pool one day, wet with the dew from the ferns. He licked himself until he was polished.

One morning there was a rustle in the leaves above. Instantly Frightful had it located. I had learned to look where Frightful looked when there were disturbances in the forest. She always saw life before I could focus my eyes. She was peering into the hemlock above us. Finally I, too, saw it. A young raccoon. It was chittering and, now that all eyes were upon it, began coming down the tree.

And so Frightful and I met Jesse Coon James, the bandit of the Gribley farm.

He came headfirst down to our private bath, a scrabbly, skinny young raccoon. He must have been from a late litter, for he was not very big and certainly not well fed. Whatever had been Jesse C. James' past, it was awful. Perhaps he was an orphan; perhaps he had been thrown out of his home by his mother, as his eyes were somewhat crossed and looked a little peculiar. In any event he had come to us for help, I thought, and so Frightful and I led him home and fed him.

In about a week he fattened up. His crumply hair smoothed out, and with a little ear scratching and back rubbing, Jesse C. James became a devoted friend. He also became useful. He slept somewhere in the dark tops of the hemlocks all day long, unless he saw us start for the stream. Then, tree by tree, limb by limb, Jesse followed us. At the stream he was the most useful mussel digger that any boy could have. Jesse could find mussels where three men could not. He would start to eat them, and if he ate them, he got full and wouldn't dig any more, so I took them away from him until he found me all I wanted. Then I let him have some.

Here are a few of my notes on how to fix mussels:

Scrub mussels in spring water. Dump them into boiling water with salt. Boil five minutes. Remove and cool in the juice. Take out meat. Eat by dipping in acorn paste flavored with a smudge of garlic and green apples.

Frightful took care of the small-game supply, and now that she was an expert hunter, we had rabbit stew, pheasant potpie, and an occasional sparrow, which I generously gave to Frightful. As fast as we removed the rabbits and pheasants, new ones replaced them.

Beverages during the hot summer became my chore, largely because no one else wanted them. I found some sassafras trees at the edge of the road one day, dug up a good supply of roots, peeled and dried them. Sassafras tea is about as good as anything you want to drink. Pennyroyal makes another good drink. I dried great bunches of this and hung them from the roof of the tree room together with the leaves of winterberry. All these fragrant plants I also used in cooking to give a new taste to some not-so-good foods.

The room in the tree smelled of smoke and mint. It was the best-smelling tree in the Catskill Mountains.

Life was leisurely. I was warm, well fed. One day while I was down the mountain, I returned home by way of the old farmhouse site to check the apple crop. They were summer apples, and were about ready to be picked. I had gathered a pouchful and had sat down under the tree to eat a few and think about how I would dry them for use in the winter when Frightful dug her talons into my shoulder so hard I winced.

"Be gentle, bird!" I said to her.

I got her talons out and put her on a log, where I watched her with some alarm. She was as alert as a high-tension wire, her head cocked so that her ears, just membranes under her feathers, were pointed east. She evidently heard a sound that pained her. She opened her beak. Whatever it was, I could hear nothing, though I strained my ears, cupped them, and wished she would speak.

Frightful was my ears as well as my eyes. She could hear things long before I could. When she grew tense, I listened or looked. She was scared this time. She turned round and round on the log, looked up in the tree for a perch, lifted her wings to fly, and then stood still and listened.

Then I heard it. A police siren sounded far down the road. The sound grew louder and louder, and I grew afraid. Then I said, "No, Frightful, if they are after me, there won't be a siren. They'll just slip up on me quietly."

No sooner had I said this than the siren wound down and apparently stopped on the road at the foot of the mountain. I got up to run to my tree, but had not gotten past the walnut before the patrol cars started up and screamed away.

We started home although it was not late in the afternoon. However, it was hot, and thunderheads were building up. I decided to take a swim in the spring and work on the moccasins I had cut out several days ago.

With the squad car still on my mind, we slipped quietly into the hemlock forest. Once again Frightful almost sent me through the crown of the forest by digging her talons into my shoulder. I looked at her. She was staring at our home. I looked in that direction, too. Then I stopped, for I could make out the form of a man stretched between the sleeping house and the store tree.

Softly, tree by tree, Frightful and I approached him. The man was asleep. I could have left and camped in the gorge again, but my enormous desire to see another human being overcame my fear of being discovered.

We stood above the man. He did not move, so Frightful lost interest in my fellow being. She tried to hop to her stump and preen. I grabbed her leash, however, as I wanted to think before awakening him. Frightful flapped. I held her wings to her body, as her flapping was noisy to me. Apparently not so to the man. The man did not stir. It is hard to realize that the rustle of a falcon's wings is not much of a noise to a man from the city, because by now one beat of her wings and I would awaken from a sound sleep as if a shot had gone off. The stranger slept on. I realized how long I'd been in the mountains.

Right at that moment, as I looked at his unshaven face, his close-cropped hair, and his torn clothes, I thought of the police siren and put two and two together.

"An outlaw!" I said to myself. "Wow!" I had to think what to do with an outlaw before I awoke him.

Would he be troublesome? Would he be mean? Should I go live in the gorge until he moved on? How I wanted to hear his voice, to tell him about The Baron and Jesse C. James, to say words out loud. I really did not want to hide from him; besides, he might be hungry, I thought. Finally I spoke.

"Hi!" I said. I was delighted to see him roll over, open his eyes, and look up. He seemed startled, so I reassured him. "It's all right; they've gone. If you don't tell on me, I won't tell on you." When he heard this, he sat up and seemed to relax.

"Oh," he said. Then he leaned against the tree and added, "Thanks." He evidently was thinking this over, for he propped his head on his elbow and studied me closely.

"You're a sight for sore eyes," he said, and smiled. He had a nice smile—in fact, he looked nice and not like an outlaw at all. His eyes were very blue, and, although tired, they did not look scared or hunted.

However, I talked quickly before he could get up and run away.

"I don't know anything about you, and I don't want to. You don't know anything about me and don't want to, but you may stay here if you like. No one is going to find you here. Would you like some supper?" It was still early, but he looked hungry.

"Do you have some?"

"Yes, venison or rabbit?"

"Well—venison." His eyebrows puckered in question marks. I went to work.

He arose, turned around and around, and looked at his surroundings. He whistled softly when I kindled a spark with the flint and steel. I was now quite quick at this and had a tidy fire blazing in a very few minutes. I was so used to myself doing this that it had not occurred to me that it would be interesting to a stranger.

"Desdemondia!" he said. I judged this to be some underworld phrase. At this moment Frightful, who had been sitting quietly on her stump, began to preen. The outlaw jumped back, then saw she was tied and said, "And who is this ferocious-looking character?"

"That is Frightful; don't be afraid. She's quite wonderful and gentle. She would be glad to catch you a rabbit for supper if you would prefer that to venison."

"Am I dreaming?" said the man. "I go to sleep by a campfire that looked as if it was built by a boy scout, and I awaken in the middle of the eighteenth century."

I crawled into the store tree to get the smoked venison and some cattail tubers. When I came out again, he was speechless.

"My storehouse," I explained.

"I see," he answered. From that moment on he did not talk much. He just watched me. I was so busy cooking the best meal that I could possibly get together that I didn't say much either. Later I wrote down that menu, as it was excellent.

Brown puffballs in deer fat with a little wild garlic, fill pot with water, put venison in, boil. Wrap tubers in leaves and stick in coals. Cut up apples and boil in can with dogtooth-violet bulbs. Raspberries to finish meal.

dog-toothed violet

When the meal was ready, I served it to the man in my nicest turtle shell. I had to whittle him a fork out of the crotch of a twig, as Jesse Coon James had gone off with the others. He ate and ate and ate, and when he was done, he said, "May I call you Thoreau?"

"That will do nicely," I said. Then I paused—just to let him know that I knew a little bit about him, too. I smiled and said, "I will call you Bando."

His eyebrows went up, he cocked his head, shrugged his shoulders, and answered, "That's close enough."

With this he sat and thought. I felt I had offended him, so I spoke. "I will be glad to help. I will teach you how to live off the land. It is easy. No one need find you."

His eyebrows gathered together again. This was characteristic of Bando when he was concerned, and so I was sorry I had mentioned his past. After all, outlaw or no outlaw, he was an adult, and I still felt unsure of myself around adults. I changed the subject.

"Let's get some sleep," I said.

"Where do you sleep?" he asked. All this time sitting and talking with me, and he had not seen the entrance to my tree. I was pleased. Then I beckoned, walked a few feet to the left, pushed back the deer-hide door, and showed Bando my secret.

"Thoreau," he said, "you are quite wonderful." He went in. I lit the turtle candle for him; he explored, tried the bed, came out, and shook his head until I thought it would roll off.

We didn't say much more that night. I let him sleep on my bed. His feet hung off, but he was comfortable, he said. I stretched out by the fire. The ground was dry, the night warm, and I could sleep on anything now.

I got up early and had breakfast ready when Bando came stumbling out of the tree. We ate crayfish, and he really honestly seemed to like them. It takes a little time to acquire a taste for wild foods, so Bando surprised me the way he liked the menu. Of course he was hungry, and that helped.

That day we didn't talk much, just went over the mountain collecting foods. I wanted to dig up the tubers of the Solomon's-seal from a big garden of them on the other side of the gorge. We fished, we swam a little, and I told him I hoped to make a raft pretty soon so I could float into deeper water and perhaps catch bigger fish.

When Bando heard this, he took my ax and immediately began to cut young trees for this purpose. I watched him and said, "You must have lived on a farm or something."

At that moment a bird sang.

"The wood pewee," said Bando, stopping his work. He stepped into the woods, seeking the bird. Now I was astonished.

"How would you know about a wood pewee in your business?" I grew bold enough to ask.

"And just what do you think my business is?" he said as I followed him.

"Well, you're not a minister."

"Right!"

"And you're not a doctor or a lawyer."

"Correct."

"You're not a businessman or a sailor."

"No, I am not."

"Nor do you dig ditches."

"I do not."

"Well . . ."

"Guess."

Suddenly I wanted to know for sure. So I said it.

"You are a murderer or a thief or a racketeer, and you are hiding out."

Bando stopped looking for the pewee. He turned and stared at me. At first I was frightened. A bandit might do anything. But he wasn't mad; he was laughing. He had a good, deep laugh, and it kept coming out of him. I smiled, then grinned and laughed with him.

"What's funny, Bando?" I asked.

"I like that," he finally said. "I like that a lot." The tickle deep inside him kept him chuckling. I had no more to say, so I ground my heel in the dirt while I waited for him to get over the fun and explain it all to me.

"Thoreau, my friend, I am just a college English teacher lost in the Catskills. I came out to hike around the woods, got completely lost yesterday, found your fire, and fell asleep beside it. I was hoping the scoutmaster and his troop would be back for supper and help me home."

"Oh, no." My comment. Then I laughed. "You see, Bando, before I found you, I heard squad cars screaming up the road. Occasionally you read about bandits that hide out in the forest, and I was just so sure that you were someone they were looking for."

We gave up the pewee and went back to the raft-making, talking very fast now and laughing a lot. He was fun. Then something sad occurred to me.

"Well, if you're not a bandit, you will have to go home very soon, and there is no point in teaching you how to live on fish and bark and plants."

"I can stay a little while," he said. "This is summer vacation. I must admit I had not planned to eat crayfish on my vacation, but I am rather getting to like it.

"Maybe I can stay until your school opens," he went on. "That's after Labor Day, isn't it?"

I was very still, thinking how to answer that.

Bando sensed this. He turned to me with a big grin.

"You really mean you are going to try to winter it out here?"

"I think I can."

"Well!" He sat down, rubbed his forehead in his hands, and looked at me. "Thoreau, I have led a varied life—dishwasher, sax player, teacher. To me it has been an interesting life. Just now it seems very dull." He sat awhile with his head down, then looked up at the mountains and the rocks and trees. I heard him sigh.

"Let's go fish. We can finish this another day."

That is how I came to know Bando. We became very good friends in the week or ten days that he stayed with me, and he helped me a lot. We spent several days gathering white-oak acorns and groundnuts, harvesting the blueberry crop, and smoking fish.

We flew Frightful every day just for the pleasure of lying on our backs in the meadow and watching her mastery of the sky. I had lots of meat, so what she caught those days was all hers. It was a pleasant time, warm, with occasional thundershowers, some of which we stayed out in. We talked about books. He did know a lot of books and could quote exciting things from them.

One day Bando went to town and came back with five pounds of sugar.

"I want to make blueberry jam," he announced. "All those excellent berries and no jam."

He worked two days at this. He knew how to make jam. He'd watched his pa make it in Mississippi, but we got stuck on what to put it in.

I wrote this one night:

August 29

The raft is almost done. Bando has promised to stay until we can sail out into the deep fishing holes.

Bando and I found some clay along the stream bank. It was as slick as ice. Bando thought it would make good pottery. He shaped some jars and lids. They look good—not Wedgwood, he said, but containers. We dried them on the rock in the meadow, and later Bando made a clay oven and baked them in it. He thinks they might hold the blueberry jam he has been making.

Bando got the fire hot by blowing on it with some homemade bellows that he fashioned from one of my skins that he tied together like a balloon. A reed is the nozzle.

August 30

It was a terribly hot day for Bando to be firing clay jars, but he stuck with it. They look jam-worthy, as he says, and he filled three of them tonight. The jam is good. The pots remind me of crude flowerpots without the hole in the bottom. Some of the lids don't fit. Bando says he will go home and read more about pottery-making so that he can do a better job next time.

We like the jam. We eat it on hard acorn pancakes.

Later. Bando met The Baron Weasel today for the first time. I don't know where The Baron has been this past week, but suddenly he appeared on the rock and nearly jumped down Bando's shirt collar. Bando said he liked The Baron best when he was in his hole.

September 3

Bando taught me how to make willow whistles today. He and I went to the stream and cut two whistles about eight inches long. He slipped the bark on them. That means he pulled the wood out of the bark, leaving a tube. He made a mouthpiece at one end, cut a hole beneath it, and used the wood to slide up and down like a trombone.

We played music until the moon came up. Bando could even play jazz on the willow whistles. They are wonderful instruments, sounding much like the wind in the top of the hem-

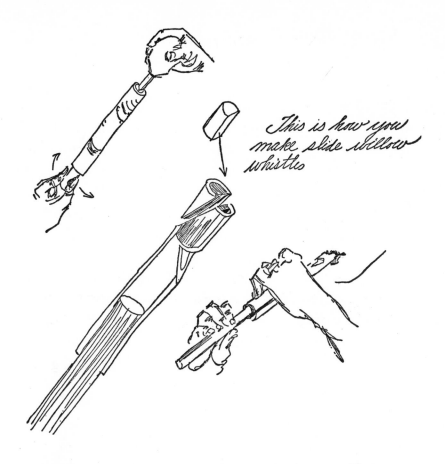

This is how you make slide willow whistles

locks. Sad tunes are best suited to willow whistles. When we played "The Young Voyageur," tears came to our eyes, it was so sad.

There were no more notes for many days. Bando had left me, saying: "Good-by. I'll see you at Christmas." I was so lonely that I kept sewing on my moccasins to keep myself busy. I sewed every free minute for four days, and when they were finished, I began a glove to protect my hand from Frightful's sharp talons.

One day when I was thinking very hard about being alone, Frightful gave her gentle call of love and contentment. I looked up.

"Bird," I said, "I had almost forgotten how we used to talk." She made tiny movements with her beak and fluffed her feathers. This was a language I had forgotten since Bando came. It meant she was glad to see me and hear me, that she was well fed and content. I picked her up and squeaked into her neck feathers. She moved her beak, turned her bright head, and bit my nose very gently.

Jesse Coon James came down from the trees for the first time in ten days. He finished my fish dinner. Then just before dusk The Baron came up on his boulder and scratched and cleaned and played with a fern leaf.

I had the feeling we were all back together again.

Sharing Sam's Adventure

1. The author could have begun her story on page 28. Why do you think she chose to begin with a December entry for Sam's diary? What questions does the first section answer before you learn how Sam started on his venture?

2. Sam is telling his own story to the reader, shuffling his notes and quoting excerpts from his diary as he tells it. Does the author's use of the first person make the story more interesting? more believable? Give the reasons for your opinions.

3. What do you think made Sam persevere in his venture after his first miserable night away from home? Have you ever stuck with something that was at first as unpleasant as this? What was it?

4. What made the tree Sam chose a perfect one for his home?

5. When Sam told his father of his plan, his father had said, "Sure, go try it. Every boy should try it." Do you think most parents would react in the same way? Sam doesn't mention his mother's reaction. What do you think it might have been?

6. Much of Sam's nature know-how came from reading he had done. Name the helpful things he learned in this way.

7. Although Sam skillfully mastered the techniques of survival, and had a growing satisfaction about his independence, what do you think he may grow to miss as time passes?

8. Natural sounds became more intense for Sam the longer he stayed in the mountains. Recall some sounds he heard that "city folk" might not notice at all. Have you ever heard these sounds?

9. Of Sam's encounters with human beings during his stay on the mountain, which do you think was most profitable for him? most enjoyable? Why?

10. Sam came to the conclusion that a mother falcon couldn't count. On what incident was this assumption based?

11. Describe the kind of boy you think Sam was, and tell which incidents in the story make you think of him as you do.

12. There are many details in Sam's journal that show he had a sense of humor. For example, on page 63 he says to his falcon, "Frightful, you are a raving beauty." What are some of the other things that seemed funny to you?

13. In her dedication the author says, "This book is dedicated . . . to the bit of Sam Gribley in the children and adults around me now." What does this mean? Do you think there is a bit of Sam Gribley in you? Why or why not?

The selection is but a part of Sam's account. What new things do you think he will learn during the winter ahead of him? You will no doubt want to get Mrs. George's book from a library or bookstore to read of his continued adventures and the way his story ends. What are some possible endings for it?

Going Beyond the Book

1. Do you know the game of ninepins to which the strawberry lady referred? The story of which she spoke is *Rip Van Winkle* by Washington Irving. If you haven't read it, you may want to get a copy and do so.
2. If you could share just one of the experiences described in the book, which would you choose? Why?

Comparing Two Naturalists

The following information will help you understand why Bando, after enjoying Sam's hospitality in his woodland home, asked, "May I call you Thoreau?"

Henry David Thoreau lived from 1817 to 1862 in and near Concord, Massachusetts. Thoreau thought that most people spent so much time trying to make money and acquire possessions that they never had time to enjoy living. He himself cared nothing for luxuries, and thought that the truly important things of life were exploring nature, reading books, thinking, and writing. So when he was twenty-eight years old, he set off into the woods. By the shore of Walden Pond he built a hut for $28.12½. Here he lived for the next two years and two months. One result of his venture was his famous journal *Walden*.

In the following sentence from this journal Thoreau explains his purpose in going to the woods: ". . . I went to the woods because I wished to live deliberately, to front only the essential facts of life and see if I could not learn what it had to teach and not, when I came to die, discover that I had not lived."

Sam does not explain his purpose so definitely, but he hints at different reasons why he decided to spend a year in the woods. What were some of those reasons?

The following quotations are some others taken from *Walden*. Find observations made by Sam Gribley on the same subjects, and write them in your notebook. When the thoughts and activities of these two "naturalists" are compared, Bando's nickname for Sam becomes even more understandable.

Regarding a Home
". . . I lived alone, in the woods, a mile from any neighbor, in a house which I had built myself . . . and earned my living by the labor of my hands only."

Regarding Clothing
"I cannot believe that our factory system is the best mode by which men may get clothing."

Regarding Baking
"Bread I first made of pure Indian meal and salt, genuine hoe-cakes, which I baked before my fire out of doors on a shingle or the end of a stick of timber sawed off in building my house . . . I tried flour also; but have at last found a mixture of rye and Indian meal most convenient and agreeable."

Regarding Birds of the Air

"On the 29th of April . . . I observed a very slight and graceful hawk, like a night hawk, alternately soaring like a ripple and tumbling over a rod or two over and over, showing the underside of its wings, which gleamed like a satin ribbon in the sun or like the pearly inside of a shell."

The Day Will Bring Some Lovely Thing

by GRACE NOLL CROWELL

"The day will bring some lovely thing,"
I say it over each new dawn:
"Some gay, adventurous thing to hold
Against my heart when it is gone."
And so I rise and go to meet
The day with wings upon my feet.

I come upon it unaware—
Some sudden beauty without name:
A snatch of song—a breath of pine—
A poem lit with golden flame;
High tangled bird notes—keenly thinned—
Like flying color on the wind.

No day has ever failed me quite—
Before the grayest day is done,
I come upon some misty bloom
Or a late line of crimson sun.
Each night I pause—remembering
Some gay, adventurous, lovely thing.

Robinson Crusoe's Story

by CHARLES EDWARD CARRYL

The night was thick and hazy
When the *Piccadilly Daisy*
Carried down the crew and captain in
the sea;
And I think the water drowned 'em
For they never, never found 'em
And I know they didn't come ashore
with me.

Oh! 'twas very sad and lonely
When I found myself the only
Population on this cultivated shore;
But I've made a little tavern
In a rocky little cavern,
And I sit and watch for people at the door.

I spent no time in looking
For a girl to do my cooking,
As I'm quite a clever hand at making stews;
But I had that fellow Friday,
Just to keep the tavern tidy,
And to put a Sunday polish on my shoes.

From *Davy and the Goblin* by Charles E. Carryl. Boston: Houghton Mifflin Company.

I have a little garden
That I'm cultivating lard in,
As the things I eat are rather tough
  and dry;
  For I live on toasted lizards,
  Prickly pears, and parrot gizzards,
And I'm really very fond of beetle-pie.

  The clothes I had were furry,
  And it made me fret and worry
When I found the moths were eating
  off the hair;
  And I had to scrape and sand 'em
  And I boiled 'em and I tanned 'em,
Till I got the fine morocco suit I wear.

  I sometimes seek diversion
  In a family excursion
With the few domestic animals you
  see;
  And we take along a carrot
  As refreshment for the parrot
And a little can of jungleberry tea.

Then we gather as we travel,
Bits of moss and dirty gravel,
And we chip off little specimens of
    stone;
    And we carry home as prizes
    Funny bugs, of handy sizes,
Just to give the day a scientific tone.

If the roads are wet and muddy
We remain at home and study,—
For the Goat is very clever at a sum,—
    And the Dog, instead of fighting,
    Studies ornamental writing,
While the Cat is taking lessons on the
    drum.

We retire at eleven,
And we rise again at seven;
And I wish to call attention, as I close,
    To the fact that all the scholars
    Are correct about their collars,
And particular in turning out their
    toes.

More Books to Read

BOSTON, L. M. *A Stranger at Green Knowe.*
New York: Harcourt, Brace and World, Inc., 1961.
Hanno, a baby gorilla, is captured in the Congo and taken to a zoo in London. He is befriended by Ping, a Chinese refugee orphan who easily understands his plight. When Hanno escapes, Ping is delighted and does all he can to make good the gorilla's escape.

DEFOE, DANIEL. *The Life and Adventures of Robinson Crusoe.*
Cleveland: The World Publishing Company, 1946.
A classic story of shipwreck, savages, and suspense that has been fascinating readers for nearly two hundred and fifty years.

IRVING, WASHINGTON. *Rip Van Winkle and other stories.*
New York: Doubleday and Company, Inc., 1963.
Here you will meet Rip Van Winkle, a famous story character who wandered into the Catskill Mountains one day and witnessed the little men's game of ninepins. He fell asleep there in a haunted hollow and woke twenty years later.

JOHNSON, JAMES R. *Anyone Can Live Off the Land.*
New York: Longmans Green and Company, Inc., 1961.
Sam Gribley himself might have chosen this book to study before beginning his adventure, for in it is all the information one would need to "live off the land." It gives in detail unusual methods of keeping warm, finding and preserving food, first aid, and finding one's way in the woods.

KRUMGOLD, JOSEPH. . . . *And Now Miguel.*
New York: Thomas Y. Crowell Company, 1953.

Miguel Chavez, a boy of New Mexico, is neither old enough to get everything he wants or young enough to be satisfied with what he has. The story of his last great adventure as a boy and his first as a man won the 1954 Newbery Medal.

MONTGOMERY, RUTHERFORD. *Kildee House.*
New York: Doubleday and Co., Inc., 1949.

The delightful story of Jerome Kildee, who went off to be a hermit and ended up sharing his privacy with a bevy of forest animals. A runner-up for the Newbery Medal in 1950.

NORTH, STERLING. *Thoreau of Walden Pond.*
Boston: Houghton Mifflin Company, 1959.

The absorbing story of a man who, like Sam Gribley, sought the peace that only nature could provide. Thoreau, the great American writer and naturalist, also kept a diary, and much of it is quoted in this interestingly written biography.

SPITTEL, RICHARD. *The Savage Island.*
Great Meadows, New Jersey: S. G. Phillips, Inc., 1959.

Hans, a young Dutch boy, is shipwrecked on a deserted jungle coast. He learns the hard rules of survival by befriending wild animals and proving himself to a tribe of primitive natives.

Sid Fleischman, a New Yorker by birth and a Californian by upbringing, became interested in magic when he was in the fifth grade. He learned everything he could about it, mostly from library books, and in the last days of vaudeville he traveled as a professional magician. This interest, knowledge, and practice made the subject of *Mr. Mysterious & Company* a good choice for him. He wrote it with his children in mind—Jane, Paul, and Anne, as in the story. It has been translated into Norwegian and Finnish, and is soon to be published in the Arabic language.

Mr. Fleischman began writing during World War II when he served in the Naval Reserve aboard a destroyer escort in the South Pacific and Asia. Later he became a newspaperman, writer of mystery novels, and a screen writer.

At present, Mr. Fleischman, his wife Betty, and their children live in Santa Monica, California.

MR. MYSTERIOUS & COMPANY

SID FLEISCHMAN

with illustrations by
ERIC VON SCHMIDT

The family of Andrew Perkins Hackett was no ordinary family, for Andrew Perkins Hackett was no ordinary man. Even his wagon stood out among the others traveling west in the summer of 1884.

The Hacketts, a family of traveling magicians, were known to audiences as Mr. Mysterious & Company. For years they had traveled about giving shows in one town after another. But their traveling days are coming to an end—Mother and Father Hackett have decided that the children need roots and proper schooling. The troupe is making its last tour and plans to be in California by Christmas. Little do they know what excitement is in store for them before they settle down. All a-boar-r-rd!

MR. MYSTERIOUS
& COMPANY

BY SID
FLEISCHMAN

Illustrated by ERIC VON SCHMIDT

An Atlantic Monthly Press Book
LITTLE, BROWN AND COMPANY
Boston • Toronto

For
the real Jane
the real Paul
&
the real Anne

CONTENTS

CHAPTER 1

It was a most remarkable sight. Even the hawks and buzzards sleeping in the blue Texas sky awoke in midair to glance down in wonder.

A covered wagon was lurching west along the barren trail to Cactus City, but it was like no other wagon seen in those parts before. To begin with, it was the wrong color. Its canvas was bright red and could be seen for miles. The wheels were painted gold, like a circus wagon, and the horses (if seeing was believing) were as white as swans.

The man driving this most remarkable wagon and these white horses was himself a most remarkable man. He wore a stovepipe hat as tall as Abe Lincoln's and just as black, and had a smiling red beard even sharper than the letter V. If the hawks and buzzards could have read, they would have seen his name in golden letters a foot high on the sides of the wagon:

MR. MYSTERIOUS & COMPANY

The day was hot, and the hour was noon. The gentle-man (for even at this distance you could tell he was a gentleman) led the horses to the shade of a lone oak tree and pulled back on the leather reins.

"Whoa, Hocus," he said in a voice as deep as a bull fiddle. "Whoa, Pocus."

The horses looked so much alike that it was difficult to tell one from the other. When strangers would ask Mr. Mysterious (who was a friendly man and always spoke to strangers) the secret of telling his white horses apart, a twinkle would come into his eye. A magician, as every-one knows, never explains his secrets, and Mr. Mysterious was a traveling magician. But in the matter of his horses there was no real secret to it at all. The animal on the left was Hocus, and the one on the right was Pocus—un-less they got mixed up, which sometimes happened. In that case it was better to talk about the weather, which was hot everywhere that late summer in the year 1884.

The moment the wagon came to a halt, three young faces, in an assortment of ages from six to twelve, ap-peared in the puckered canvas opening behind the driv-er's seat. Two girls and a boy had been doing their school lessons farther back in the wagon.

"Are we almost in Cactus City, Pa?" the boy asked.

The gentleman lifted his hat and kissed them each in the order of their ages and said, "Be patient, young 'uns. We'll be in Cactus City by show time and in California by Christmas."

The children ranged in size like organ pipes, and they had the bluest eyes in any six counties. They climbed to

the ground in their bare feet, and Jane, who was the oldest, smiled to herself. She enjoyed smiling to herself and
sometimes practiced in Pa's shaving mirror. She wondered how she could wait both for Christmas and for the
new life Pa had promised them in California. For the
first time she would have a chance to make friends her
own age and keep them for more than a day at a time.
Jane was almost twelve and beginning to consider herself a young lady, despite her bare feet. It seemed to
her, during secret moments at Pa's shaving mirror, that
she appeared very grown-up when she smiled to herself.
And one day Mama would let her wear her hair up like
the older girls she saw.

"California," Paul grimaced, turning up his toes from
the hot earth, which stung like bees. He was nine and
wore a pair of Pa's suspenders cut
down to size. "Shucks, who'd
want to go to California?"

"Me," Anne said,
clutching a rag doll
that had long legs
and a fixed smile.

Anne longed to take dancing lessons when they reached California. She had never seen a real ballerina, but she had seen a picture of one on Pa's magic-lantern slides. From that moment she had begun to walk on her toes and to dream of satin dancing slippers. Everything seemed possible to her once they reached California.

"We might never get there," Paul said. At least every other day he changed his mind, and this was a day he didn't want to go to California. "We might get stuck in the mud."

Jane cast an unworried glance over the trail ahead of them. "What mud?"

"It might rain."

"It might not."

"Well, we might get scalped by Indians, then." Paul said that just to see his sister flinch. At that moment Mama, in her white sunbonnet, appeared at the wagon opening.

"Now that you mention it," she said, "you'd better have a haircut before show time. It's a wonder you can see three feet ahead of you with all that hair in your eyes."

Pa lifted her to the ground, and she began to busy herself with the noon meal. Mama had once been a schoolteacher, and now she taught the youngsters their lessons as the wagon traveled from town to town. She also played the small portable piano inside the wagon and could sing all the Stephen Foster songs. "We're almost out of water, Andrew," she said.

"We'll get water and supplies in Cactus City," he nodded.

His name was not, as one might suppose, Andrew Mysterious. It was simply Andrew Perkins Hackett—which hardly sounded mysterious enough for a man who could pluck coins from the air and turn hens' eggs into silk handkerchiefs. He had, therefore, adopted a stage name, according to the custom among show folks. As Mr. Mysterious & Company, the family entertained settlers and pioneers in the small towns of the Old West, which at the time was Brand New.

The brightly painted show wagon carried all the tricks and props of a magician's trade. It was full of lacquered boxes with trap doors and secret compartments, colored scarves and ribbons. There were velvet tables with gold fringes, cabinets, and strange vases. Tucked in a corner was a hutch of white rabbits, waiting to be pulled out of hats. On occasion Mr. Mysterious had pulled rabbits out of ten-gallon cowboy hats, Mexican sombreros, coonskin caps, and even ladies' bonnets.

Pa printed up handbills on a small hand press. These were sent ahead to be posted on walls and fences to announce the show's arrival. Handbills had already been sent to Cactus City, where Mr. Mysterious & Company would present its show at seven o'clock sharp—unless the wagon got stuck in the mud. It hadn't got stuck in the mud since last February in Iowa.

"Let me make the sourdough biscuits, Mama," Jane said, adjusting the yellow ribbon in her hair. She looked rather plain in her dark calico dress, but on show nights she was able to wear her pink gingham and float through the air. She looked enchanting behind the footlights

Pa would pass a barrel hoop around her to prove there were no wires holding her up. It amazed everyone except Jane herself, who quite naturally knew how the trick was done. Pa had sworn her to secrecy, and she had never told a soul. But then, she hardly knew a soul outside the members of the family.

"Do we have to have biscuits again?" Paul groaned. Jane had recently learned how to make sourdough biscuits, and it seemed as if the family ate them three times a day.

"Come along, my lad," Pa called. "We'll need to root up some wood for the fire."

Paul had already climbed onto the stilts he had patiently whittled out of old wagon boards. He practiced every time the wagon stopped, and sometimes he took his meals standing as long-legged as a young giraffe. The stilts made him almost as tall as Pa himself, but of course Paul didn't have a smiling red beard as sharp as the letter V. But one day he would have, for he dreamed of becoming a magician like his father. Pa had already taught him to palm coins and small balls. He could untie knots in a rope with his toes. But it would take years of hard practice to master the difficult feats Pa did before the kerosene footlights.

Pa had brought along a shovel, and he began to dig for mesquite roots. "My lad," he smiled, "you can't dig roots from up there on stilts."

Reluctantly Paul jumped back to earth and brushed the hair out of his eyes. He began hunting a mesquite root. Firewood was rarely found lying on the prairies and badlands. Wood was so hard to find that houses were often built of adobe or sod, and after a rain you could see new grass growing on the roofs. But there was mesquite to be found, and the roots made a good fire. Nothing else was at hand except Paul's stilts, and they didn't count.

"Pa," he said, pulling up a fat root and shaking the dirt out, "I wish we didn't have to go to California. Settle down, I mean."

"You'll like living on a cattle ranch," Pa said. "I grew up with cattle. Ranching is the only other trade I know."

"I'd rather travel around just the way we do. Seeing things and having adventures—why, we have adventures every day. Sometimes twice a day."

Pa shook his head. "The matter is settled, my lad. Your mother and I have talked it over from front to back and side to side. You young 'uns ought to have a regular house to grow up in and be getting a regular schooling."

"Mama's the best schoolteacher there is, I bet."

"No doubt about it," Pa said. He stepped on the shovel with his dusty boot. "But a show wagon is no place to get your schooling. No, my lad, we're going to homestead some land and raise beef, like your Uncle Fred in San Diego. And your mother will have a house with a real kitchen and curtains on the windows. No two ways about it—this is going to be the last tour of Mr. Mysterious and Company."

Paul fell silent. He had to admit it might be exciting to live on a cattle ranch. There were some days when he thought he'd rather grow up to be a cowboy than a magician. A sheriff, maybe, or a U.S. marshal. But on show nights, with the footlights blazing up at Pa's face as he performed one miracle after another, there was no doubt in Paul's mind. He wanted to grow up just like Pa. He would rather be a magician than ten sheriffs. He wanted to keep traveling the countryside in the bright red wagon and never wanted to see California.

"Come Christmas," Pa said, "this family is going to settle down for good, like other folks."

There were times when Paul noticed a certain sadness come into his father's eyes at the thought of laying aside his magic wand. Pa loved entertaining folks and making them laugh, but once he made up his mind, it stayed made. "I hope Christmas never comes," Paul said under his breath.

He didn't really mean that. He liked Christmas as much as the Fourth of July and birthdays and Abracadabra Day. Sometimes he thought Abracadabra Day was the best holiday of all. It was listed in no almanac and printed in no calendar. It was a secret holiday that belonged to the show family. They had invented it, and no one else knew about it.

The secret was this: no matter how bad you were on Abracadabra Day or no matter what pranks you pulled, you would not be spanked or punished. It was the one day in the year, in the Hackett family at least, on which you were *supposed* to be bad.

As Pa had once explained it to them, "The way we live, moving about all the time, you young 'uns have got to be good. But no young 'uns ought to have to be good three hundred and sixty-five days in the year. So you each have one day to be bad."

There was only one rule about Abracadabra Day. You must not tell anybody the day you had chosen to be bad. The children sometimes planned for weeks or months just what prank they would pull on Abracadabra Day. No matter what it was, they couldn't be spanked, which was why they had named it Abracadabra Day. It was like magic to do something naughty and not get punished.

Paul was digging out another mesquite root when there came a shouting and a commotion behind them at the show wagon. He turned and saw Mama and Jane and Anne, all three, waving their arms like windmills.

"Andrew—come quick!" shouted Mama.

"Pa! Hurry!"

Pa dropped his shovel and whipped off his hat so he could run all the faster. Paul dropped a root and climbed on his stilts, but tripped over the shovel. To add to the confusion, it must be admitted at this point that horses and rabbits were not the only livestock traveling with Mr. Mysterious & Company. There was Madam Sweetpea. Madam Sweetpea didn't perform in the show; she tagged along behind. Madam Sweetpea was a black-and-white cow. Despite her name, there was nothing very sweet about Madam Sweetpea except the fresh milk she provided for the three Hackett youngsters. She was by nature proud, ornery, and the laziest cow north of the Rio Grande River (and south of the Rio Grande as well). She walked very slowly, and since she was tied to the rear of the show wagon by a rope, the wagon could never go any faster than Madam Sweetpea walked.

"Pa!" Jane said. "Look!"

"Calm down, now. Look at what?"

"Behind the wagon," Mama exclaimed. "Madam Sweetpea! She's gone!"

"Vanished into thin air!" Jane added.

"The cow jumped over the moon," Anne said.

CHAPTER 2

Jane watched Pa tap the stovepipe hat firmly on his head and stride on his long legs to the rear of the show wagon. It was true: Madam Sweetpea was gone. Her rope was gone. The flies she switched with her tail were gone.

Even her hoofmarks had vanished from the earth.

"A spendid mystery," Pa mused. He stood sharpening the point of his beard and wondered how a full-grown, ornery cow could disappear into thin air.

"Pa, it's *impossible*," Jane said.

"Nothing is impossible, Sister," Pa said. "Not if we put our minds to it."

Jane brushed a wisp of hair from her forehead and tried to put her mind to it. She knew that Pa needed mirrors or threads or trick boxes to make things disappear. But she had never seen a mirror or trick box large enough to hide a cow. And Madam Sweetpea, who weighed more than half a ton, could hardly have been plucked out of sight with threads.

"Andrew," Mama said gently. She was very worried. "What are we going to do? Poor Madam Sweetpea. There'll be no milk for the children."

The doll in Anne's arms continued to smile. "Jane can't make biscuits now," Anne said. She was not smiling. She liked Jane's sourdough biscuits. It wouldn't be possible to make biscuits even with water. The water barrel was almost empty. The wagon had crossed a creek bed just five minutes before, on the other side of a small hill, but the creek was as dry as dust.

"A splendid mystery," Pa said again, examining the spot where Madam Sweetpea should have been but wasn't. Even her fat shadow was gone.

"What's all the fuss?" Paul said, hurrying up on his stilts. His arms were loaded with firewood so he wouldn't have to go back for it. Paul hated to go back for things.

"Now that we have all assembled," Pa said, "let us get at the bottom of this mystery. Is anyone carrying a grudge against Madam Sweetpea?"

"She kicks," Jane said. "She kicked you when you weren't looking, Pa—just last Tuesday."

"How well I remember," Pa nodded with a look of pain and sorrow.

"She ate Mama's hat," Anne said. "Her Sunday-go-to-meeting hat. The one with the wax cherries on it."

"That cow will even eat rusty nails," Paul put in. "She's got no sense at all."

"Maybe so," Pa admitted. "Madam Sweetpea eats straw hats and rusty nails and kicks grown men. Those are ornery traits in a cow—or in a horse or a mule, for that matter. But she gives milk, and I suppose we'd better overlook her bad habits."

Jane glanced at Paul, and it seemed to her he was almost glad that now she wouldn't be able to make sourdough biscuits for the noon meal. But he wasn't old enough to make a cow disappear. He wasn't a magician, like Pa.

Pa lifted his hat to scratch his head. "Who last heard a sound from Madam Sweetpea?"

"She went *moo*," Anne said.

"When?"

"When we crossed the dry creek, Pa."

"Thank you, Sister." A twinkle was coming into Pa's eye. "Then she was last heard about five minutes ago —just before she vanished into thin air."

"Pa!" Jane exploded. "Maybe Madam Sweetpea just ran away."

"But she was tied to the wagon. A good stout knot, too. I tied her myself."

All eyes suddenly turned to Paul, who remained on stilts and was casting a shadow as long as his father's. Paul, they knew, had been practicing untying knots with his toes.

"Young man," Pa said. "Did you untie Madam Sweetpea's rope as we were crossing the dry creek?"

Paul straightened his shoulders and said, "Yes, Pa."

"So I couldn't make biscuits!" Jane said.

"In that case," Pa declared, "the mystery is solved. Madam Sweetpea is just behind that small hill at the dry creek bed."

And at that moment they all heard a *moo* from the other side of the hill. It was Madam Sweetpea's voice, as loud and clear as a foghorn on the Mississippi River.

"Paul!" Mama said. "How could you do such a naughty thing?"

"You walk yourself behind the wagon there," Pa said, "and I'll administer a first-rate spanking."

Paul, who had kept a perfectly straight face, now burst out, "Abracadabra Day!" And then he began to laugh so hard that he almost lost his balance high up on the stilts. "Abracadabra Day!"

There was a stunned silence from Pa and Mama and Jane and Anne. He had taken them all by surprise.

"So that's what you've been up to, you rascal!" said Pa, starting to laugh himself.

Mama forgot her anger and found herself joining in the laughter. A moment later all five of them stood merrily on the bare Texas badlands, laughing as hard as at a circus—which woke the hawks and buzzards again as they napped on the high winds in the sky.

"By gosh and by golly," Pa said. "I can't very well give you a hiding on Abracadabra Day, so why don't you and I go fetch Madam Sweetpea?"

They walked back over the hill, still chuckling, and found the cow munching a tuft of buffalo grass. She was standing right over her shadow, switching flies with her tail, and her rope dragged in the dust. Paul, on his stilts, walked her back to the wagon—or rather, pulled and tugged on her rope, for she didn't want to leave the dry creek bed. He had planned his prank for more than a week. He had heard Pa call out that they would stop for the noon meal at the shade tree up ahead. That was when he had untied Madam Sweetpea with his toes. Now he had surprised them all—and he had even fooled Pa, for a moment or two at least. It had been like a magic trick.

After the noon meal Mama got out a soup bowl, put it on Paul's head, and trimmed his hair around it. Most of the boys on the frontier had their hair cut that way until they outgrew the bowl.

Finally the family packed the cooking utensils and continued on the trail to Cactus City. If they got to town early enough, they would be able to visit the general store and buy all kinds of supplies and perhaps some candy.

The red covered wagon creaked and lumbered over the trail, and Madam Sweetpea walked along behind, with her rope well knotted to the tail gate. The family rode together on the wooden seat, watching the passing sights.

Most of the time they chuckled about Paul's Abracadabra Day. They would laugh many times, and even for years to come, over the day Paul made a cow disappear!

CHAPTER 3

Jane was the first to notice Cactus City off to the left of the trail. There was no sign pointing the way, but she could see the top of the church steeple. The town appeared sunk in a small valley, as if hiding from sight.

"You children get back in the wagon and put on your shoes," said Mama. "We're not going to ride into town looking like a band of gypsies."

Paul hated to wear shoes. With shoes on he couldn't practice untying knots with his toes.

"Hurry, Pa," Anne said. "So we can go to the general store before it comes show time."

She had been thinking of the candy jars for hours. Pa had promised them five cents' worth of candy each. That was more than a week ago, and her mouth had been watering ever since.

"Plenty of time," Pa said. He looked at his fine gold watch that chimed the hours. He was prouder of his watch than anything he owned. "Two hours yet before show time. I didn't figure we'd be getting to Cactus City this early. Plenty of time."

The trail forked off, and the wagon followed the dusty road leading down into the hidden valley. The family always felt an air of excitement as they rode into town. There were things to see and people to talk to and news to catch up on. And, of course, a show to give.

"Jane," Mama said. "Hand me my new sunbonnet. It's hanging right there over your head."

Jane unhooked the bonnet and handed it out to her mother. It was as white and stiff as starch could make it. Mama took a great deal of care to keep the girls' bonnets as crisp as her own. She made her own starch, either from the settlings of potato water or by soaking wheat and using the starchy dregs that settled to the bottom.

Jane brushed out her long hair and tied the ribbon freshly in place. Now that they were so near, she could hardly wait for Cactus City. There would be other girls, town girls. How wonderful it would be to live in a town, she thought, and carry her books to school and go to parties. She had never been to a real party in her life. She had never been to a taffy pull or a box social or even a sewing bee. The family had been on the move as long as she could remember. It was fun being part of a show wagon, but there were times when she felt a longing and a loneliness as hard to bear as a toothache. But now, with the rooftops already in view, her eyes sparkled and her mood was light as a smile.

"Is my ribbon straight, Mama?" she asked.

"Straight as can be," Mama said, doing up Anne's shoes with a buttonhook.

Pa was knocking the dust off his trousers. "It wouldn't surprise me if they hadn't had a wagon show in here for a year at least," he said. "Maybe more. Everybody must be waiting for us."

"Looks like a pretty town," Mama smiled, tying the bonnet strings under her chin. "Joy, all freshly painted like it was born yesterday."

"Mighty quiet, though," Pa said, casting a glance along the main street.

The town was indeed neat and freshly painted and quiet as a clock that had run down. There was something strange about this town. Jane looked about, but there wasn't even a dog to be seen on the street or a horse hitched to a rail. Pa noticed that not a single handbill had been posted to announce the coming of the magic show. Not a man, woman, or child was on the boardwalks to greet them.

LAST CHA

There was not a soul to be seen anywhere.

The town stood empty.

Pa pulled up in front of the barbershop and looked around. "Mighty strange," he murmured. "A town without folks in it."

Paul gazed at the silent street. It was kind of spooky.

All the excitement Jane had felt a moment before was gone.

"Pa," Anne whispered. "I'm scared."

Mama held Anne a little closer, and Anne held her rag doll close enough to burst a seam.

"Andrew," Mama murmured, "where is everyone? It looks like the earth has swallowed everybody up."

"Look," Jane said quietly, trying not to sound scared. "There's a fresh washing hanging on the line. Behind that green house."

Pa tapped the stovepipe hat firmly on his head and climbed to the ground. He left the wagon where it stood in the middle of the street. The sun was getting so low that the wagon seemed to cast a shadow from one end of town to the other. "You and the young 'uns wait there," he said. "I'll have a look around."

"I'll get your rifle, Pa," Paul said.

"Won't need it. It doesn't look like there's even a jack rabbit to shoot at around here."

Jane watched Pa cross to the boardwalk and try the door of the general store.

It was shut tight. Padlocked.

"Bet it's a ghost town," Paul said to Jane.

"I'm not afraid of ghosts."

"You are, too."

"Well, how could there be ghosts in the daytime?"

Mama told them to get back inside the wagon, where they would feel safer. But even under the red canvas they talked in whispers. Finally Paul lifted the canvas so they could peek out. Pa was trying doors farther along the boardwalk.

"The whole town is padlocked," Jane said.

And Paul said, "Maybe everyone is hiding."

"Why?"

"They might be expecting an Indian attack."

Anne, whose heart was beating lickety-split, suddenly pointed toward Pa. "Look! There's an Indian!"

"Where!"

"I see him!" Paul said, forgetting to whisper. "Just behind Pa!"

Now Jane saw him, too—an Indian standing with full warbonnet, face painted, and a tomahawk raised in the air! "Pa!" she shouted. "Indian!"

"Behind you!" Paul cried.

Pa turned quickly and saw the redskin, too. And then the youngsters watched an amazing sight. Pa didn't duck and he didn't run. He merely stood there looking at the Indian, and the Indian stood looking at Pa. The children stood frozen, except Jane, who had shut her eyes.

"The rifle, Mama!" Paul shouted.

But Mama didn't make a move. Couldn't she see what was happening? Paul wondered. He couldn't see too well himself, with the lowering sun full in their faces.

But then he saw Pa do a most remarkable thing. As if he had hypnotized the redskin, Pa bit off the end of a fresh cigar and struck a match on the deadly tomahawk.

Jane couldn't stand it any longer. She opened her eyes and saw Pa blow a smoke ring in the savage's face. Then he tipped his hat politely and walked away.

And the redskin just stood there as if frozen.

Mama (who had almost reached for the rifle when the children first began shouting) turned with a gentle smile. "You ninnies," she said. "Don't you know a wooden Indian when you see one? It's standing in front of the cigar store."

Jane let out her breath. She felt a little silly, but no sillier than Paul. Still, the sun *had* been in their eyes.

Pa crossed to the other side of the street and stood for a moment scratching his head.

"Look," Anne said again, pointing her finger.

"What do you see now?" Paul asked. He wasn't going to be fooled a second time. "Another wooden Indian?"

"A doggy. Under the sidewalk. See? Here, doggy."

Jane and Paul couldn't help looking, and there was indeed a dog hiding under the wooden boardwalk.

"Jump, doggy," Anne said, forgetting all about Indians. "Jump."

And right before their eyes, the dog, who was black and furry, with great laughing brown eyes, crept out into the sun and made a backflip in the air.

"That dog's been trained," Jane said. She loved animals, whether they were trained or not. She lifted the canvas up high. "Jump. Jump here!"

And the dog jumped into the wagon.

"Mama!" Jane called. "We found a dog!"

Mama turned, her sudden smile framed in the white sunbonnet. "Joy! Why, the poor thing. He looks thirsty. His tongue is hanging out." Even though the water barrel thumped empty, she added, "Jane, get the dipper and see if you can scrape him up a drink."

Jane scooped out a dipper of water and poured it into a tin pan. The dog lapped it up so fast the water seemed to disappear as if it were one of Pa's magic tricks.

"His master couldn't be very kind," Jane said, stroking his furry back, "letting him go thirsty this way."

"Maybe he doesn't have a master," Paul said.

"Then who taught him tricks?"

"Maybe his master disappeared, like everybody else in this town. Then we could keep him."

Pa returned from the far end of the street, taking long and merry strides as if marching in a parade. His eyes twinkled, and a smile lifted his eyebrows high up under his hat brim. There was a slip of paper tucked in his hatband, and even Mama wondered what it could be as he mounted the wagon seat.

"Git up, Hocus! Git up, Pocus!"

"Andrew," Mama said, "what did you find out? You're smiling like a jack-o'-lantern."

"I'll put up in front of the bank, and you tell me what you see."

"What's that note under your hatband?"

"Git up."

The wagon creaked forward, and Madam Sweetpea protested with her foghorn voice. Half a block farther along, Pa pulled up on the reins.

"Paul," he said. "Read off the name on that bank."

Paul shaded his eyes and read the gold lettering afire in the sun. "First Bank of Lone City, Texas."

"Lone City?" Jane exclaimed. "Pa, that bank is in the wrong town." She stopped suddenly. "Unless——"

"Exactly," Pa laughed. *"We're* in the wrong town. This isn't Cactus City at all. It's Lone City!"

And then he whipped out the note tucked in his hatband and read it. He had found it tucked up on the door of the feed store.

Gone to Cactus City to see the magic show.

Mama took the note and read it again. "I declare," she smiled.

Pa turned the wagon around in the middle of the main street. "Folks are waiting for us," he said. "They padlocked their town to see a magic show—and by gosh and by golly, we're going to give it to them."

"Git up, Madam Sweetpea," Anne said.

CHAPTER 4

Pa heard a dog bark.

"It must be a squeak in the wheels," he said. "We've got two horses, a cow, and six rabbits, but we don't have a dog."

"Yes, we do!" Jane laughed, snapping her fingers at the dog farther back in the wagon. "And he can do tricks. Sit up!"

Pa turned and saw a black dog sitting up on Mama's trunk.

"Can we keep him, Pa?" Anne begged.

Pa stopped the wagon in front of the livery barn, and the dog climbed into Jane's calico lap. Pa shook his head. "That's a fine-looking dog, but he belongs to someone here in Lone City. We can't take him with us." Pa climbed to the ground. "Hand him to me, Sister."

Sadly Jane handed down the dog. His tail started wagging, stirring up a breeze, and he began to lick Pa's face—red beard and all.

"Now don't you go trying to break our hearts," Pa said. "You can't come along. You belong here in Lone City. Now get along home."

Pa mounted the wagon seat once more, and the dog sat in the hot dust. His tail was still.

"Git up, Hocus. Git up, Pocus."

Pa was silent a long time. The young 'uns had always wanted a dog, he knew, but it would only be another mouth to feed. There was no place in the show for a dog. All the animals earned their keep; Hocus and Pocus pulled the wagon, Madam Sweetpea gave fresh milk, and the rabbits popped out of hats. A dog was just a dog.

Jane tried not to look back. No one said a word, and there wasn't a smile on even one of the five faces. The wagon creaked and swayed along the rutted trail, and finally a sign appeared:

Cactus City--One Mile

It was Mama who broke the silence when she glanced behind to make sure Madam Sweetpea was still tied to the wagon.

"Look—he's following us," she exclaimed.

They all turned to look. The dog was indeed following in Madam Sweetpea's tracks.

Pa stopped the wagon and strode to the dog.

"Now see here, little dog. You don't belong to us. You go along home."

The black tail wagged a half circle in the dust.

"Hear me, little dog? You turn around and get home."

The tail stopped wagging. Pa took the reins once more, and the wagon lurched forward. But every time someone glanced behind, the black dog was there, following in Madam Sweetpea's tracks.

"He likes us," Jane said. "He wants to come along."

"Maybe he's trying to run away from home," Paul said.

"Andrew," Mama said. "His tongue is hanging out. All that walking in the sun and dust—he's thirsty again."

Pa leaned back on the reins once more. He sat a moment thinking hard, and the children held their breath. Then he tapped his hat firmly in place. "All right," he said. "There's no point in sending him home when we're so close to Cactus City now. Get him in the wagon. We'll find his owner and return him."

"Jump!" Anne shouted. "Jump, doggy!"

"Here!" Paul added.

"In the wagon!" Jane called out.

The dog leaped into their laps. Everyone was smiling again. The wagon moved on, and the children scraped another dipper of water out of the barrel.

The sun sat on the horizon like a huge pumpkin. The rooftops and false fronts of Cactus City stood on a mesa covered with cactus.

Much as the children had traveled, they had never seen so much cactus in one place in their lives. It was like driving the wagon through an enormous pincushion. Jane saw barrel cactus as big as nail kegs. Paul cast an eye over beavertail cactus by the dozens. Anne watched jumping cactus, hoping to see one jump. They didn't jump so fast that you couldn't get out of the way; in fact, Pa said they didn't really jump at all, but grew in leaps and bounds. Mama saw pancake cactus, which hardly looked good enough to eat, even with butter and molasses.

The whole town was waiting for the wagon show when Hocus and Pocus, lifting their white legs smartly, led the spinning gold wheels along the main street.

"There they are!" went up the shout. "Here comes Mr. Mysterious and Company!"

Pa lifted his stovepipe hat, and the youngsters waved to the crowds along the boardwalks. The show wagon traveled the length of the main street. Folks in the hotel leaned out of the upstairs windows to watch. Boys and girls followed along the street (some of them doing cartwheels out of pure joy). They were dressed in their best calicos and homespuns. The ladies wore bustles, and some of them carried parasols.

Pa halted the wagon across the very end of the main street, and the townspeople gathered around. The show had been promised for seven o'clock sharp, which was just ten minutes away. There wouldn't be time to go to the general store—there wouldn't even be time for supper.

A man wearing a heavy silver watch chain across his ample vest stepped forward and raised his arm. The townsfolk quieted to a whisper.

"As mayor," he said, "I welcome you folks to Cactus City. Where's the show going to be?"

"In this very spot," Pa said. "With your permission."

The mayor nodded. "Our young 'uns have been waiting all afternoon. We figured you got lost."

"We drove into Lone City by mistake."

"Don't stand there jawin', Mayor!" someone shouted. "Let's get on with the show."

Pa pulled out his gold pocket watch. "My timepiece here says seven minutes to seven. We've been on the trail all day, and we're a mite dusty. But our handbills promised you a magic show at seven o'clock sharp—and by gosh and by golly, we'll give it to you!"

With only seven minutes to set up the props, the family had to work fast. Mama flew to the wooden trunk for their show costumes. Jane unpacked the colored silk scarves and flags her father would produce from "empty" vases and tin tubes. Paul set up the magician's table with the red velvet drape and the gold fringe. Anne brushed the lint off her father's black tailcoat.

Pa rolled up a sidepiece of the canvas cover and let down a wooden side section of the wagon itself. It folded out like a tabletop to rest on two stout legs, and formed the stage. Then he lit the four kerosene footlights to be set out when the show started.

Inside the wagon a backdrop was hoisted and screens set up like stage wings. Jane changed into her pink gingham, and Paul buttoned up his blue assistant's uniform. Pa shifted Mama's portable piano behind one of the wings, and she took her place on the stool.

"All ready?" he whispered to his show company.

There was a nod all around, and Pa slipped into his tailcoat. Everyone forgot about the black dog. In the

151

rush and confusion he darted between Pa's legs and across the stage.

"Hey! That's my dog!"

A man shouldered his way forward. Anne peeked out and saw him first. Her heart began to race at the sight of him. He wore wide suspenders and a dirty hat, and his face whiskers stuck out like the quills of a porcupine.

"You there!" he shouted. "Come out here! You stole my dog Blue!"

Blue had disappeared behind the wagon drapes and was hidden, shaking and whining softly, behind a trick box.

Then the man climbed right up on the stage. Jane peeked out from one side and Paul from the other. The kerosene lamps lit up the man's face, and it was something fierce to see. The next thing Paul knew, the man had caught hold of his arm with a grip like a vise and yanked him out from behind the wings.

"You there!" the man growled. "You're nothing but a pack of rawhiders and thieves—even you young 'uns. Trying to make off with my dog!"

"Honest, mister——" Paul protested.

Pa strode out in his tailcoat and stovepipe hat—and he looked even more angry than the stranger. "Take your hand off that boy," he said in a voice so sharp it could have split a rock.

The man turned, and his whiskers shook. "Where's my dog? Trying to hide him, were you?"

"Not a bit. He followed us with his tongue hanging out. He wouldn't turn around and go home. We figured his master would be here in Cactus City, so we let him come along. Sister, bring him out."

"Oh, you're not fooling Jeb Grimes," the man snapped. "I'm onto you actor folks. I'll get the sheriff and have you all thrown in jail!"

Jane picked up Blue and hugged him tight. There was a quick tear in her eye. She was sorry that he had to go home with the whiskered stranger. But she did what she was told. She set Blue at his master's feet. Almost at once the dog backed and growled.

"Come here, you lazy critter," Jeb Grimes said.

But Blue kept growling and then hid under Jane's long skirt.

Jeb Grimes faced Pa again. "You put a hex on my dog," he growled. "You turned him against me."

"No," said Pa. "Maybe you turned him against yourself. But he's yours, and there's not much I can do. Now take that fine dog and get off this stage."

But Jeb Grimes planted his stout legs firmly where he stood and peered out at the townspeople. "Sheriff Johnson—you're out there, and you seen it for yourself. These show folks tried to steal my dog!"

The sheriff moved through the crowd. The star pinned to his vest glinted like silver. He leaned his big hands on the edge of the makeshift stage. "Jeb, you've got your dog back," he said. "Now stop making a fuss. These people look to me like they're telling the truth. That dog of yours follows everyone but you."

"They had Blue in their possession, Sheriff—and that's thieving."

"Maybe and maybe not," Pa said. "Take off your hat, Mr. Grimes."

"What?"

"Remove your hat, sir."

"What in tarnation for?"

"You just said possession is thieving."

"Well, it is."

"Then do me the kindness to take off your headgear."

Jeb Grimes squinted and looked around him, and the sheriff said, "What are you afraid of, Jeb? You hiding all your gold pieces under your hat?"

"I'm a poor man," Jeb Grimes declared, and everyone laughed—the folks from Cactus City as well as Lone City. They all knew he hoarded every dollar that came his way.

Finally he took off his old and battered hat. Pa beat the dust out of it and then rolled up his right sleeve. Very slowly he reached his hand deep into Jeb Grimes' hat—and pulled out a live and kicking white rabbit!

The townspeople gaped in amazement. They were so startled they forgot to applaud.

But Pa didn't perform the trick for applause. He was still simmering with anger. "Now then, Jeb Grimes," he said, "what are you doing with my rabbit hidden in your hat? Sheriff—that's thieving!"

Now the audience burst into a roar of laughter and whistling. Everyone laughed but Jeb Grimes.

He grabbed back his hat and pulled it down almost to his ears. "Blue!" he shouted. "Come here, you ornery, ungrateful critter."

154

"Just a moment," Pa said. "Mr. Grimes, I'd like to buy your dog."

"He ain't for sale," Jeb Grimes said.

At that moment the watch in Pa's vest pocket struck the hour. It was show time.

Pa lifted out the watch, and the chimes sounded again and again—seven times. The chimes were clear and beautiful—as golden as the watch itself.

Jeb Grimes' eyes opened in wonder. He had never seen a chiming watch before. Pa had bought it in Kansas City.

"Blue ain't for sale," he said again. "But that's a mighty pretty gold watch you got there. Rings out like a church bell, don't it?"

"Get off the stage, Jeb Grimes!" someone yelled. "Let's have the show."

But Jeb Grimes didn't move. "Yes, sir, a mighty fine watch. I'd like to have a watch like that, mister. You want my dog? I might trade for that watch of yours."

Pa closed his hand over the watch. He had saved a long time to buy it, and he needed a timepiece. There wasn't another watch like it within five hundred miles, and he didn't want to give it up. But then he glanced at Jane and Paul and Anne peeking out from the wings. And he could even see Blue sticking his muzzle out from under the hem of Mama's dress, where he was now hiding.

All their eyes were on him. A dog didn't belong in the show, and he ought to leave well enough alone.

"It's a trade!" Pa said firmly. He unclasped the watch from his chain and put it into Jeb Grimes' gnarled hand.

"Not just the watch," Jeb Grimes said. "The chain, too. Or it ain't a bargain."

"Jeb Grimes," Pa declared. "You must have been raised on sour milk. Here, take the chain and get off this stage."

With that, he strung the chain loose from his fancy vest, which Mama had decorated with fine needlework. He dropped it into Jeb Grimes' waiting hand. Sorry as the children were to see Pa lose his watch and chain, it meant Blue would never again have to go home to Jeb Grimes.

"Blue!" Jane said. Her face lit up with sheer happiness. "Blue! You're ours!"

And Paul grinned, "You can come out now."

Blue crept out from under Mama's skirts and began to wag his tail once more. And Pa raised both arms to the audience.

"Folks!" he announced, and he was smiling again. "The show is about to begin! We present for your amusement, edification, and jollification our traveling temple of mysteries! A program of wonders and marvels for young and old! Feats of legerdemain and tricks of prestidigitation! Magic, mirth, and music!"

At this, Mama struck up a heavy chord on the small piano, and Paul, his buttons gleaming, hurried out with Pa's black wand.

"Folks!" Pa continued, with a gesture of the wand. "I present—MR. MYSTERIOUS AND COMPANY!"

CHAPTER 5

Jane was floating in the air.

Pa passed the barrel hoop from her head to her toes and back again.

"Behold!" he said.

The townspeople stared up in silent wonder at the small stage. Jane floated behind the footlights with her eyes closed as if she were sleeping in a magic trance. Her pink gingham had the enchanted look of gossamer. There was not a sound to be heard from the crowd. The men forgot to puff on their cigars, and their eyes seemed as large as silver dollars. The children stared up in amazement, and their eyes were at least as large as nickels.

"Is it real?" said Pa. "Can it be done? You see it before your eyes. A feat first performed by the magicians of China and India. Today it can be seen on the stages of London, Paris, New York—and Cactus City!"

Hardly an eye in Cactus City blinked.

"Now then, Sleeping Princess," Pa said very softly, "you will rise still higher."

And Jane, who was already floating three feet off the stage, rose another foot. She appeared as light as a feather. It seemed as if a sudden breeze would blow her away!

"Behold!"

The mayor hooked his thumbs in his vest and wondered if it was done with mirrors.

The sheriff hooked his thumbs in *his* vest and wondered if it was done with wires.

While Jane seemed to be in a mysterious sleep, like the fairy princess herself, the truth of the matter was that she was trying hard not to giggle. And Paul wasn't helping matters.

He was out of sight in the wings. "There's a fly on your nose," he whispered across the stage.

"And now, Sleeping Princess," Pa said, passing his black wand over her, "you will return to the enchanted sofa and awaken."

As if under the power of Pa's magic stick, she floated lower and lower to the velvet sofa on the stage. Even though she tried to put the fly out of her mind, she could almost feel it on the tip of her nose, and she had to fight back the giggles. It would have broken the spell, of course, but the harder she tried to keep from wrinkling her nose and bursting into giggles, the harder she had to clamp her teeth together. Paul! she thought. I'll get even with him!

Finally she settled onto the sofa like a gently falling leaf. "Rub my nose, Pa," she said in a desperate stage whisper. "It itches something terrible."

Pa, who had been standing with his eyes fixed on the audience, glanced down. "No wonder," he replied in a stage whisper. "There's a fly on your nose."

And at that she almost *did* giggle. Paul hadn't been teasing her at all!

Pa brushed the fly away with a pass of his wand, and then he clapped his hands.

"Awake, Sleeping Princess!"

Now she could open her eyes at last. She awoke and curtsied to the audience. Pa bowed deeply beside her. Then she ran off into the wings to a round of applause.

The moment she was out of sight she put her face in her hands—and giggled.

The show held the townspeople spellbound for well over an hour. It grew dark, and the footlights flickered. Pa made handkerchiefs disappear. He passed his wand over an egg, and it turned into a turnip. Paul, as the magician's assistant, showed a tin tube that looked as empty as a stovepipe, and Pa produced yards of ribbons from it. He changed red silks into green ones and green ones into yellow ones.

During many of the feats Mama created a mysterious atmosphere by playing softly at the piano. At the same time she was kept busy seeing to it that the youngsters got on and off the stage on cue, and she had to make sure the trick boxes and tubes were ready when Pa needed them. There was no time for Blue, who sat at Mama's feet and watched the goings on. But in whispers the youngsters had already decided among them to think of a new name for the dog.

"Mama," Anne whispered, "I'm hungry. My doll's hungry, too."

"In a moment, Sister," Mama replied. She was playing dark and mysterious chords. "The show is almost over."

One miracle followed another, and all the time Pa sharpened his beard and smiled. He set up the magic lantern while Paul and Jane blew out the footlights to make the stage dark. Then Pa projected still pictures on a white sheet, for the magic lantern was nothing more than a "picture show."

A photograph of President Chester A. Arthur shot up onto the sheet, and everyone applauded. The picture was dim, and it flickered badly, but no one minded. Magic-lantern shows were very popular in the frontier towns, for they gave the settlers a look at famous people and faraway places.

The black lantern box smoked and sputtered. Pa put in a slide of a Mississippi steamboat, and it seemed as if one could almost hear its whistle blow. Then came Civil War scenes, including a picture of Abe Lincoln by the famous photographer Mathew Brady. Pa showed a slide of a large Napoleon cannon, which looked as if it were going to fire right down the main street of Cactus City. It scared the ladies and small children. Pa himself had been wounded at Gettysburg. The Civil War had ended nineteen years before, but one still saw men in bits and pieces of their old army uniforms, for nothing went to waste on the frontier. Wives had made their husbands trousers, and even shirts, from old army blankets.

Finally, Pa showed slides of the Niagara Falls and the pyramids of Egypt and London Bridge. "And now a special treat for you ladies," he said.

With that, he showed photographs he had made in Kansas City at a grand reception where women were dressed in the latest fashions from Paris.

The frontier women, in their plain calicos and sunbonnets, looked on with "Oh's" and "Ah's." The slim-waisted ladies in the lantern pictures wore feathered hats and beribboned bustles. It was enough to make a ranch wife's mouth water—and it did. But the frontier ladies made quick mental notes of what they saw, and in the months to come they would attempt to make similar costumes for themselves. The show would provide man, woman, and child with something to talk about all through the winter. They would argue their opinions on how this trick was done, or that, but they could never be sure—and they might even discuss it till spring.

Anne watched for the slide showing a ballerina. On the tips of her toes, the dancer seemed to come to life in the swirl of her costume. Anne was enchanted. Sometimes for days on end she found herself walking on her toes. Perhaps, when the family settled on the ranch near San Diego, Mama would find her a dancing teacher.

"And now, my friends," Pa announced as he relit the kerosene footlights, "our entertainment is at an end. The show is over. We don't sell tickets, and if you have a mind to, you can turn around and go home without paying the price of admission. Some wagon shows give an entertainment and then sell soap or patent medicines.

Well, sir, we're not in the soap business *or* the patent-medicine business. All we've got to sell is good family entertainment—and you all look like good family people."

The crowd smiled at this, and Jane and Paul set two tambourines at the two corners of the stage.

"If you liked our traveling temple of mystification, education, and jollification," Pa went on, "the price you saw on our handbills was twenty-five cents for adults and a nickel each for children. If you didn't like the show, it was free. I see some of you brought along barter instead of cash money, and we'll be happy to accept it. My family and I haven't had our supper, and that pie you're holding, madam, has been making our mouths water."

"It's wild plum," the woman said.

"Sara makes the best wild-plum pie in Texas," the man beside her called out.

Mama struck up a Stephen Foster song on the piano. The townspeople, if one could judge from the rattle of money against the tambourines, had liked the show, one and all. Soon the edge of the stage was piled with things to eat. Folks were used to trading what they had for what they needed or wanted. Not everyone had coin money to spend. Paul saw a watermelon that must have weighed twenty-five pounds, and he licked his lips. Jane had her eye on a big basket of apples. Two pumpkins appeared; a dozen eggs, a jar of honey, almost a bushel of corn, a jug of sorghum molasses, turnips and potatoes, and several jars of preserved vegetables. The edge of the stage began to look like a county fair!

163

Meanwhile, Paul and Jane and Anne changed out of their show costumes. Mama packed things away carefully for the next performance. They were as busy *after* the show as they had been *before*. Jane had the silks and flags to fold and put away. Paul had the magic table to take apart, leg by leg, to allow more room in the wagon. Anne began carrying in the barter from the stage.

"Don't drop those eggs," Mama said. "We'll need them for breakfast."

Soon the crowd had gone, and Pa blew out the footlights. He carried in the watermelon and found a place for it under the wagon seat. Mama filled her "grab box" with barter. It was nothing but a large tin cracker box where she kept the smaller food supplies, together with her silverware and frying pan. Tomorrow she would cut the pumpkins into strips and dry them for winter. They would make a nice Christmas pie, she said to herself.

Finally, Pa folded the small stage platform back into the side of the wagon and let down the red canvas. Then he mounted the seat and drove the team to a clearing at the edge of town, where they would camp for the night.

"Paul," Mama said. "Get a bucket of water at the town pump, and I'll start supper. You children are hungry."

"Hold on," Pa said, a smile breaking over his face. "This family is going to eat in the hotel restaurant tonight. We made twenty-two dollars and eighty cents. I just counted it. Hard money. We're going to celebrate!"

And celebrate they did—although Paul had to bring a pail of water from the pump just the same. Mama wasn't going to let her family show up at the hotel restaurant unless everyone was scrubbed up clean.

Pa ordered the six-course supper for everyone. They had left Blue to guard things at the wagon, and they spent the first two courses of the meal trying to decide on a new name for him.

They tried Trixie and Wags and Blackie and Tray and Spot (even though he didn't have spots) and Duke and Pal and sixteen other names. But nothing seemed right.

"That dog needs a special name," Pa agreed. "He's as smart as a professor. He's entitled to an educated name."

"That's it!" Jane almost shouted. *"Professor!"*

Even Paul's eyes lit up. He tried the name on his tongue. "Professor," he said. "Pro-fessor. Yup, that suits him just fine."

Anne liked it, too, and that settled the matter. Then, between the second and third course, everyone fell quiet.

"Now don't you youngsters go feeling bad about my watch," Pa said. "A watch is only a thing made of springs and wheels and gears. It doesn't live and breathe. It can't shake hands with you or wag its tail when it's happy or lick your face. Most of all, a watch can't love you— but a dog can. No, sir, we got a fine bargain."

They all felt better after Pa's speech.

The hotel restaurant was a grand place, with wax flowers on the tables and two large oil paintings in gold frames on the walls. The family enjoyed just sitting there, listening to the peaceful ticking of the pendulum clock near the door. Pa told stories of his boyhood on an Illinois ranch. He had apprenticed himself to a traveling magician—and had been traveling ever since.

Jane looked around, but all the girls her own age seemed to have vanished from the town.

They were finishing their dessert when the mayor stopped at their table. "A mighty fine show," he beamed, hooking his thumbs in his vest. "Are you heading for Dry Creek, New Mexico?"

"We expect to play there a week from next Saturday," Pa said. "We'll be on our way in the morning."

"I've got a brother in Dry Creek," the mayor said. "Newt Hastings. You look him up and tell him I said to treat you folks right. He's the sheriff there."

It was past nine o'clock when the family returned to the wagon. Anne had fallen asleep, and Pa carried her against his shoulder.

The Professor (for they informed him of his new name at once) was waiting with his tongue hanging out and his tail wagging. Jane and Mama had brought him table scraps wrapped in a handkerchief, and he had his dinner while the youngsters got ready for bed. Jane and Anne shared the sofa that was used in the Sleeping Princess act. Pa had once laughed, "Our girls never walk in their sleep —but sometimes they float!" Paul slept nearby, rolled up in a down-filled quilt. Later, Mama and Pa would make up a bed out of blankets and a buffalo robe in the rear of the wagon.

"Paul," Jane said softly while Pa was unhitching the horses. "Are you asleep yet?"

" 'Course not."

"I wish there was some way of getting Pa's watch back. He was mighty proud of that watch."

"There's no way to get it back," Paul said. "It belongs to Jeb Grimes now—and he wouldn't give it up for anything."

"If we could make some money, maybe we could buy Pa another watch just like it."

"It would take us a hundred years. Two hundred, maybe. It was all gold and everything."

"I know. But we've got to think of something," Jane added.

And they fell asleep, thinking.

CHAPTER 6

The sun came up hot and clear, as if it had been cut out of a prairie fire with a pair of scissors. Pa was already setting up his hand press. He would print up handbills for Dry Creek and other towns and send them ahead by stagecoach.

"Sister," Mama called to Jane. "Madam Sweetpea needs milking."

"I'm brushing my hair."

Jane seemed to spend hours brushing her long hair and still more hours wondering what it would be like to wear it pinned up on top like the older girls.

"I don't know a way in the world to make pancakes with a hairbrush," Mama called.

Mama wouldn't let Jane wear her hair on top. Jane was too young. A girl had to be fourteen or fifteen before her mother let her give up braids or a simple ribbon in back. It seemed to Jane, as she fetched the milk pail, that she would never reach fourteen or fifteen.

"Brother," Mama called. "We need another bucket of water."

"I'm helping Pa print handbills." Paul wasn't exactly helping, but he *was* watching. The printing press, like anything mechanical, fascinated Paul.

"I can't make coffee with handbills," Mama said. "You run down to the pump and hurry back."

Paul climbed onto his stilts, unhooked the wooden bucket, and went loping down the main street as if to catch up with his own shadow.

Pa stopped to build the breakfast fire and then returned to his press. The handbills, still wet with ink, read:

169

ONE NIGHT ONLY!

DRY CREEK, NEW MEXICO

MR. MYSTERIOUS & COMPANY

Wonders! Marvels! Magic!

☞ **SEE** ☜

The Sleeping Princess – She Floats in Mid-Air!

The Miser's Dream – Coins From Nowhere!

The Sphinx – He Talks!

The Doll House

MAGIC LANTERN PICTURES

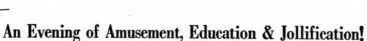

An Evening of Amusement, Education & Jollification!

FUN FOR ALL!
BRING THE WHOLE FAMILY!

SATURDAY NIGHT

Adults 25 cents   Children 5 cents

After breakfast Pa would take the handbills to the Wells Fargo office. The stagecoach, due about noon, would carry them on to Dry Creek and points west. A stagecoach could cover forty or fifty miles in a day. The show wagon, with Madam Sweetpea at a slow walk behind, rarely traveled more than ten miles a day. The handbills would reach Dry Creek long before Mr. Mysterious & Company.

Mama was ready to start the coffee, but Paul hadn't yet returned with fresh water. "Now where can that scamp be?" she declared. "Sister, look out and see if he's coming."

Anne looked, but there was nothing to be seen on the main street but a few chickens. "Maybe he got lost, Mama," she said.

Jane had finished milking, and Mama started the pancake batter.

"How could anyone get lost in Cactus City," Jane said patiently, "with only one street?"

Jane was anxious to be done with breakfast so they could go to the general store. She liked to look at all the bolts of calico and the ribbons and buttons, and imagine herself dressed up like the ladies in Pa's magic-lantern slides.

Suddenly Mama caught her breath. "Andrew!" she said. "Put down those eggs. You'll break them!"

Pa had taken up the breakfast eggs and was juggling three of them in the air. "I've got to keep my fingers in practice," he laughed. "It's not often a man gets to practice with fresh hen fruit."

"Put them down!"

Pa tossed one egg behind his back. It went up over his head. Mama stood breathless. Just before the egg hit the ground, he caught it in his hat.

Anne applauded.

Mama breathed again. Sometimes being married to a magician was a trial. Once she had caught Pa juggling three of her best china plates, which she used only on Sundays. It was a wonder, she thought, that he didn't try to juggle their three youngsters!

Mama put the three eggs in her apron pocket for safe-keeping and poured out the flapjack batter. The griddle was sizzling-hot, and the pancakes turned golden. "Jane," she said, "you'd better go fetch your brother."

"Here he comes now," Pa said. "And he's running as if a swarm of bees were after him."

Paul, high on his stilts, came sprinting toward the wagon like a long-legged goose. Chickens in the street scattered before him.

"Pa!" he shouted, the water sloshing in the bucket as he loped along. "Pa!"

One of the stilts plunged into a gopher hole, Paul took a tumble, and the water bucket went rolling in the dust.

"Jack fell down and broke his crown," Anne laughed.

"Pa!" Paul yelled.

"Something's wrong," Mama said.

Paul gathered up his stilts and ran the rest of the way on his bare feet. When he arrived at the wagon, he was panting so hard he could scarcely talk.

"What is it?" Pa said. "What happened?"

"I was pumping water," Paul started. "And——"

"Now catch your breath and tell us what happened," Mama said.

"And the pump's right next to the sheriff's office. And —and——"

"And *what?*" Jane asked.

"And I heard them talking. Him and the mayor. And —and——"

"My lad, if we could turn your *and*'s into steers, we'd have a whole herd by now."

"They were talking. About what happened last night."

"Well, what *did* happen last night?" Pa demanded.

Suddenly Mama remembered the flapjacks and turned them just in time.

"Well," Paul panted, "they were talking about Jeb Grimes. The sheriff is going to get up a posse!"

"For Jeb Grimes?"

"No," Paul said. "Jeb Grimes was driving his wagon back to Lone City last night and——"

"Get to the point, lad."

"Well, he came around a bend, and there was a man waiting. With a handkerchief around his face. And he held Jeb Grimes up! Quick as you please. Took everything he had. The sheriff said Jeb Grimes carried gold pieces in a sack around his neck and the bandit took them. And your chiming watch, Pa! We'll never get it back now!"

"Never mind my watch, boy. Do they know who did it?"

Paul nodded quickly. "The sheriff said it was the Badlands Kid! He's big and mean—meaner even than Jeb Grimes. The sheriff said he picks his teeth with a bowie knife and would as soon cut out your gizzard as look at you."

Pa shook his head sadly. "I'm right sorry about Jeb Grimes losing all his gold pieces," he said. "There's good in every man, even if it is hard to see at times."

But the flapjacks were going to burn on the griddle if everyone stood around talking any longer. Mama got busy with tin plates and poured off fresh milk into tin cups, and the family started breakfast. But when Mama reached for the three eggs in her apron pocket—they were gone!

She raised an eyebrow and looked at Pa. Pa was sharpening his beard. "Andrew," she said crisply, for she knew how Pa liked to play his magic tricks off the stage as well as on. "Andrew—you give me back those eggs. I know you've got them. You 'magicked' them out of my apron pocket."

"Why, I wouldn't do such a thing," Pa said blandly. "You must have mislaid them."

"Andrew," Mama said, and she raised the other eyebrow. The children watched now with expectant smiles and forgot all about the Badlands Kid. Pa liked to tease Mama, but he always made her laugh in the end. "Andrew—when a hen goes to all the trouble of laying an egg, I'm not going to *mislay* it. Now, you hand them over this minute!"

Pa patted Madam Sweetpea on the rump. "Young 'uns," he said, "have you ever seen a cow lay eggs?"

"No, Pa," they answered together.

"Watch and behold!"

With that, Pa sat on the milking stool. He rolled up his sleeves and reached under Madam Sweetpea as if he were going to draw a squirt of milk.

But an egg fell into his hand instead.

Then a second.

Then the third!

Anne's eyes popped. Soon they were all laughing— even Mama. It was indeed a comical sight to see a cow "lay eggs"!

"Joy," Mama smiled, as she cracked the eggs into the frying pan. "The next thing I know you'll be telling us a chicken can give milk."

"I'm working on that one," Pa laughed.

The show wagon pulled up between the sheriff's office and the town pump. Paul worked the pump handle while his father emptied bucket after bucket into the water barrel strapped to the side of the wagon. But Paul's mind wasn't on his work.

The posse was forming right out in front of the sheriff's office. Paul counted eleven horses and riders. He wished he could go along. There might even be a reward for catching the outlaw!

Mama wondered whether it would be safe for the show wagon to leave Cactus City—what with an outlaw in the neighborhood. But Pa had his rifle if there was trouble. "And anyway," as he said, "that posse means business. They'll track him and catch him."

"I hope so," Jane said. She didn't like outlaws at all—especially if they picked their teeth with a bowie knife.

Pa went over to talk to the sheriff. A few moments later the posse lit out of town. There was a great rattle of hoofs and a cloud of dust, and the posse was gone.

"The Badlands Kid must not amount to very much as an outlaw," Pa said when he returned. "There's not even a nickel reward on him."

Once the water barrel was full, Pa led the wagon across the street for the long-awaited visit to the general store. Pa gave the youngsters a nickel each to spend. Paul and Anne headed straight for the tall candy jars filled with butterballs and licorice and rock candy. Jane made a beeline for the bolts of calico. The material sold for eight-and-a-half cents a yard. Mama had promised to help Jane make a dress for herself, and Jane had already saved up more than a dollar. That would be enough for the material and the buttons and maybe a little lace for the cuffs and the neck.

But there was so much to look at that it was like a visit to the dime museum in Kansas City. Chairs hung from hooks on the ceiling, and there were harnesses and kerosene lamps by the dozens. There was a smell of coffee beans in the air. There were black potbellied stoves and Stetson hats and buggy whips. There was a keg of horseshoes in all sizes. There was no end of things to look at.

The storekeeper had a round, jolly face and mutton-chop whiskers as bushy as squirrel tails. Pa bought two sacks of grain for the animals, and Mama ordered a fifty-pound sack of flour and a fifty-pound sack of meal. She picked the sacks out carefully, for each was a different color with a different pattern of flowers. A flour sack was nothing to be thrown away when it was empty. One made shirts or blouses out of it—or even underwear.

"Poor Jeb," the storekeeper said. "He never would spend a penny on himself, and now it's gone. Of course, he's probably got more buried in his yard. I guess he's the richest man in these parts, though you wouldn't know it to look at him."

"How did he come by such a fine dog?" Pa asked.

"Help yourself to the crackers and cheese," the storekeeper said, lifting the wooden cover off the cracker barrel. "That dog belonged to his wife. She's dead now, rest her soul. Jeb kept the dog. There's some men that need a dog to kick, and Jeb's one of them. It keeps a man from kicking himself, and that's been Jeb's trouble for thirty years. Now that he's traded you folks his dog, maybe he'll finally have to give himself a right smart mulish kick."

Mama helped Jane pick out five yards of calico in a sky-blue color, a spool of blue thread, and a dozen mother-of-pearl buttons, all for less than sixty cents. Paul and Anne kept staring at the candy jars and kept changing their minds. Finally Paul chose rock candy, Anne chose licorice, and Jane decided on the butterballs. The choices were important because the youngsters knew they would have to make their candy last for weeks to come.

The storekeeper helped Pa load the sacks of flour and meal and grain into the wagon. The family climbed up onto the seat, and the Professor stretched himself across Jane's lap. He wagged his tail in Paul's face and licked Anne's ear.

"Git up, Hocus," Pa said finally, cracking his whip in the air. "Git up, Pocus!"

And the show wagon, creaking under its load, rolled away along the main street. Madam Sweetpea tagged along behind and snapped her tail at a fly.

Pa reached for his pocket watch out of habit, to see what time it was. The watch was gone. Reaching for it was a habit he would have to break.

CHAPTER 7

The horizon stretched out as tight as a clothesline with the long day hanging out to dry. A cloud of dust was rising in the distance, and Pa figured that was the posse on its way back to Cactus City. Two days had passed, and perhaps the men had rounded up the outlaw.

School was under way inside the show wagon. The children sat with their slates on the buffalo rug while Mama assigned them arithmetic problems.

"Brother," Mama said, "if a man walked five miles to town and five miles back every Saturday for a year, how many miles would he have walked in a year?"

Paul set to work on the problem. He was quick at figures, but he wondered how the man knew it was exactly five miles. It was too far to measure with a yardstick. Perhaps he had measured it with a wagon wheel. A few weeks before, Pa had pointed out a rancher figuring a property line. The man had tied a handkerchief to a wagon wheel and then counted the number of times the handkerchief spun around.

Jane was doing long division. But her mind wasn't on it. If she went to a regular school, she'd be in the sixth grade. And she wouldn't be the *only* student in her class as she was in the wagon school. There was no one to pass notes to, and there were no boys to tease her except Paul, and he didn't count. How thrilling it would be, once the family settled in California, to have a graduation day. There would be speeches and frilly white dresses and maybe even a band playing. But now she felt very much alone as the wagon jogged along, and she tried to concentrate on her long division.

Anne was scratching out a pig on her slate. The Professor had grown tired of school an hour before and had climbed up beside Pa on the wagon seat.

"It looks like the posse heading this way," Pa called out.

"I'll make up some coffee," Mama said, closing up the book in her hands. And then, with a smile, she added, "Noon recess."

The wagon headed for the shade of a stand of cottonwood trees. Jane cleaned off her slate with a small rag dipped in water. Paul spit on his slate and wiped it on his shirt sleeve. "School," he murmured. "I wish I could figure some way to play hooky."

"You can't," Jane said.

"I know it."

He had never once played hooky. If he did, the wagon school would leave him behind!

"When we get to California, that's what I'm going to do," he said. "Play hooky. Every day, maybe."

With the dust cloud still a long way off, Mama hooked the coffee pot over the noon fire. Pa cut open the watermelon, and Jane took the Professor exploring in the cottonwood trees. It felt good to stretch her legs and spit out watermelon seeds as she walked.

Jane often wandered off alone to think her private thoughts. Sometimes she would bring a book along and wish she could sit for hours, lost in the enchantment of *The Old Curiosity Shop* by Charles Dickens or *Romeo and Juliet* by William Shakespeare. Mama had only a few books, and Jane had read them over and over. But with the Professor at her heels she forgot her loneliness and sent a rock skipping for him to chase.

When she caught up with him, the Professor stopped suddenly, and a growl rumbled in his throat.

"What do you see, Professor?" Jane asked. "Why, that's only an owl in the trees."

But it wasn't an owl that started the Professor barking. When Jane took a step forward, she froze.

A man was sitting there.

She could see him clearly now, through the trees.

He sat on a fallen log, finishing up his noon meal. He was eating a strip of jerky—dried beef—which filled out one cheek like a wad of chewing tobacco. He had scowling, bloodshot eyes, as if he had been riding all night. His hat was as black as chimney soot. His eyebrows shot up when he saw Jane, and the horse behind him whinnied at the Professor's barking.

"Howdy," the man said. "You lost or something, young 'un?"

Before Jane could answer, the man began to pick his teeth with a bowie knife!

She froze all over again. "The Badlands Kid," she said under her breath.

Without a word, she turned and ran. Her heart was beating like a string of Fourth of July firecrackers. The Professor left a final bark in the air and followed Jane toward the wagon.

The posse had just pulled up, and Mama was filling coffee cups.

"That outlaw don't appear to be hiding around here," Sheriff Johnson said. "We stopped over at the Angus place, and the only news around here is Mrs. Angus had her baby early this morning.

"Pa!" Jane shouted.

Mama whirled round in fright. "What is it, child?"

"The Badlands Kid!" Jane exclaimed, out of breath. "I just saw him! Hiding back in those trees!"

Paul almost choked on a mouthful of watermelon seeds. The sheriff put down his tin cup. "Are you sure?"

"I saw him!" Jane declared.

The sheriff studied Jane for a moment and then turned to the posse. "Boys, come on."

Pa drew his Winchester from the rifle boot. "I'll join you, Sheriff."

The sheriff nodded. "Pete, you and Charlie and Jasper circle around back. The rest of you boys spread out. All right, let's go."

Mama hugged Anne to her skirt, and Jane held on to the Professor, who wanted to go with Pa. Paul wished he were old enough to join the posse—although Jane had said the Badlands Kid looked mighty scary.

They waited beside the wagon while the men disappeared in the trees. There wasn't a sound except the switching of Madam Sweetpea's tail.

Any moment, it seemed, there would come a burst of gunfire. The seconds fell away as silently as sand in an hourglass. Madam Sweetpea began to swish her tail like a pendulum. Still not a sound from the trees.

And then the men appeared, with the outlaw in their midst. They wore long and solemn faces. Not a shot had been fired, but they had their man. The sheriff stopped the posse in front of Mama.

"Madam," he said, "is this the critter your daughter saw in the woods?"

Mama, still clutching Anne to her skirts, glanced at Jane. Jane nodded.

"He sure looks bloodthirsty, don't he?" the sheriff said.

"He does," Mama admitted.

At that, all the long faces broke into smiles, and a howl of laughter went up. Even the outlaw himself burst into guffaws.

"Madam," he said, "this sun-beat face of mine is enough to frighten me myself at times, but I beg your forgiveness." He bowed low to Jane. "I'm sorry to disappoint your young 'un, but I'm not the Badlands Kid."

"It's only Doc Bradley," the sheriff said. "He was on his way back from delivering Mrs. Angus' baby this morning. Hasn't had any sleep all night, which is why he looks so mean and ornery!"

"But he was picking his teeth with a bowie knife," Jane protested. "Just like the Badlands Kid."

"Young 'un," the sheriff said, "if I had to arrest every bachelor in these parts who picks his teeth with a bowie knife, I could fill every jail from Texas to California."

"Doc," Pa said, putting away his rifle, "you sit down and have a cup of coffee with us."

"I'd be rightly obliged," the doctor replied. "This is quite an occasion. It's not every day I'm taken for a famous outlaw!"

Jane traded a glance with Paul and felt as silly as a goose, but no one really seemed to mind.

As Dr. Bradley said before he left with the posse, there was nothing better to mix with a cup of coffee than sweet laughter.

184

CHAPTER 8

Every day the horizon looked the same. There seemed
no end to Texas, especially when you jogged along at
about ten miles a day. Jane wondered if they would
ever cross the line into New Mexico Territory. Would
Pa really get them to California in time for Christmas
dinner with Uncle Fred and Aunt Emma?

The show wagon crossed the New Mexico line on
Friday. And the horizon looked just as flat and empty
as it had in Texas. There were greasewood and mesquite and humps of tumbleweed waiting for a wind to
come up. Dry Creek lay somewhere ahead.

Pa wasn't thinking of Christmas dinner. He shook
the reins and wondered how to make a chicken give
milk. He had been thinking about it for days, and finally,
with the sun lowering, his eyes lit up. He had it! He
knew how it could be done. He might even perform
it the next evening in Dry Creek.

The Hacketts were not alone on the trail. They saw cowboys herding cattle north. They met a traveling preacher and stopped to talk. When they made camp that evening beside a trickle of running water, they were joined by another covered-wagon family. Everyone said "Howdy" and made friends at once.

The father, who had green eyes and hair the color of Kansas wheat, was a wandering newspaperman. He carried a hand press and type cases in his wagon. "Our name's Keith," he said. "We're heading south to Bear Claw, to set up a newspaper."

Mr. Keith introduced his wife Ruth and their three daughters—Susan, Martha, and Ellen.

Jane glowed with delight. Martha, with two blond pigtails, was just Jane's age. Paul was disgusted. Ellen was his own age—but she was a girl. Susan was fifteen and wore her hair up. Jane could hardly keep her eyes off Susan.

There was another hour of sunlight left, and the youngsters used every moment of it. They couldn't go swimming in a trickle of water, but they did get their feet wet. They played Blindman's Buff and Drop the Handkerchief. They ran three footraces to a cottonwood stump and back.

Then, while the women were getting dinner ready, Mr. Keith took a surprise from his wagon.

A bicycle!

Jane and Paul and Anne had never seen anything more exciting. Bicycle riding had just become a popular sport in the larger towns, but a two-wheeler was

still a rare sight in the small towns of the West. The front wheel was almost as tall as a wagon wheel, and the rear one wasn't much larger than a soup plate. Pa rode it to the cottonwood stump and back, with the youngsters waving him on as if he were a rodeo rider on a bucking bronco. He almost lost his stovepipe hat but finished bravely, still holding on to both hat and handlebars.

Then Mr. Keith gave each youngster a ride. He held them on, keeping the bicycle upright, for the round trip to the cottonwood stump.

"Supper!" Mama called.

"Time to eat!" Mrs. Keith called.

The two families had shared the makings of dinner. It was, for one and all, a feast. There were ears of roasted corn, salt beef, two pans of corn bread, beans, canned oysters, fresh milk—and for dessert, plum pie, fruit, and a slice of cheese.

The Professor dug up an old buffalo bone for *his* dessert.

"I can't say I've ever heard of Bear Claw, New Mexico," Pa said during dinner.

"No wonder," Mr. Keith smiled. "Bear Claw won't really exist until we get there. I'm a town-starter."

Then he explained that several ranchers in the area had decided to start a town. They had hired Mr. Keith to set up his printing press. "I'll print up the praises of Bear Claw," Mr. Keith said, "and then the newspaper will be mailed out to Eastern folks, folks with a hankering to head out West and start a new life. I'll write about the fine climate of Bear Claw, the clean air, the grand future. And folks will come, one by one. Soon there'll be a church and then a schoolhouse and a general store, and more folks will come. And pretty soon the town fathers will have themselves a real town with real people in it—and maybe a hundred years from now it'll be as big as Kansas City or St. Louis. Yes, sir, it takes all kinds to settle a big, empty land like this—and sometimes there's a printing press out in front of the Conestoga wagons and the emigrants. Why, I've started up six or eight towns already with my hand press."

After dinner, after it was already dark except for the flickering of the campfire, Pa and Mr. Keith moved Mama's small portable piano to the ground.

"I haven't seen a piano in a month of Sundays!" Mr. Keith exclaimed. "Folks, let me at it."

He sat himself at Mama's piano stool, cleared his coattails, and sent notes chasing each other into the night air. He played in a grand manner.

"Everybody sing!" he demanded.

The youngsters joined their parents around the piano and raised their voices mightily in choruses of "Buckeye Jim," "Old Dan Tucker," "Nelly Bly," "Susannah," and "Old Folks at Home."

Another traveler joined them during the second time around on "Nelly Bly." Quick introductions were made. He wore a tin star and said he was a U.S. marshal out hunting the Badlands Kid.

"But I heard all the merriment," he said, "and if it's agreeable to you folks, I'll bed down by your campfire."

"There's plenty left to eat," Mrs. Keith smiled.

"I'll pour you some coffee," Mama added.

"And there's all the songs you can sing," Pa said.

The marshal was tall and lean, with polished boots and fine silver spurs. After a plate of salt beef and beans, he carried his coffee cup to the piano and burst into song. He had a ringing baritone voice.

Mr. Keith's fingers never tired. He seemed to find notes that had been hiding in the piano for years. He shook chords, like a fall of leaves, from the keyboard. But finally the younger voices gave out, the piano was lifted back into the wagon, and Anne was put to bed.

The campfire was kept blazing. The marshal went to unsaddle his mare, and the youngsters tagged along.

"When do you think you'll catch the Badlands Kid?" Paul asked.

"Tomorrow for sure."

"Golly," Martha said.

"I might be a lawman," Paul said, "unless I learn to be a magician like Pa."

The marshal took off his badge and pinned it on Paul's shirt. "Try it on for size, young fella."

Paul stuck out his chest. It was a glorious feeling— but it lasted only a moment. As the marshal lifted off the saddle and set it beside his bedroll for a pillow, Paul heard something. Jane heard something. They both heard the chiming of a watch, clear and sharp, from the marshal's shirt pocket!

It sounded exactly like Pa's watch striking the hour! Jane and Paul exchanged a quick, startled glance.

Was it really Pa's watch they heard? Who was this stranger? Was he a U.S. marshal—or the Badlands Kid?

Paul didn't dare move. A creepy feeling went up Jane's back. They wanted to run but only backed away.

The stranger looked up. "Don't run off with my tin star, young fella," he said.

"Y-y-yes, sir," Paul muttered in a cold sweat.

Paul reached up to unpin the badge, but his hands were trembling so hard he couldn't get it off. The man reached out with his long arms and unpinned the star.

"Good night, young 'uns," he said.

"Good night, sir."

"And time you were in bed," Mama said from the campfire a few feet away.

190

"You, too," Mrs. Keith said to Susan, Martha, and Ellen, who couldn't make out why Jane and Paul were acting so strangely.

"But, Mama——" Jane whispered.

"No arguing, now. In bed."

Pa and Mr. Keith were exchanging stories, and neither Jane nor Paul could catch Pa's eye. They made all kinds of silent faces, for they didn't dare let the stranger know that they suspected him. Pa only looked up to say, "You scamps ate too much. You look ready to burst."

It was no use. There seemed nothing to do but say good night to the Keith children and retire to the wagon. Once under canvas and out of sight, Jane and Paul whispered to each other across Anne's sleeping figure.

"We'll stay awake," Jane said. "Then, as soon as Pa comes to bed, we'll tell him."

Paul agreed. It wouldn't be hard to stay awake. Who could sleep with the Badlands Kid close enough to hit with a bean shooter?

"He's probably just waiting to cut out everybody's gizzard," Paul breathed.

"Unless he isn't really the Badlands Kid," Jane said.

"But he has Pa's watch. I heard it!"

"Maybe it isn't really Pa's watch at all. But one just like it. Then everyone would only laugh at us. Just like they did before."

Paul nodded in the darkness of the wagon. The stranger *might* be a lawman, after all.

But the more they whispered about it, the more uncertain they became. It *had* sounded like Pa's watch.

CHAPTER 9

A wind came up in the night, scouring the landscape as if with a broom. When dawn broke, clumps of tumble-weed had gathered against the wheels of the show wagon like brittle cobwebs. The sounds of five people sleeping under the canvas wagon cover could be heard, if anyone at all was listening.

Paul awoke first. He sat bolt upright, as if triggered by a spring. He couldn't believe he had shut his eyes, even for a second—and yet the red canvas glowed with the light of morning.

"Jane!"

Her eyes popped wide open and she sat up, too—so suddenly that Anne tumbled out of bed.

"We fell asleep!" Paul exclaimed.

"The Badlands Kid," Jane whispered in sudden alarm. It was all the footracing, she thought, and bicycle riding and song singing that had tired them out.

"What about the Badlands Kid?" Anne yawned, but Jane put a hand over her mouth.

"Sh-h-h—he'll hear you."

"We better tell Pa," Paul said.

They crawled to the rear of the wagon, Jane in her cotton nightgown and Paul in his nightshirt. Anne crept along, too. "What's so secret——"

"Sh-h-h!"

They shook Pa awake. Before he could yawn, they began telling him about the chiming of the watch and their suspicions about the stranger. Pa listened to every word. He pursed his lips and frowned. "It sounded like my watch, did it?"

"Just like it," Jane said.

Mama awoke. "What's all this whispering? What's happened?"

Pa pulled on his boots. He walked forward on the wagon bed in his long nightshirt and got his rifle. "Now all of you stay put."

Then he left the wagon, and the family waited. A moment later Paul heard him cock the rifle, and Anne put her hands over her ears.

"Now what is all this?" Mama insisted.

Jane explained, and Mama turned white.

A moment later Pa reappeared at the wagon opening. "He's gone," Pa said, uncocking the rifle. "Pulled out in the night. He's long gone."

The Hacketts and the Keiths shared the same breakfast fire. They discussed the mysterious stranger. Was he really the outlaw, or had a U.S. marshal come into a chiming watch exactly like Pa's? At any rate, the man was gone, and he had not harmed them.

It was Paul's turn to milk Madam Sweetpea, but Susan and Martha and Ellen asked for turns, and Paul was very obliging. The girls giggled, and Madam Sweetpea turned her head as if she were looking for a straw hat to eat. After the cream had risen, Mama skimmed it off and poured it into the butter churn. Then Pa roped the churn to the side of the wagon. By the time they reached Dry Creek, all the swaying and jiggling of the wagon would churn the cream to butter.

While the horses were put back in harness, the youngsters found time for a few rounds of jump rope. Martha's pigtails flew. Susan could jump rope blindfolded. The Professor watched these goings on with an anxious eye. Then suddenly he leaped into the game to try it for himself. He cleared the rope once, twice—but the third time around caught him with his feet flat on the ground. He slunk away as if disgraced.

"I've got it!" Jane said, her eyes brightening. "If we can teach the Professor to jump rope, maybe Pa will put him in the show."

"Will you, Pa?" Paul asked.

"That's a smart dog," Pa said. "But I've never heard of a dog jumping rope."

"We'll teach him," Anne said. She was walking around on her tiptoes again.

"You'll have to catch him first," Pa laughed, looking up from the harness. "He's gone off to hide."

They broke camp a few minutes later. The two families said their good-bys. Finally the Keith wagon, loaded with printing equipment, creaked and swayed to the south. Jane stood a long time waving to Martha. The two girls had become old friends in a matter of hours, but they would probably never see one another again.

Pa took up the reins. "Everybody in?"

"Where's the Professor?" Anne asked.

Pa laughed. "I warned you. That dog doesn't want to jump rope. Brother, you better go fetch him."

Paul jumped down from the wagon and found the Professor digging a deep hole beside the cottonwood stump. "Come on, boy. We're leaving."

But the Professor wouldn't listen. He kept digging until all that showed was his tail. Paul pulled him out, picked him up, and started back to the wagon. But the Professor leaped out of Paul's arms and returned to the hole as if it were full of buried buffalo bones.

"Pa, he won't come!"

"Get hold of him and don't let go. We can't wait all morning."

Paul tried again. He dragged the Professor out of his hole, and, sure enough, there was an old bone between his teeth. "Smart dog," Paul grinned. "You didn't want to leave it behind."

But something bright in the bottom of the hole caught Paul's glance. It looked like the oyster can from last night's supper. Was that what the Professor had smelled? Maybe, Paul thought, he had been trying to *bury* the bone in the soft earth and had sniffed the oyster scent farther down. But how had the oyster can got way down there? Once more, like a greased pig, the Professor twisted out of Paul's hands to return to the hole. This time Paul pulled up the can—and a dozen shimmering gold pieces poured out at his bare feet.

"Pa!"

Pa came running. There was no doubt about it now. It *was* the Badlands Kid who had spent the night around their campfire. And sometime during the night, he had buried Jeb Grimes' gold pieces in an oyster can.

Dry Creek was a small cattle town that leaned with the prevailing wind. The store fronts, the hitching posts, and even the shade tree in front of the livery barn stood at a slant. It was Saturday noon, and one by one the ranchers and their families were coming to town in buggies and spring wagons. Wheels and hoofs lifted the summer's dust so that you could hardly see from one end of the main street to the other. There was a great coming and going on the boardwalks and a jingling of spurs. The cowboys were coming to town, too, in their checked shirts, their neckerchiefs, and their Stetson hats.

"Joy," Mama said, clearing the air in front of her face with an embroidered handkerchief, "this town needs a good dusting."

"We'll have a fine crowd tonight," Pa smiled. "Nothing perks up a town like Saturday night."

They found a vacant lot for the show wagon between the livery barn and the barbershop. The side of the barn was tacked with posters that read:

RE-ELECT

NEWT HASTINGS

SHERIFF of DRY CREEK

"Howdy, Sheriff," Pa said. "When's the election?"

The sheriff, chewing a piece of straw, had wandered over to the show wagon even before Pa unhitched the horses. "About two weeks now," the sheriff said. He had a young, friendly grin and stood straight as an awning post. Paul, who was already out on stilts, was fond of sheriffs in all sizes and shapes, but this one was different. Sheriff Newt Hastings had a broken leg. It was bound up with splints, and he walked with a hickory stick. He tipped his hat politely to the ladies—to Mama and Jane and even Anne. Jane smiled to herself.

"Why, he's hardly more than a boy," Mama said.

Jane straightened her hair ribbon and hoped the sheriff would turn his grin on her again.

"My horse ran over a cutbank and threw me," he was telling Pa, tapping his splint with the hickory stick. "And this broken leg is going to lose me the election. I can feel it in the wind."

"Folks can't put you out to pasture for a thing like that," Pa said. "Your leg'll heal."

"Maybe they can."

"Who's running against you?"

"My no-account deputy. He's out hunting the Badlands Kid right now. We haven't had many outlaws around here, and if my deputy brings the Kid in—folks will elect him for sure."

Jane began helping Mama hang out their show costumes to air and was listening to every word. How could he be expected to go out chasing outlaws with his leg in splints?

"Sheriff," Pa said, "I wish we could help you. The truth is the Badlands Kid spent the night around our campfire. When we realized who he was, he was already gone. But he can't be far."

"Then my deputy will pick up his trail for sure—though we don't know what the Badlands Kid looks like. He's new in these parts. The stage came through from Cactus City warning us about him. Jeb Grimes has put up a fifty-dollar reward."

Pa lifted his hat and scratched his head in pure surprise. "You mean Jeb Grimes is going to part with fifty dollars?"

"For information leading to the arrest of the Badlands Kid—as the saying goes. It's as good as in my deputy's pocket."

Paul's ears pricked up. He and Jane had let that reward money slip through their fingers.

Pa turned the oyster can of gold pieces over to the sheriff. "I guess Jeb is beginning to change his ways. These gold pieces are his. The Badlands Kid buried them for safekeeping, but the Professor here dug 'em up."

"I'll see Jeb gets 'em back," the sheriff said. "What time's your show?"

"Seven o'clock sharp."

"The whole town's waiting."

With that, he smiled and tipped his hat again to the ladies and walked off toward the sheriff's office. Jane watched him on his lame leg, and her heart went out to him. She hoped he wouldn't lose the election. She wished there was something they could do.

Pa took Madam Sweetpea into the livery barn for a new set of shoes, for even cows had to be shod when on the trail.

The blacksmith told Pa that Newt Hastings was planning to get married. "Got his heart set on Mary Jo Abbey," the blacksmith said. "She lives almost the other side of New Mexico. But if he loses the election, I guess he'll have to put the wedding off." The blacksmith gave a shake of his bushy head. "A man isn't apt to take himself a wife if he don't have a job."

Jane and Paul and Anne spent a good part of the afternoon trying to teach the Professor to jump rope. They raised so much dust that the dog changed color —from black to brown. But the youngsters' thoughts kept straying from the rope. Jane couldn't get the sheriff out of her mind. He had such a nice grin— even while chewing on a piece of straw—and such courteous ways. But really, she thought, he had hardly noticed her. If only she were five years older! It seemed to Jane that growing up was taking forever. She wished Pa could wave his magic wand and turn her into a grown-up—even if just for one day. Then the sheriff wouldn't dismiss her with a polite tip of his hat!

Pa was busy with his new trick. He was going to make a chicken give milk during the show that night. He had bought a funnel at the hardware store, and now he got out his toolbox. He was careful that no one was watching over his shoulder as he tinkered with the funnel. Within an hour he was finished, and he smiled with satisfaction. Pa caught a chicken and tried it out, and the trick worked.

He reached for his watch—and remembered it was gone. He checked the sun instead. It would soon be show time.

"You young 'uns get cleaned up," he said. "And that goes for the dog as well."

They threw the Professor into a nearby horse trough, where he swam from one end to the other and changed back from brown to black.

CHAPTER 10

"Ladies and gentlemen," Pa smiled. "Gentlemen and ladies. Boys and girls, and girls and boys. We present for your amusement, edification, and jollification our traveling temple of mysteries! A program of wonders and marvels for young and old! Feats of legerdemain and tricks of prestidigitation! Behold! Magic, mirth, and music!"

The kerosene footlights were ablaze. Mama struck up a chord on the piano, and Pa, in his fancy vest, his frock coat, and his stovepipe hat, bowed low. He looked mysterious indeed. The Hackett youngsters, behind the wings of the small stage, knew every word of Pa's introductory speech by heart. It seemed to Paul that he had heard it at least a million times, and he had learned to recite the speech backwards. Under his breath, while waiting to walk on stage with Pa's magic wand, he muttered:

"Music and mirth, magic. Behold! Prestidigitation of tricks and legerdemain of feats. Old and young for

201

marvels and wonders of program a. Mysteries of temple traveling our jollification and edification, amusement your for present we."

"Brother!" Mama whispered urgently from the other side of the stage.

Pa was waiting for his magic stick. Paul hurried from the wings and tripped on his left foot. The magic wand went flying. The crowd burst into a roar of laughter, and Paul's face turned as red as an apple. His store-bought shoes, he thought. They had tripped him. How could anyone walk without tripping in store-bought shoes!

Someone handed the wand up to Pa, and Paul retreated to the wings. He wished he could disappear in a puff of smoke. On most nights the show went smoothly, but some nights everything went wrong. Threads would break, secret panels would stick, or the bottom would fall out of trick boxes. The show family sensed at once that this was going to be a night of errors and disasters. But Pa didn't drop his smile for a moment. If an audience sensed that things were going wrong, it would end up in howls of laughter and hoots and catcalls.

The Saturday-night crowd gathered in a thick crescent of faces around the wagon-stage. Benches had been brought from the schoolhouse and arranged up front for the smaller youngsters. Some of the older ones brought along boxes to sit on; there were a few camp chairs for the ladies, and in the rear several cowboys sat on their horses to watch the entertainment. Twilight was darkening the town, knitting shadows together, and soon the first stars would appear.

202

Pa was thinking fast. He had to win the audience—convince folks, somehow, that the show was running smoothly. "I have the pleasure this evening," he was saying, polishing the magic wand on his coat sleeve, "of introducing a new and marvelous, baffling and never-before-seen feat of conjuring. For this experiment I will need an ostrich. Did anyone in the audience bring an ostrich with him?"

The crowd laughed, for everyone knew there wasn't an ostrich in the whole territory of New Mexico.

"No?" said Pa. "Then may I borrow a peacock? A swan? A sea gull? A stork?"

"I can get you a chicken," the blacksmith called out. "How will that do?"

"That will have to do," Pa said, as if in disappointment. "Make it a hen."

While the blacksmith hurried away for a chicken, Pa addressed the audience again.

"Is there anyone here who has seen a hen give cow's milk?"

There was a chorus of "No's."

"How about you, sir?" Pa asked, pointing to a thin man with a long, gloomy frown. He was the town barber and undertaker, and hadn't been known to crack a smile in twenty years.

"I never heard of such tomfoolery," the man answered in a crotchety voice. "A hen can't give milk. Everybody knows that."

"Will you accept a challenge, sir?"

"What challenge?"

"If I can make a hen give milk, will you drink it?"

"No, sir. I can't abide the stuff."

Pa smiled. "But if I can't make a hen give milk, you won't have to drink it."

"Go on, Clem," someone yelled. "Take him up on it."

The barber-undertaker shook his gloomy head. "I ain't drunk milk in forty-odd years," he said. "But you can't get anything but eggs from a hen. I'm onto your fakery. You got everything up your sleeves."

"If I roll up my sleeves?"

"Then it's a bargain. I'll drink the milk."

Pa rolled up his sleeves to the elbow, and the blacksmith returned with the hen. She was a big fat one, with red, flapping wings and a temper. Pa held her by the legs and called for his props. Paul had the funnel, but he hated to face the crowd. What if he tripped again? He stood in the wings, unable to move.

"Hurry, my lad."

There was a tone of command in Pa's voice, and Paul swallowed hard. Then he put one foot carefully in front of the other.

"Trip again," Pa whispered.

Paul could hardly believe his ears. Did Pa want to make him a laughingstock all over again?

"Do as I say."

Paul tripped. Tears all but sprang into his eyes as the crowd howled. Pa caught the funnel in midair.

"Thank you, my lad. Now if you will fetch a glass."

Paul returned to the wings for the glass and wanted to run clear away. He would become a cowboy. He didn't want to return to the show—to the stage—to Dry Creek. He looked around for Jane. Where was she? Why couldn't she bring Pa his glass?

But Jane wasn't in the wings, and Anne was across the stage with Mama. Paul picked up the glass. He took another breath and started on stage once more.

"Trip again," Pa whispered.

Paul fought back tears and tripped again. Pa caught the glass, and the crowd howled.

But picking himself up, Paul realized that the laughter had changed in tone. It had a good-natured sound. Folks had come to believe his clumsiness was part of the show! That was what Pa had in mind! What had begun as an embarrassing fall had been turned into entertainment. The audience loved it!

Paul returned to the wings smiling. Maybe, he thought suddenly, they ought to keep the comic falls in the show every night. That made him a kind of performer—almost like an acrobat. But where, he wondered, was Jane?

On stage, Pa showed the glass and looked through the tin funnel. "Empty glass, empty funnel, fat chicken," he smiled. "Behold!"

He set the glass on the velvet-topped table with gold fringe. He nested the chicken on top of the funnel opening. Then he held the chicken and funnel over the glass.

"Madam Hen," he commanded. "A glass of milk for the gentleman, if you please."

There was a hush over the audience. The chicken looked around as if spoiling for a fight.

Not a drop of milk
poured out of the funnel.

"Madam Hen," Pa
repeated. "Do as I say."

Not a drop. The undertaker,
who hadn't bothered to smile
in twenty years, almost grinned.

"Madam Hen," Pa said angrily.
"A glass of milk, if you
please—or I will turn you
into chicken soup."

Instantly a long stream of
milk poured out of the funnel
and filled the glass!

The undertaker's gloomy
face lengthened. The townsfolk roared. Sheriff Newt
Hastings called out, "Clem—
you promised to drink it!"

"But I ain't tasted the stuff
in forty years!"

"You're about to now!"

Pa gave out the glass, which
was passed from hand to hand
until it reached the undertaker.

"It's all yours, Clem!" a
cowboy called out.

"But——"

"A man that don't stand by
his word don't amount to much."

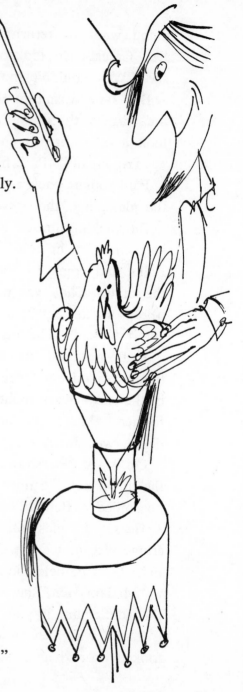

The undertaker smelled the milk and wrinkled up his thin nose. "I always stand by my word—but I can't stand the smell of milk."

"Then I'll hold your nose for you," a neighbor laughed.

With the neighbor's fingers clamped like a clothespin to his nose, the undertaker poured down the milk. The people watched, smiling all the while, and then applauded —for they were enjoying themselves. When the glass was almost empty, the undertaker took a final gulp and lowered the glass, and a strange expression came over his face. He licked his lips. His eyes lit up. He smiled!

Folks around him could hardly believe what they saw. A smile on their undertaker's face. And a large, toothy smile at that!

"I declare," the undertaker beamed. "Why—I declare. That stuff don't taste half bad. Reminds me of when I was a kid."

"Clem," said a gray-haired woman standing nearby, "you haven't cracked a smile since you were a kid, either."

"But milk from a chicken—I never saw such a thing!"

Pa's new trick was a complete success. If the show had started out badly, Pa, using tactics like a general in battle, had won his audience. There would be no catcalls now. The chicken trick had fooled them, but Pa had performed an even finer miracle. He had put a smile on the undertaker's face!

In the wings, Paul whispered urgently, "Jane!"

There came no answer. Jane seemed to have vanished—and Pa would be needing her in the very next trick.

CHAPTER 11

The footlights held Pa's wizard's face in a flickering glow. His voice was strong and deep. "Mystery of mysteries," he said. "The possible impossible. The impossible possible. The greatest feat of the ages. Suspension by sorcery. Levitation by magic. I present—the Sleeping Princess Illusion."

That was Jane's cue. He turned for her entrance.

But Jane didn't enter.

"I present," Pa said again, with a flashing glance at the wings—"the Sleeping Princess Illusion."

Jane wasn't at the wings. But there was a flutter behind the back curtain.

The curtains parted, and Jane appeared. She held her head high and avoided Pa's eyes. She had been hiding, as still as a stick of furniture. Her heart thumped. She had hesitated to show herself, but now it was too late to change her mind. Like Pa himself, once she made up her mind it stayed made.

"Sister," Pa breathed in a stage whisper. He was almost too stunned to go on with the trick. "What in tarnation have you done to your hair?"

"I put it up, Pa."

"I can see that."

Mama missed a chord on the piano and stared at Jane as if she were a stranger. Jane had pinned up her hair like the older girls. She looked fifteen. "Jane Hackett," Mama whispered across the stage. "Wait till I get my hands on you!"

With an audience on the other side of the footlights, Pa had to go on with the trick. There was no time now for a tongue-lashing.

Within moments, Jane was floating in midair. She could feel Sheriff Newt Hastings' eyes on her. In the pink gingham and with her hair up, she felt enchanted. She felt like a real sleeping princess. It was like a dream, and she would hate to come back to earth and be awakened. She would like to go on dreaming this way for twenty years.

Behind the wings, Anne turned to Mama. "I want my hair up—like Jane."

"Be still," Mama said. She had to admit that Jane looked lovely. But she didn't want to see her youngsters grow up too fast. "Next thing I know, she'll be wanting to wear a bustle."

"I want to wear a bustle, too," Anne exclaimed.

"You'll both get a hiding."

Pa held his magic stick over Jane and commanded her to descend. Soon her act would be over. She didn't want it to be over. What was the sheriff thinking? That she was mysterious and beautiful? She didn't want the sheriff to stop looking at her. She had read in books about young ladies swooning with love, and she wondered what *that* would be like.

"Awaken, Sleeping Princess," she heard Pa command in his deep voice.

But she didn't awaken. She refused to open her eyes. She felt like swooning. She would pretend she was swooning.

"Awaken," Pa said again, clapping his hands over her eyes.

But Jane kept her eyes tightly shut.

"Wake up," Pa whispered.

"Abracadabra Day," Jane whispered back.

Pa stopped short. And then he couldn't help smiling to himself. "You rascal," he said under his breath.

She had declared a holiday and was determined to make the best of it. But Pa couldn't let her sleep on stage throughout the performance. He began to stroke the lapel of his coat, where he kept a straight pin on the underside, and before she knew it, Jane felt a pinprick. Her eyes popped open—and the trick was over.

Applause thundered out over the show wagon. As she curtsied to the audience, she could see the sheriff clapping hardest of all. She felt entirely pleased with her special performance. She left the stage smiling and touched her hair as if to assure herself that it really was piled on top of her head.

"Abracadabra Day, Mama," Jane said in the wings.

"What——" Mama's anger gave way. "And I've been waiting here to get my hands on that hair of yours."

Jane gave her mother a kiss. "I'll take it down after the show."

"I want my hair up," Anne protested.

"Girls," Mama said. She had only a moment, for Pa was beginning the next trick and she had background music to play. "I love you both dearly and enjoy seeing you happy and smiling. Pa does tricks to entertain folks. Putting your hair up to look older is only a trick, too—but a different kind of trick. To deceive folks. Because no matter what you do to yourself, you're still a twelve-year-old. Your hair can't change that. Only time can. If I was angry, it was because I don't like to see you deceive yourself as well. Why, it's wonderful to be twelve or five or sixteen or sixty. Every age is a wonderful age. Now go along with you."

In front of the footlights, one mystery followed another. As Pa expected, however, there was a second mishap. A thread broke when he was causing a finger ring to rise and fall on his wand. But he managed to cover his embarrassment by making the ring disappear entirely, and the audience was no wiser.

Pa was performing in front of a drawn stage curtain. Behind it, Paul was being prepared for the Sphinx Illusion. Mama put on him a stringy black wig (it looked a fright—and was called, as you might expect, a fright wig) and then affixed a drooping mustache and beard with spirit gum. She marked lines on his face with a grease pencil. When she finished, he looked two hundred years old—almost as old as the Sphinx himself.

A three-legged table was placed in center stage, and Paul, climbing into a secret place, disappeared from sight. One could see under the table—or so it seemed —but no one could see Paul, his fright wig, his mustache, or his beard.

"And now," Pa announced at the footlights. "The Great Sphinx—he talks, he knows all, he will answer three questions! Open the curtains, if you please."

Jane pulled the cords, and the front curtains parted. There was nothing to be seen on stage but the three-legged table, which stood in perfect innocence.

"And now," Pa exclaimed, with a clap of his hands, "bring out the Egyptian Box."

Anne, knowing her cue, hurried out with a wooden box, painted red and gold, and handed it to Pa. She was careful not to trip on the floor boards.

The Egyptian Box was a foot square. It had a front door that opened on brass hinges. Pa opened the door and showed everyone that the box was empty. Then he placed it on the table.

"And now, my friends—behold!"

After a pass of his magic stick, he opened the door —slowly. The hinges creaked, and shivers went up a few backs.

"The Sphinx . . ." Pa announced.

The empty box was no longer empty. A face with dark eyes looked out of the box. It was a face that looked two hundred years old!

"A living head in a square box," Pa said. "It thinks, it speaks—it can wrinkle its nose."

Paul wrinkled his nose and twitched his mustache. Many folks who had taken the head in the box for a dummy now leaned closer. Where was the body? They could see under the table, but there was nothing to see —no shoes, no legs, no chest, no arms.

"Good evening, Sphinx," Pa said to the head in the box.

Paul, in reply, pitched his voice as low as he could. "Good evening, Mr. Mysterious."

"Will you answer three questions for these kind people?"

The Sphinx nodded, and Pa turned to the crowd.

"Who has a question for the Sphinx?"

"I do," called out a rancher. "Is the sheriff here going to get himself re-elected?"

Paul watched his father's hands for a signal and then answered. "Yes," he said deeply.

This prediction met with smiles and applause. Everyone liked Newt Hastings, but some had doubts about re-electing a sheriff who might be hobbling on a lame leg for another six months.

A lady called out, "Who stole four of my chickens?"

As the Sphinx, Paul was often asked about stolen chickens, and he had learned a pat answer. "Coyotes," he declared.

And then Sheriff Hastings stepped closer. "Sphinx," he said. "Where's the Badlands Kid?"

There was a general titter over that question, for not even the wise Sphinx could be expected to answer it.

With his head in the box, Paul looked out at the footlights and the sea of heads beyond the stage. Everyone was looking at him—even Pa—and waiting for an answer. It was hot in the box, and his face was sweating. As his eyes scanned the youngsters on benches, the ladies on camp chairs, and the cowboys sitting their horses at the rear—his false eyebrows shot up. He saw a familiar face.

He saw the Badlands Kid himself!

"Well?" Pa asked. "What is your answer, Sphinx?" In a stage whisper, Pa added, "Say he's somewhere in Texas."

But Paul didn't say a word. The beat of his heart sounded as loud as a peckerwood. Was it really the Badlands Kid at the back of the crowd? Had the outlaw come to town—unable to resist watching the magic show? And sure he wouldn't be recognized?

"Sphinx," Pa said impatiently, "we're waiting for your answer."

"The Badlands Kid——" Paul hesitated. It *looked* like the outlaw, but with the footlights in his eyes Paul couldn't be sure. The man sat hunched over his saddle horn and was smiling as friendly as could be. Paul peered as hard as he could.

And then he saw the flash of a marshal's badge on the horseman's vest.

It had to be the Badlands Kid! Paul was sure of it.

But if he said so out loud, there would be gunplay right in the crowd. Youngsters might get hurt and some of the ladies, too.

Sweat poured down Paul's made-up face. His drooping mustache drooped still lower. He could feel the sweat trickling clear down into his shoes—even if no one could see his shoes.

"I'll whisper the answer in the sheriff's ear," he croaked at last.

Pa could tell that something was wrong.

"All right," he said. "Sheriff, step up here."

A box was placed near the edge of the stage, and Newt Hastings climbed up, broken leg and all. "I'm ready, Mr. Sphinx," he smiled.

"Lean closer," the Sphinx said.

The sheriff leaned closer.

"Closer than that," the Sphinx said.

The sheriff leaned his ear right in front of the Egyptian Box.

And then the Sphinx whispered, "There, Sheriff! Near the water trough. Sitting his horse. Look—he's picking his teeth with a bowie knife! That's him!"

The sheriff straightened. He looked around at the crowd and winked at the folks. "The Sphinx here says the Badlands Kid is back across the line in Texas," he announced loudly. "Boys, hand me my rope. As long as we're having an evening of tricks, I'd like to do a few rope stunts."

"Pa!" Jane whispered from the wings. "I see him! The Badlands Kid. He's out there!"

Aware now of what the sheriff was up to, Pa said, "I'll step aside for a good rope trick any time. Spin away, Sheriff."

215

The sheriff, despite his broken leg, got the lariat swirling over his head like an enormous halo. And then, suddenly, the rope flew out over the crowd.

It darted as true and swift as an arrow. The loop fell over the head of the Badlands Kid. Before the out-

law could reach his guns, the sheriff pulled back sharply. The loop tightened over the Kid's chest and pinned his arms in tight. His horse shied and threw him to the ground. The sheriff pulled him in, like a man with a fish on the end of the line.

"Take his guns, boys," the sheriff said. "This here is the Badlands Kid. And it looks like the Sphinx has won himself the reward money."

The show was over. The outlaw was locked in jail, and the Saturday-night crowd headed for home in buggies and spring wagons. It was quite a show, folks agreed, that featured the capture of a notorious badman.

But Pa's chiming watch would never again strike the hour. It was a thing of dangling springs and broken hands. In that sudden moment when the outlaw's horse threw him, the watch had fallen to the ground. An iron horseshoe had split it open. Jane and Paul found it in the dust, and the sheriff gathered it up as evidence to send back to Cactus City. It would link the Badlands Kid to the holdup of Jeb Grimes.

Later the sheriff returned to the wagon with a fresh piece of straw between his teeth.

"Hello, Sheriff," Mama smiled. "You're just in time for a cup of coffee."

"Thank you, ma'am."

"It looks like you'll win the election, broken leg and all," Pa said. "Now that you captured the Badlands Kid."

"It'll help my chances. We'll know election day."

But Mr. Mysterious & Company would be long gone by that time. They might never know how things turned out.

"Mr. Sphinx," the sheriff grinned. "You gave me information leading to the capture of the Badlands Kid.

Here's your fifty dollars reward money. I deducted it from them gold pieces of Jeb Grimes' that the Kid buried."

"Thank you, sir," Paul said.

"What you going to spend it on?"

Paul was noncommital. "Things," he said. But he had already talked it over with Jane and Anne and sworn them to secrecy. They would buy Pa a new watch.

Traveling with the Hacketts

1. Paul liked the family as it was—as Mr. Mysterious & Company. He said, ". . . why, we have adventures every day. Sometimes twice a day." What were some of the adventures that the family enjoyed?

2. In what ways was the Hackett family's trip west different from others you have read and heard about, or even experienced yourself?

3. The author has mentioned the ages of the Hackett children. If he had not, certain remarks that Anne made would have given away her age of six years. What were some of them?

4. Mr. and Mrs. Hackett had made their decision—the family would settle in California. Anne and Jane were happy about the decision for different reasons. What were the reasons of each? Were the reasons typical of their ages?

5. Pa demonstrated a special kind of showmanship by making every accident or unexpected incident seem part of the show. Tell about some times when his quick thinking and his use of "tactics like a general in battle" saved the day. Which incidents prove that he was an entertainer, even in family situations?

6. What is the meaning of the word *coincidence*? List some of the coincidences that led to the involvement of the Hackett family in the Badlands Kid adventure. Note how far back the first coincidence occurred.

7. Mrs. Hackett had only a moment to explain her anger about Jane's hairdo on p. 211. Do you think

that Jane understood her explanation? Were you convinced by it? Would Jane then have agreed that "every age is a wonderful age"?

8. Do you know of any traveling shows such as Mr. Mysterious & Company? Tell about them. Do you think it would be more difficult for such a family to earn its living today than in 1884? Explain your answer.

9. What kind of advertising did Mr. Hackett use to sell his show? Compare it with some of today's entertainment advertising. Read the message on the handbill shown on page 170. Is there any important information left out? Where would you put this information? Draw and decorate a handbill that you might use for this same show or one of your own.

10. Which incidents demonstrated the neighborliness of the people in this story? Tell of some ways in which people show qualities of neighborliness today.

11. Have you ever wished for an Abracadabra Day? Tell of the time when such a day would have helped you most.

12. What would you have liked best about being a member of Mr. Mysterious & Company? What would you have liked least?

Changing Times

This story takes place in the year 1884, so many of the things and events described that were common then seem strange to us today. Read the following sentences from the story, taking particular note of the underlined words in them. Rewrite the sentences, replacing the underlined terms or phrases with ones that might be used today. The first one is done for you as an example.

1. A covered wagon was lurching west along the barren trail to Cactus City . . . (A station wagon was speeding west along the open highway to Cactus City.)

2. She had never seen a real ballerina, but she had seen a picture of one on Pa's magic-lantern slides.

3. As Mr. Mysterious & Company, the family entertained settlers and pioneers in the small towns of the Old West . . .

4. Wood was so hard to find that houses were often built of adobe or sod . . .

5. "No, my lad, we're going to homestead some land and raise beef . . ."

6. "Jane," Mama said. "Hand me my new sunbonnet."

7. She had never been to a taffy pull or a box social or even a sewing bee.

8. Pa stopped the wagon in front of the livery barn . . .

9. Then he lit the four kerosene footlights to be set out when the show started.

10. Jane was anxious to be done with breakfast so they could go to the general store.

11. There were black potbellied stoves and Stetson hats and buggy whips.

12. But she [Mama] didn't want to see her youngsters grow up too fast. "Next thing I know, she'll be wanting to wear a bustle."

Enjoying Word Pictures

When Sid Fleischman describes Madam Sweetpea's voice, he writes that it is "as loud and clear as a foghorn on the Mississippi River." Other descriptions in the book create pictures that are just as vivid. The following sentences are taken from the story. In your notebook write the comparisons as you remember them. Then check back to the pages given to see what Mr. Fleischman wrote.

1. The wheels were painted gold, like _____, and the horses (if seeing was believing) were as _____ as _____. (page 123)
2. The children ranged in size like _____ . . . (page 124)
3. The sun sat on the horizon like a _____. (page 149)
4. He [Jeb Grimes] wore wide suspenders and a dirty hat, and his face whiskers stuck out like _____ _____. (page 152)
5. The horizon stretched out as tight as a _____. (page 179)
6. The seconds fell away as silently as _____. (page 183)
7. Madam Sweetpea began to swish her tail like _____ _____. (page 183)
8. He seemed to find notes that had been hiding in the piano for years. He shook chords, like a _____, from the keyboard. (page 189)

Mr. Mistoffelees

by T. S. ELIOT

You ought to know Mr. Mistoffelees!
The Original Conjuring Cat—
(There can be no doubt about that).
Please listen to me and don't scoff. All his
Inventions are off his own bat.
There's no such Cat in the metropolis;
He holds all the patent monopolies
For performing surprising illusions
And creating eccentric confusions.
 At prestidigitation
  And at legerdemain
 He'll defy examination
  And deceive you again.
The greatest magicians have something to learn
From Mr. Mistoffelees' Conjuring Turn.
Presto!
 Away we go!
  And we all say: OH!
   Well I never!
   Was there ever
   A Cat so clever
    As Magical Mr. Mistoffelees!

 He is quiet and small, he is black
From his ears to the tip of his tail;
He can creep through the tiniest crack,
He can walk on the narrowest rail.
He can pick any card from a pack,
He is equally cunning with dice;
He is always deceiving you into believing

224

That he's only hunting for mice.
He can play any trick with a cork
Or a spoon and a bit of fish-paste;
If you look for a knife or a fork
And you think it is merely misplaced—
You have seen it one moment, and then it is *gawn!*
But you'll find it next week lying out on the lawn.
And we all say: OH!
Well I never!
Was there ever
A Cat so clever
As Magical Mr. Mistoffelees!

His manner is vague and aloof,
You would think there was nobody shyer—
But his voice has been heard on the roof
When he was curled up by the fire.
And he's sometimes been heard by the fire
When he was about on the roof—
(At least we all *heard* that somebody purred)
Which is incontestable proof
Of his singular magical powers:
And I have known the family to call
Him in from the garden for hours,
While he was asleep in the hall.
And not long ago this phenomenal Cat
Produced *seven kittens* right out of a hat!
And we all said: OH!
Well I never!
Did you ever
Know a Cat so clever
As Magical Mr. Mistoffelees!

Prologue for a Magician

by ARTHUR GUITERMAN

Dear victims, kindly bear with me a minute:
You see this hat? There's not one rabbit in it.
Observe these pockets? Not a bit of money
In any of them, and it's far from funny;
Moreover, as I trust you will believe,
There's positively nothing up the sleeve.

So, should I conjure kings and queens and aces
And even coins from unaccustomed places,
Or should I do extraordinary things
With handkerchiefs and ribbons, balls and rings,
Should objects come to sight that were not there
And subsequently vanish into air,
Such miracles must find their explanation
In Magic or in Prestidigitation.

Now watch me. You can do it if you try;
The quickness of the hand deceives the eye!

More Books to Read

ANNIXTER, JANE and PAUL. *Wagon Scout.*
New York: Holiday House, 1965.

An exciting, probing story of a westward journey during the post-Civil War period. Young Eric assumes responsibility for the wagon train in times of danger and hardship and proves himself a leader.

FLEISCHMAN, SID. *By the Great Horn Spoon!*
Boston: Little, Brown & Company, 1963.

The most hilarious quest for gold that was ever begun—Praiseworthy, a loyal butler, and Jack Flagg, his companion, join the California Gold Rush of 1849.

FRANCHERE, RUTH. *Hannah Herself.*
New York: Thomas Y. Crowell Company, 1964.

Pioneers going west in the 1800's had as many hardships as those who landed at Jamestown in 1607. Hannah Fairfield discovers this when she makes a trip west to visit her sister, Ellen.

McGRAW, ELOISE. *Moccasin Trail.*
New York: Coward-McCann, Inc., 1952.

Eleven-year-old Jim Keath is rescued and raised by Crow Indians in this exciting runner-up for the 1953 Newbery Medal.

STODDARD, E. *The First Book of Magic.*
New York: Franklin Watts, Inc., 1953.

The author gives the beginning magician clear instructions for performing thirty-one magic tricks. Also included is information on giving magic shows and on famous magicians.

Helen Griffiths was born in London in 1939. Ten months later, at the beginning of World War II, she was evacuated to Yorkshire, a county in northern England. There in the country she became interested in and grew to love animals. When her family returned to London, the Zoo and Natural History Museum became her favorite places.

Miss Griffiths studied a commercial career until she was sixteen. At that time she persuaded her parents to allow her to "escape" to a farm, where she spent six glorious months tending cows and just being with the animals she loved. Upon her return to London she found horseback riding a good substitute for the farm and learned a great deal about horses in the next year or so.

A fascination for Argentina led Helen Griffiths to study Spanish, and through exchanged language lessons she met her husband. As Helen Griffiths Santos, her life has become somewhat nomadic. As you read this, she and her husband and children may be in Lausanne, Madrid, Palma de Mallorca, or London. But wherever she is, Helen Griffiths Santos continues to write. Her first book, *Horse in the Clouds*, was published when she was sixteen. Since then she has written six more animal tales, of which *The Wild Heart* is her favorite.

THE WILD HEART
by HELEN GRIFFITHS

ILLUSTRATED BY
VICTOR G. AMBRUS

When young creatures are orphaned and forced into independence too soon, they must learn the rules of survival quickly if they are to cope with life at all. Often the struggle to survive leaves lasting scars of bitterness.

One such orphan, called La Bruja—The Witch—by gauchos who did not understand her, was left motherless as a very young foal. She survived, but only because of her exceptional speed and ruthless determination to live.

The author of *The Wild Heart* depicts both human and animal life on a South American pampa, but the story is La Bruja's. The first half of her story is included in *Wide Horizons.* Decide as you read whether you think the book was given an appropriate title.

THE
WILD HEART

by HELEN GRIFFITHS

Illustrated by VICTOR G. AMBRUS

Jacket painting by SAM SAVITT

DOUBLEDAY & COMPANY, INC.
Garden City, New York

Pronunciation Guide for Some of the Words Used in *The Wild Heart*

You may need to use the pronunciation key in the glossary of *Vistas* or in the *Thorndike-Barnhart Junior Dictionary*.

Ángel (än′hel)
boleadoras (bō′lā ä dō′räs)
criollo (crē ō′yō)
estancia (es tän′syä)
Felipe (fā lē′pe)
fiesta (fē es′tä)
gauchos (gou′chōs)
Gregorio (grā gō′ryō)
guanacos (gwä nä′kōs)
La Bruja (lä brü′hä)
maté (mä tā′)
ombú (ôm bü′)
pampa (päm′pä)
pampero (päm pā′rō)
payador (pä yä dôr′)
Pegaso (pā gä′sō)
poncho (pôn′chō)
pulpería (pùl pä rē′ä)
Ranito (rä nē′tō)
Thamár (tä mär′)
Trapalanda (trä pä län′dä)
vizcachas (vēs kä′chäs)

The Wild Heart by Helen Griffiths
Copyright © 1963 by Helen Griffiths
Reprinted by permission of Doubleday & Company, Inc., New York
and Hutchinson and Company (Publishers) Ltd., London.

Contents

Chapter One • SCARECROW FILLY

1.

The gauchos say that there is a heaven for horses. They call it Trapalanda. It is a place of great beauty, fresh and constantly green, with running water that never fails, shady trees, blue skies, and warm sun. It is a place where no flies sting, where men are nonexistent. Nor are there pumas and wild dogs. Winter never comes to Trapalanda, and everywhere is peace.

Ángel, often called Ranito, liked to believe that Trapalanda truly existed, especially when he thought about La Bruja, the mare whose life had been hard until she came almost miraculously into his hands. Perhaps she was there now, filling her belly with luscious grass, dribbling cool water through her lips, kicking up her heels like the filly she once had been, snorting and rubbing noses with Pegaso, who was white and winged and the king of horses. Life could not be so cruel that there was no rest at the end of it.

Ángel often thought of La Bruja. She had been a savage brute when she first took shelter with him, yellow teeth constantly ready to tear, nervous hoofs ever alert, and she was named La Bruja—The Witch— because of her disposition. Ángel was to know her better nature, but the name stuck because, after all, it was her name.

But the story of La Bruja began long before she came into Ángel's keeping and long before she was coveted by man.

It began on the empty pampa when the midday sun was at its zenith in the azure sky and a lone mare sweated below it, straining with the pangs of labor. She had endured many hours thus, and the foal was long in coming, seemingly unwilling to leave the dark haven in which it had been succored for so long.

The mare was thirsty, but there was no water near. There was grass in plenty—tall, thick grass which obscured her up to the knees—but the grunting animal was not hungry. She labored patiently, passing the long hours staring at the horizon, moving in a slow circle, sometimes sinking down to rest. She did not rest often, a constant fear of danger keeping her alert while she was so helpless.

The horizon was deserted. Grass stretched endlessly about her, touching the sky in the distance, and the green on earth below her hoofs was matched by the blue of the sky above her head, unbroken by a single cloud. She saw no suspicious movement, heard no suspicious sound; and the slight wind that breathed constantly through the grasses brought no scent of danger to her widely distended nostrils. So far she was safe.

Suddenly the mare felt strong movements within her, and she knew her time had come. First two tiny hoofs, followed by a quivering nose; a big damp head with flattened ears; neck, shoulders, flanks, and haunches, with a straggly bit of tail at the end; an ungainly foal, which the mare had long awaited, tumbled into the grass.

It was a filly foal, La Bruja, and the world was dark to her just then, before her eyes could see. There was naught in her world as yet, except perhaps shock and confusion and then a warmth which began slowly stealing over her as the rough tongue of her mother began to stimulate her skin.

She snorted and kicked and trembled. Life was strong within her, and the blood began pulsing through her veins in tune with her fast-expanding lungs. A second struggle produced a minor bleat from a mouth newly opened; and the flattened ears began to prick, the straggly tail to shake itself, and the gangling legs to tremble.

Wild kicks followed as La Bruja fought to find some usage for her legs, and she struggled helplessly on her flank for several minutes, while the mother looked on and licked occasionally, until a sense of balance came to her with an urge to push herself upward.

Her first attempts were failures, but La Bruja was new to the world and did not know when she was beaten. She stretched her legs and forced her weight upon them. At times she forgot to straighten her hoofs first, so that she overbalanced before she could even stand. When she remembered to put her hoofs on the ground first and managed to stand steadily on all four sticklike legs, she did not know what to do next. For a moment or two she swayed back and forth, trying to lift one leg and shuffle it forward, and her efforts took time and patience, for more often than not she failed and fell into the grass.

While La Bruja struggled thus, the mare resumed her steady watch of the horizon. Her thirst was greater now, and she was anxious to leave the birthplace of the foal, the warm smell of which would travel on the wind and reach the searching nostrils of some hungry hunter; but until the foal had learned to use her legs, flight was impossible.

The sun was westward bound, but the sky was still bright in the east, where darkness comes first. The destination of the mare lay in the east, where others of her kind were gathered. When the foal should be fit to travel, the mare would seek the company of the herd, and she stared anxiously toward the eastern horizon, waiting for the foal.

La Bruja learned. She had several falls, but surprise was greater than any injury, and before much time had passed, she was prancing awkwardly around the mare, poking, sniffing, and prodding with her rough, large head, hunger the strongest instinct that was now within her.

The mare stood still and patient, wise to the ways of foals; and after much experimenting, nibbling at her mother's tail, sucking her knees and hocks and belly, La Bruja found the right place. She stood with her legs splayed wide apart, her neck twisted, and her tail flicking excitedly, gulping mouthfuls of warm, sweet milk until her skinny belly was bloated and she gasped for breath.

Then the mare grew rougher, for shadows were creeping over the eastern pampa and she was still far from the safety of the herd which awaited her. She pushed the foal aside whenever La Bruja searched again to suck, and she began moving slowly toward the herd.

La Bruja stood still, uncomprehending. The mare looked round and nickered a soft command to follow. La Bruja did not understand. She stamped her hoof and bleated angrily, milk still dribbling from her wet, pink jaws, and she flicked her rag of tail.

The mare came back to her and gently nudged her forward, but La Bruja still did not understand. The mare tried again, and, pushing with head and breast, sometimes roughly, sometimes gently, she gradually persuaded the foal to come.

In this erratic manner, with La Bruja sometimes bounding ahead and sometimes lagging far behind, staring longingly after the retreating mare, the two of them traveled slowly in the direction of the herd, darkness before them and failing light behind.

Thus were La Bruja's first hours on the pampa.

2.

La Bruja was never coveted by any man for her beauty, for she was far from beautiful. Even as a foal, when babyhood lends a natural attractiveness to clumsy figures, La Bruja was ugly.

Her sire was of the *criollo* breed, and she inherited his Roman nose but none of his pride of carriage. Her head was overlarge, held always too high, as if constantly in search of danger, and her ears seemed to be too small in comparison, half hidden in a fuzzy forelock and untidy mane. Her body was long and always skinny. Even though she fed well on her mother's milk, there never seemed to be any flesh to cover her bones, and with bloated belly but ribby flanks she looked more like a scarecrow than a filly foal.

The length of her legs was amazing, more than that of any other foal in the herd, so that she was taller than all her brothers, and her long legs and long body revealed that she was not pure-blooded and that there was more of her mother's sire in her than her own.

La Bruja's mother was only half *criollo*. Her sire was a thoroughbred stallion, newly imported to the land, who, unable to resist the call of freedom which whispered constantly to him through the grass and on the wind, broke away from his master and claimed as his own the first wild mare he found. In the resultant offspring the hardy *criollo* blood proved strongest, and La Bruja's mother seemed to possess none of the ancient blood of her sire. But in La Bruja, granddaughter of the thoroughbred, nature had reverted itself, and she was three parts like her grandsire and only one part native pony.

Her coloring was vague, a sort of liver-brown with mottled haunches, and her eyes and nostrils were pink-rimmed, giving her a vicious appearance long before hatred became part of her nature. Her ragged tail and brushlike mane were of a gingery tone, and, all in all, she looked as though she had been thrown together in a hurry with no particular care being taken to see that all the parts fitted or matched.

But though so ugly, she was healthy and strong, and for a wild horse there is nothing more important than these two things. The wild horse has little cunning; therefore it must have strength.

La Bruja's games with the other foals in the herd strengthened the muscles of her legs, taught her how to twist and turn with alacrity, how to defend herself from unexpected attacks—playful though they might be—and La Bruja became the most energetic foal in the herd, for she never tired of running and playing and teasing. Even the hot summer sun seemed to affect her but little, and when the others were often listless, flopped out in the grass, La Bruja would be circling round them on her gawky legs, nibbling and lightly kicking, trying to coax them to play.

The herd to which La Bruja belonged was small in comparison with many another wild herd in those days, which sometimes numbered sixty or seventy or even a hundred horses. There were only twenty-one animals in

La Bruja's herd, including eight foals, but the stallion who led them was satisfied.

He was a young animal, little more than a colt, and this was his first herd. The eight foals were the first of his offspring, and, excluding La Bruja, all had inherited his good looks. Small but strong-chested, with wiry legs and solid frame, he pranced proudly about his little herd, and by his constant watchfulness and anger against any mare who showed the slightest disobedience he revealed the fact that this was his first command.

How grandly he arched his neck, the muscles showing thick in the curve; how alert and eager were his sparkling eyes; how gaily held was his tail as, reveling in the sheer joy of being strong and young, he galloped across the flat grassland, circling his mares at wide distances but never for one moment removing his gaze from them. His khaki coloring was broken only by a clear white star on his forehead, black mane, tail, and fetlocks. He was proud in his youth and strength, and his strength was in the number of his mares.

His sons and daughters feared him, all except La Bruja. The ungainly half-breed filly foal feared nothing. Even as a youngster she was proud, for she inherited this from her sire if nothing else, this and her love of freedom. She listened to the pounding hoofs of the restless stallion and watched him as he swooped around his mares; while she listened and watched, her own legs would tremble, and her heart would beat faster, for even as a foal she loved to run.

One day the watching and listening became too much for her. Recklessly she flung herself after the racing stallion and followed far behind him, not kicking and bucking as did he, but loping with all the vigor her young body possessed. The mares and colts watched in sudden astonishment, for they knew the bad temper of their master when crossed in his commands.

The mother of La Bruja whinnied shrilly, demanding the filly's return, but the blood was in her head, and her heart expanded thrillingly. La Bruja ignored her mother. This was everything.

The stallion became aware of his tiny follower, and he whirled suddenly to face her. La Bruja, astonished, halted, and she trembled, not from awe or fear but from exertion. Ugly head held high, she awaited the stallion's approach, unmoving while he stalked about her, sniffing and curious, not angry.

In general the stallion ignored his sons and daughters. They were too young yet either to interest or antagonize him, but La Bruja beheld him fearlessly, and he was curious. He touched the panting body with his soft muzzle, and it was a gentle touch. Then he turned sharply away again and dashed toward his herd, careering through the startled mares, scattering them deliberately so that he might round them up again.

La Bruja followed him, and ever after that she was his shadow. Neither colt nor filly could keep pace with him except La Bruja, and only this one ugly offspring would he tolerate.

How superior became La Bruja, indulging in the patronage of her sire. The older colts she battled with, the younger, she ignored, and always she had the advantage, for when she chose to flee from their combined rage, none could overtake her. How independent she became, going only to her mother for milk and nightly shelter. If she should fall asleep during the daylight hours, made sleepy by a full, contented belly, the faithful mother kept watchful guard over her and stood so that her shadow should fall across La Bruja and keep her from the sun.

La Bruja was unaware of the goodness of her mother. To the filly, the mother was a background to her life, like the sun in the daytime sky, the moon and stars at night, the grass and the wind and the earth. Her mother was food and shelter, nothing more; but when La Bruja lost her mother, her life was changed, and the joy was gone from living.

Chapter Two • *PAMPERO*

1.

As La Bruja grew, the rising and setting of the sun and moon marking off the days and weeks, the mantle of summer descended upon the land in which the herd dwelt.

The greenness of spring slowly passed away. The grass withered in the heat and became yellowy brown. The giant thistles died, their stalks becoming hollow, their roots turning to dust; but so thickly did they grow together that even rootless they stood, leaning one against the other, supporting each other in huge, rust-brown clumps. They could not fall, and they hemmed in the wild horses like high barricades, so that even the docile mares became impatient, while the high-spirited stallion was almost savage with rage, and La Bruja shared his anger.

For days, weeks, and months the thistles stood. At times the summer heat would flare into crackling flames among the tinder-dry stalks, and for miles a vast line of fire would burn, destroying the burrowing *vizcachas* and other rodents as it crept across the wide pampa, halting only at a river, stopped only by a storm, or stamped out by the men on the pampa, the gauchos.

Fortunately fire was not a peril that La Bruja's herd needed to face. The quencher of fire, the destroyer of thistles, and the killer of La Bruja's mother was the summer storm which came when La Bruja had known only four months of life.

The storm, *pampero* it is called by man, came from the southwest. The afternoon had been long, hot, and still. The north wind, which had been blowing for days with breath like the heat of a furnace, suddenly stopped, and there was a pregnant silence over the pampa as the mares and younglings sprawled upon the ground, exhausted by the heat and breathless atmosphere.

A gloom seemed suddenly to possess the sky, a gloom not cast by any cloud. Even as the horses noticed it, the gloom became a mountain of blackness, clouds of yellow dust intermingled with it, and flocks of terrified birds, flying madly before the encroaching evil, swept above the horses and caused them to spring to all fours, uttering cries of alarm.

Gulls circled and dived and mewed like injured puma kittens; golden plovers thronged with them and cried their warning, too; and a host of monster dragonflies clouded the sky when they had gone. The mares, colts, and fillies crushed together in a frightened bunch, and the stallion stayed beside them, for even he was powerless against the furies of the sky.

Hardly had the birds and insects passed when the first huge drops of rain began to fall. They came as liquid mud, falling from a sky choked with windswept dust. The horses clung to one another as sudden lightning flashed through the blackness of the clouds with terrifying thunder close in succession. Torrents of rain fell upon the cringing horses. They shrieked in fear at the vivid flashes of light and reared as the thunder rocketed in their sensitive ears.

The stallion was made savage by the tempest. The uproar of sound and sudden light among the darkness filled him with a sense of danger, and he watched over his mares with unhesitant cruelty, fearing for them in this fury of the heavens. Any mare that broke away, dashing madly she knew not whither, the stallion raced after to turn her back, kicking, biting, fearful in his rage; and the mares obeyed him, fearing his fury as much as they feared that of the storm.

The first blackness passed away, and the air was made white with fleetly falling hailstones—giant hailstones as large as eggs, flat and jagged—and they fell with fury until the pampa was made white with them.

The horses screamed and panicked. Even the stallion could not control them. Beaten by wind and rain and stones of ice, they fled hither and thither, but there was no shelter from the tempest, and one of them was blinded by the lightning which struck her as she reared in terror.

The storm passed over. The hail ceased, the thunder was silent, and by nightfall the pampa was calm again and cool. The horses slept where they stood, and when dawn came, brilliant sunshine spread over the land and the air was fresh, without a vapor.

But what destruction had the *pampero* wrought? Now the pampa was a vista of flatness unto the horizon, for every thistle had been crushed to the ground and swept away by the violent wind. Plovers lay in scores upon the earth, life crushed from them before they could escape, and many more fluttered with broken wings or limped among their dead companions because they could not fly at all.

Tiny deer which frequented the pampa lay dead, also, but among the horses the mother of La Bruja had been the only fatality. Struck between the eyes by a heavy hailstone, she fell instantly dead, and from that moment the life of her foal was altered.

All the mares wandered about stupefied, suffering from cuts and bruises, some limping as they dragged an injured leg, and they were so much hurt that for days they seemed only semiconscious. Even the proud stallion drooped his head and had no desire to stretch his sturdy legs.

This period of depression passed, for now that the storm had spent itself, the weather was beautiful and the sun shone without too great a heat and the breezes were cool instead of sultry.

The thistles were gone, and the stallion could race again, for there was nothing to impede his stride. But the fleet shadow of La Bruja no longer dogged his path, for now she was an orphan and there was none to tend her needs. All her energy must be preserved for the unfairly balanced struggle for survival, and there was no time for playing and running with the cool breezes and rejoicing in the brilliant sunshine. Now she must fight all day and dart from hating hoofs, for there was no mother to defend or feed her.

La Bruja's hope for survival lay with her persistent, strong-willed nature and her speed. To get her daily food, she had to steal from every nursing mare, pushing aside the rightful colt or filly to snatch at the udder herself. One or two swallows were all she would gain before being roughly thrust aside, and in this manner she went from mare to mare, tolerated by none, attacked by all, even by the other younglings whose milk she stole.

She had no other manner of living, and the favor of the stallion was useless to her. He could not feed her, and his mares refused. They kicked and bit her, they chased her away, and only the filly's fleetness saved her from many a cruel attack. But hunger possessed her, and pain became of secondary importance. For the milk of life she would endure much, and spent all the daylight hours robbing the mares as they grazed, regardless of how they punished her.

La Bruja became an outcast among them, a hindrance, and they did not want her. But she ignored their plainly expressed dislike of her because she needed them.

It was in the early days that La Bruja missed her mother most; the days before she learned to fend for herself, before she learned to accept the kicks and bites that were the price of a mouthful of milk; the days before she learned to sleep alone.

When the storm had passed, La Bruja searched vainly for her mother among the downcast mares, sniffing at them in order to know them and turning away lost when each time she did not find her mother. Then, bewildered, hungry, and lonely, she found her mother's body lying among the broken thistles, already stiffening into the rigor of death. She drew back, nose wrinkling with disgust, ears flattened with fear, for although this was her mother, it was not her mother, and she turned away from the cold carcass, somehow understanding that she need search no further for the mother she had lost.

What was she to do, a four-month suckling without its dam?

She saw the other colts clinging close to protective mother flanks; she saw them suckling with stamping hoofs and flicking tails; she watched them sink repleted into the grass, ready to sleep away their fullness in readiness to gorge again. She watched them standing afar off, for there was none to call her close with a gentle nicker or a toss of the head.

She was aware of great hunger as she watched, and when all had fed and fallen asleep, only then did she attempt to approach the several mothers, searching for a little kindness, a tiny neigh of welcome. There was neither. They treated her tentative advances roughly, thrusting her aside without mercy. They had milk enough for one colt only, and nature was hard on the motherless.

All that day La Bruja starved. She slept awhile, lying at a distance from the herd, and the warm sun melting over her back gave her comfort, her to whom all maternal comfort was now denied.

La Bruja felt loneliness as well as hunger. She had never slept alone before. There had always been her dam beside her, guarding her while she slumbered. Now she had no patient watcher, one to see that no puma stole upon her while she slept, that no colt or jealous mare would suddenly attack her.

With the coming of the second dawn after the storm La Bruja was desperate in her hunger, and so this day she began to rob the mares of the milk they would not give her, regardless of the cost. She ended the day battered and bruised, but her hunger had been almost satisfied, and she could sleep without pain, half contented.

So passed each succeeding day, and La Bruja thrived, thin and ragged ever but lively still. The loss of her mother became no longer a grievance with her, but for many a week she felt her absence. She had been hardly aware of her mother while she lived, but now that she was gone, La Bruja was greatly aware of her loss.

She was friendless and alone, unprotected from the daily fears and bumps in every childhood, animal or human. She did not miss her mother with an aching heart but only with a knowledge that she lacked something she needed. She had no comfort or anchorage, and life was hard because of it. Otherwise in her slight memory her mother no longer existed.

The daily disturbance among the mares roused by La Bruja was not unnoticed by the stallion, and he grew resentful toward the gangling filly who constantly scattered his herd. His former tolerance for her was forgotten, and he himself turned upon her and drove her away. La Bruja knew no fear of the stallion, and his punishments were no harder to bear than those of the mares. She side-jumped and sometimes fled, but as soon as the moment was opportune, she cautiously returned again, driven by hunger and even by defiance.

La Bruja no longer galloped behind her sire, nor did she even watch him. She cared for nothing now, intent only upon survival, and while necessity forced her, she robbed the mares of their jealously guarded milk, robbed them until she no longer needed it.

This day came gradually, week by week, as she grew. She began to notice the grass beneath her hoofs, and when she was nearing six months of age, it attracted her. She nuzzled it with her pink nostrils, snorting as its coolness tickled her; she gingerly tested it with her tongue, and slowly she took her first bites of it, finding it strange but somehow satisfying.

Soon she was daily cropping the grass, finding patches of sweet clover, a delicacy of which she never tired. Milk

became of secondary importance to her, and it was not long before she surrendered it completely and lived by grass alone.

When she became this much independent, she ignored the mares completely. Her bruises faded, her split skin healed, and a glow began to come to her coat, which before had been rough and dull.

La Bruja grazed away from her herd. She chose to be alone, scorning the others as any outcast scorns those who turn him away, but an inherent need for safety kept her within sight of the mares. Still she needed their protection, for alone she was well-nigh helpless against foes, especially at so young an age.

The stallion watched over her from a distance. He sometimes circled round her and drove her toward the herd, but she resisted all his efforts to keep her among his mares, and after a while he let her alone, seeing that she did not intend to stray.

She was a satellite, outcast like Hagar, but she was a female and belonged to the stallion. He would make certain that she did not wander. As he would drive away the colts when they reached maturity, so would he cling to the fillies and keep them near him.

Chapter Three • *SECOND SPRING*

1.

La Bruja, dwelling almost alone, learned much about the pampa on which she lived. Now that grass and clover were her diet, she no longer felt hunger, and after grazing, she found time enough to explore and discover and play.

She learned that there was other life apart from that of the herd. There were timid deer dwelling in groups that kept well apart from the horses. Their smell was strong and unpleasant, and La Bruja snorted her disgust with wrinkled nostrils whenever she came upon them.

There were guanacos, the llama of the pampa, smaller than their mountain brothers but much the same in every other respect. Their necks were tall, their ears were long, and their heads were haughtily stupid. La Bruja found them curious, and she learned that they were not to be feared.

There were the huge rheas, the flightless giant bird that lived among the guanacos and sometimes among the horses. They were powerful and fleet, vicious when aroused, and La Bruja kept well clear of them, for they often startled her.

Below her hoofs teemed much more life, for there were rodents of many kinds burrowing beneath the pampa grass. Nocturnal creatures, La Bruja saw little of them, but the vizcachas built complicated labyrinths below the ground and left evidence of this in the huge piles of sun-baked earth which were scattered generously about the pampa, conspicuous at any distance. When La Bruja was small, they were big enough to make the jumping of them an exciting game, but as she grew, they seemed to shrink and after a while no longer interested her.

While she daily discovered new things, La Bruja grew, and signs of babyhood fell away. The brushy tail vanished, and dark, slender hair grew down to her hocks. The tufts along her neck became a proper mane and forelock, falling freely about her but not adding much to her general appearance.

She grew much. Her long legs became even longer, her long body, too. There was alertness in her luminous eyes but defiance, too, which detracted from their beauty. Her liver coloring did not change, except to darken, and there was not even a white marking on her forehead to bring some small attraction to the Roman nose and gaunt, plain features. She was taller than any of her sisters or brothers, and she was fast overtaking her sire, a fourteen-hand pony, tall enough for his breed.

Winter came to the pampa, and with it came coldness and rain and days without sun, to which La Bruja was not accustomed. The summer birds fled, and the stallion considered it time to drive his herd northward to a warmer clime.

They traveled slowly, grazing in a leisurely fashion as they went, many of the mares in foal again but with a youngster still running at their heels. The grass was ever abundant, and as they journeyed northward, they came to warmer winds and more sunshine.

La Bruja traveled behind, with them but not of them. She had accepted her lonely life unquestioningly and was contented to live as she did. She felt no need of comradeship, for after being denied it so long, the desire in her had faded, and she was glad to graze alone.

All winter through they turned their heads northward, but when the first signs of spring were coming to the pampa, the stallion changed direction, and back they trekked to their own country, leaving rocky scrubland and distant forests behind them.

Fresh green grass was springing up. The patches of weeds which grew thick and tall in the summer months fell away to nothing during the winter, and the grass could find its way. The rhythm of spring was in the air. Swallows returned to their nests, flying above the heads of the horses as they journeyed swiftly to their homes. The mornings were misty and fresh, damp and clean. Lapwings cried and drummed their wings; pipits soared high and poured out songs of spring as they floated slowly earthward. The mares gave birth to the new year's foals, and the yearlings could not understand why their mothers did not heed them.

The thistles came again, and La Bruja found their huge, rhubarblike leaves good to eat. The stems were sweet, and La Bruja ignored the grass to take her fill of this new-tasting plant which she had been too young to discover before. She grew fat on these leaves, and firm flesh covered her ribs so that they were no longer conspicuous.

As time passed, the thistles grew hard and dry and were not fit to eat. Their flowers broke open in a white mass, shedding scores of silvery seeds which floated aloft in the breeze. Then the whole sky seemed to be a myriad of silvery balls, floating hither and thither, and the horses tossed their heads and sneezed but eagerly snaffled up the fallen seeds which abundantly covered the ground.

The days were spent in idleness and feasting. La Bruja watched and felt all the signs of her second spring, and her spirit grew high and glad as such flowing life came to the pampa anew.

She kicked and bucked and dashed about, stretching her long, slender legs into a wild gallop, and the mares watched her with mild surprise, having not the energy for such useless play. With new life in the herd they were fully occupied caring for their foals, and they were loath to do more than eat and doze and guard their younglings.

2.

When La Bruja was a yearling, the stallion claimed her and brought her into the herd, keeping her there with many bites and kicks, for she was unwilling to stay among the mares, she who was accustomed to dwelling alone.

The stallion was pugnacious now, more than he had ever been, and the slightest disobedience by any mare he would not tolerate. In this time of marauding stallions he was jealous for each member of his herd and would permit no straying for fear that one of his mares would be stolen away.

He first attacked the yearling colts, his three handsome sons that had hardly recovered from the separation from their dams. He drove them away with squeals of rage, eyes flashing, hoofs rearing over them, ready to strike if they did not obey his commands. Bewildered and greatly frightened, they scattered across the pampa, and the stallion chased them each in turn, biting them in the rump in order to let them know his power.

The three colts stayed together. They did not desert the herd entirely for some time, being still full of longing for their mothers and companions, unable to understand the jealousy of their sire. After a while they slowly wandered away and grew independent and proud, becoming stallions themselves one day and treating their sons as they had been treated by their father.

The stallion had his battles, too. Even though his herd was small, it was coveted, while he in his turn desired the mares of others. His biggest battle was with a small, skewbald stallion, twice his age and with twice his number of mares.

They fought hard and savagely, rearing to their hind legs and using their forehoofs to inflict damage, screaming all the while. Neither could gain the advantage, and by mutual consent they fell away from each other, returning to their respective herds, scarred and weary. La Bruja's sire had the left ear completely torn away, while his adversary went from that day on blinded in one eye by a blow from the other's hoof.

Lesser battles gained the stallion eight more mares and fewer scars. Some of his youthful handsomeness was gone, but great was his glory when he surveyed his growing herd. When the time of fighting passed, he settled down to guard his mares from their daily and often nonexistent enemies, his wounds healing, his pride increasing.

He allowed La Bruja to stray again, for he had no fear for her now. There was no stallion to molest and steal her. She had a growing foal within her and was safe.

La Bruja was unaware of the foal. She was glad to find herself free from the stallion's domination, able to dwell in her solitary fashion, for even now the mares resented her, a stranger in their midst, and they treated her no better than before. The eight new mares came in for some hazing, too, but they gradually settled down among their new companions, a thing that independent La Bruja could not do. She longed for her solitude while she was with them, and when spring had passed and summer came, she took advantage of her sire's relaxed vigilance and separated herself from them again.

The months of summer dried the grass, which wilted yellow and pale beneath the blazing sun. When the thistles and their seeds had withered, the mares' new fatness melted away. This summer there were not so many thistles, and the stallion galloped proudly around his larger herd, which now contained twenty-five mares and fifteen colts.

As time passed, La Bruja felt not so inclined to gallop. She was becoming aware of the growing foal; a slothful spirit overtook her, though she did not understand its meaning, she who had delighted in stretching her lanky legs into a race with the wind. A feeling of contentment filled her, so that she desired only to eat and doze like the others.

The burning sun dried up the lakes, and the golden plovers, which had come in hundreds from colder climes, fled the pampa in search of water. The horses traveled from district to district, searching the same, and there were many days when their thirsts remained unslaked, for it did not rain. The mud at the lakesides was cracked and dry, and the mares surveyed each parched lagoon with dismal eyes. Then came a time of fierce storms which drove away the scorching heat and filled the lakes again. But no storm this year compared in severity with that which killed La Bruja's mother.

Autumn came, bringing with it new grass, damp with luscious sap. The mares ate ravenously, and all their days were spent thus, eating and teaching their young-sters to eat. Flocks of squalling, hurrying birds sweep-ing northward warned the mares of the coldness to come, and the stallion once again looked to the north, heeding their warning, for the birds were true mes-sengers often.

Winter came and passed away, and La Bruja's third spring was nearing, the time when she would bring forth a colt or filly, as had her mother before her. She was uglier than ever in her hugeness, and it did not seem that her ugliness would ever fall away, for it in-creased with every year. Her thinness was her nature, and she could never be fat like the *criollos* because of the blood of her grandsire, the tall and slender thoroughbred who passed on his thinness but not his beauty.

La Bruja instinctively began to learn about the life within her, and somehow she knew that within a short time she must find a safe and secret place. It was not enough to stay at her present distance from the herd, for might they not search her out in curiosity and then in jealousy kill what she had nurtured for so long? No chances must be taken, this she knew, and she sought out a thicket of tall grass as she grazed, ex-amining it with care.

It was soft and warm and sheltered. As the herd wandered along, it would within a day or two be at some distance from the place La Bruja chose, near enough to return to if danger threatened but far enough to be at peace and fearless.

La Bruja chose wisely. She had not done this thing before, but instinct came to her aid without her knowing, and she did that which instinct commanded as if it were her own desire. She lingered near her chosen place, and the other mares went on. The stallion allowed her to linger this much more than usual, for he knew that after two or three days alone she would return to the herd, foal at heels, and his herd would be increased again.

Chapter Four • THE MOTHER

1.

La Bruja's time had come. She lay in the thicket and was glad to be alone. Her ears were alert, straining for any sound unusual, and she watched the birds. By their actions she would know if all was well. They would sing and swoop and play in the air, but if danger came, they would screech and flap their wings and vanish. Now they played, and their joyful twitterings and song were a soothing background to La Bruja's patient suffering.

The early days of spring were short, and the sun soon deserted the sky, leaving the pampa to the pleasure of the moon and its sparkling companions. La Bruja was restless and a little afraid. There were few nights that she had seen and none that she had experienced so completely alone.

She rose and stretched and grazed a little. She trembled at strange rustlings and the sobs of a crazy widow bird, and she returned to the thicket, which was warm still from the heat of her body.

The foal came, and it was in darkness that La Bruja began her first duties of motherhood. The moon had suddenly vanished behind a mass of cloud, and it was by smell alone that La Bruja found her youngling and cleaned it.

She heard its tiny breathing and felt its warmth, and she was flooded with rich desires to love and tend the little creature dropped in the thicket.

With such eagerness she licked it clean; with such contentment she listened to its first struggles to rise, its wavering bleats of determination, for in the darkness she could make out nothing of the foal. The moon had failed her when she needed it most.

The clouds floated on, and the moon returned once more in all its glory. La Bruja saw by its powerful light the foal she had only heard and felt. It was already rocking unsteadily on its tiny hoofs, and the spindle legs trembled at the strength with which they were suddenly empowered.

A filly foal it was, and in appearance she was all that a *criollo* foal should be, with none of La Bruja's ugliness or strangeness and all of her sire's good looks. She was tiny, of color a rusty yellow which was to become a mellowed bronze with age. Time was to bring her to captivity, and the tiny creature now filling La Bruja's heart with love and joy was to become the joy of a gaucho poet, a *payador,* who called her Thamár, for she was as beautiful as the daughter of a king.

As La Bruja had done in her time, the filly foal Thamár learned hastily the use of her legs, as must learn all young creatures born on the plain, where there are no places to hide in safety. Hunger, too, she felt, and La Bruja was aware of the eagerly searching, soft mouth with a contentment she had never known before.

Here was company at last, something of her own which would never deny her or drive her away, something which needed her as once she had needed her dam. With gladness she gave herself to Thamár and stood in patience while the foal sucked.

Dawn came in a glow of pink and gold. Below the color of the sky a thick, white mist wreathed among the grass and slowly dispersed, leaving a fresh dampness over the earth and a sparkling dew which quenched the thirsty mother as she ate, coming eagerly from the thicket with the foal dancing excitedly beside her. The mist clung ghostlike to their warm bodies, and when La Bruja plunged her head to eat, there was no sign of it. Her legs, too, were invisible, and there was little to see of Thamár, shivering beside her.

Unlike her mother, La Bruja felt no desire to return to the herd and the protection of the stallion. What was there to call to her, who had always dwelt in loneliness? She had no memories of friendliness and company, and never had the pampa given her cause to fear. Why needed she protection? What needed she to fear?

The stallion had kept her in unwilling bondage, and now she was free. With Thamár at her side she had all the company she needed, and she was unwilling to take her filly to the herd. There would be no welcoming neighs, no friendly touch of noses, only iron hoofs and cruel teeth.

Hardly aware of her intentions, La Bruja drifted away from the herd. She knew full well in which direction it was, and she turned her head the other way. As the hours passed and the sun grew warmer, La Bruja became resolved in her decision.

The filly took her fill of milk and basked beside her. La Bruja stood so that her shadow should fall across the little creature, for there were no trees on the pampa to give respite from the sun. While Thamár slept, La Bruja stood guard, and in everything she did she was contented. No danger threatened, the birds all sang and played, and nothing could persuade La Bruja to return to her rightful place. She feared nothing, for her legs were swift and her heart was strong.

When the filly woke, refreshed and lively, La Bruja watched her play. She chased the multicolored butter-flies, she reared up to snatch at the plovers as she caught their shadows overhead, and she grabbed her mother's swishing tail, anxious to prove her strength and to use her so newly discovered legs. Then La Bruja put a stop to play, for now that she had made a decision, she was anxious to put herself farther from the herd and also from the place wherein Thamár had been born.

She set off at a trot, and Thamár was glad to follow her, thinking this some new game that her mother played. She raced ahead and turned to watch her slower mother, but very soon tiredness and hunger overcame her, so that La Bruja had to halt and allow the foal to feed.

In this manner the hours passed by, and soon darkness came upon the land again. The foal slept, and La Bruja kept watch over her. Her restless spirit was somewhat quieted, for by this time she and Thamár were at some distance from the herd. From now on it was certain that they would dwell alone.

2.

La Bruja's decision to dwell alone with Thamár was not a wise one. She who had known only three springs could be scarcely aware of the dangers that awaited a lonely mare. The lion which would cautiously withdraw from a herd guarded by a watchful stallion had no fear of stragglers or strays.

Then there was man—that all-powerful, deadly creature whom La Bruja had never seen. How could she even know that man was as great an enemy as the puma and more clever? Man made slaves of horses, and these horses betrayed their own kind. La Bruja feared no horse, and she could not know that the creature he carried on his back was dangerous.

These two dangers were the greatest, for apart from puma and man there were few creatures to harm her.

La Bruja had no fears. In her ignorance she grazed and guarded her youngling with only instinct to make her sniff the air and keep her ears alert. For what was she listening? Would she recognize the scent of danger when it came?

Not only because of ignorance was La Bruja unafraid. She was aware of her great speed, and she had already learned that speed was the greatest asset in life. She could excel her own sire in the race, and because of this knowledge of her ability she was unafraid.

La Bruja rarely galloped these days. Thamár could not keep pace with her if she did, and La Bruja refused to be separated from her foal by more than a length or two. She guarded the filly with great zeal, for her heart cleaved to this little creature of her own.

With joy she watched her youngling play, showing her games at times, for she was still a filly herself and young enough to play. When Thamár grew weary, La Bruja would draw the foal to her with tenderness, gently nibbling the filly's neck and caressing her by brushing her own head against the filly's body. La Bruja was all that any foal could desire, and in the shadow of her mother's care Thamár grew strong and bold and beautiful, the latter attribute being even more striking in contrast to La Bruja's ugliness.

The daily life of mother and foal was uneventful. They passed each hour by eating, playing, sleeping, and partaking in the general activity of the pampa. They saw no other horses, and for this La Bruja was glad. She wanted no company but that of Thamár, and she was rich in contentment, for life now treated her well. But by the very order of things, La Bruja's folly in choosing to live this solitary life was made apparent, for it is ordained that her kind must live together in order to be safe.

The summer days had passed, and the first autumn chills were in the air. Grass was shooting up again, succulent and green, and La Bruja's pleasure and greed for the new season's offerings perhaps made her less wary than usual. Also, she had lived unmolested for half a year, and confidence bred contempt.

Her first awareness of danger came too late. The young, fawn puma crouching among the grass and tangled clumps of withered weeds sprang suddenly upon her, and La Bruja, in surprise, could only scream out shrilly her fear and pain as claws dug deeply into her withers and teeth gnawed at her neck.

Then instinct forced itself uppermost in the midst of her confusion. With a mighty jerk of the head, she reared high and flung the puma from her. As he flopped to the ground, La Bruja fled, and her heart beat heavily as her hoofs pounded across the pampa, fear subsiding a little as she recognized her power in speed. She gave not even a backward glance to delay her, but dashed away, forgetting the pain, forgetting everything in her dread of the puma.

A terrified cry smote upon her ears, a cry she knew at once for that of Thamár. She had forgotten her foal in her moment of danger, and the sudden realization of this halted instantly her crazed career. She swirled about and saw the lithe and hungry puma bounding after her youngling, almost within reach but never quite. Thamár was not so swift as her dam, but fear lent speed to her, and her legs galloped swiftly while her heart was frozen.

The mother came to her rescue. Moments earlier the puma had terrified her, but now her heart was filled with scorching rage against the creature that threatened Thamár. Speed had carried her to safety; now it brought her back into danger with the strength and fury of a whirlwind.

She charged upon the puma, mouth open, teeth bared, eyes rolling white, screaming with wild rage as she attacked him. The puma gave up his second prey and turned to face his attacker with snarls and hisses, not swift enough to flee. He crouched to the ground and clawed at her, and La Bruja's heavy hoofs came slicing down upon him. He dodged them and sprang at her before she could strike again, and now he was upon her back, clinging like moss to a stone, and La Bruja could not shake him off.

Undaunted, she flung herself upon the ground and rolled over, and the puma jumped aside to save himself. He was quicker than La Bruja, and before she could spring to her feet, he had grabbed her neck, sure that this time he was the victor. But he had not reckoned with a mother's love, and La Bruja somehow managed to strike him as he clung to her, dashing him to the ground.

Dazed, he could not escape her now. She crashed her hoofs upon him again and again, white froth foaming from her jaws, blood streaming from her in many places. The puma hissed and cried and howled, but

La Bruja, with the cry of her own youngling still in her ears, had no mercy for her defeated foe.

She crushed his soft body completely, even when he was dead. Not until the flesh was pulp and the bones all cracked did La Bruja cease her stamping, and when she stopped, her rage had cooled, and she had forgotten Thamár's terrified cry. Then she became aware of soreness and exhaustion and also a violent thirst. She was trembling, every limb aching with exertion, but her first concern was Thamár.

She nickered softly to the frightened foal and drew her gently to her, searching all parts of the slender body in order to discover if it had received any injury. Thamár was whole, however, and La Bruja's heart was eased.

Together they trotted to the nearest watering place, and by nightfall the fear of the afternoon had completely faded, although La Bruja was never to forget the experience and forever afterwards held a deep hatred for the pampa lion.

Chapter Five • THE ROUNDUP

1.

La Bruja's wounds healed. Several scars marked her neck and withers ever afterwards to tell of the battle she had fought with the puma, but no injury was deep enough to cause any permanent damage or impede her swiftness. The scars made her more ugly, but of this La Bruja was unaware. Thamár was unharmed, and this was her only interest. She learned to guard herself and her youngling with more care, and never again was she taken unawares by a puma.

That autumn La Bruja also caught her first sight of man. She was grazing unconcernedly, with Thamár not far distant sniffing at the clover and taking her first taste of it, when she suddenly heard fast hoofbeats a short distance from her. She looked up, startled, staring with pricked ears and watchful eyes at the horse whose hoofs she heard, and saw a strange creature upon his back.

The horse was galloping madly not toward La Bruja but away, and therefore she did not stir from where she stood, curiosity overwhelming any slight instinct of danger. The horse she understood well enough, but what was it he carried astride him? Some living creature assuredly, for it made sounds and moved.

The gaucho wore a poncho round his shoulders, and this streamed out behind him as he raced against the wind, adding to the strangeness of his figure. Perhaps he did not see La Bruja, or perhaps he saw only her ugliness and regarded her as worthless. Certainly he did not turn toward her but left her unmolested where she stood to wonder at this oddity which she had never seen before.

The horse and rider passed by, but because the pampa is flat, La Bruja was able to watch them for some time, growing smaller in size, fainter in sound, until eventually she lost interest and returned to grazing.

This was La Bruja's first sight of man, and it was not alarming. Like a bird that sweeps overhead, so came and went the gaucho and his horse, pausing for nothing. La Bruja soon forgot him, and when man came again, she was unafraid, having no reason to fear.

La Bruja should have feared the second time, which shortly followed the first. A great roundup of wild horses had been arranged by the gauchos. They wanted the horses for two reasons. The first reason was to sell hides and grease to traders who sent them across the seas to other lands; the second was to keep and break any of the ponies too worthy of such an end.

They had planned the roundup with care. They built a huge stockade, and they sent out riders to learn where the horses dwelt, so that they should know how great a drive they would need to make in order to capture them all. The first rider La Bruja saw was such a man, and he returned with reports of two large herds and a few odd strays within the district he had searched. Other reports were similar, and the gauchos concluded that, with luck, they should within a week ensnare perhaps two hundred horses.

The gaucho of those times had more Indian than European blood in his veins. His skin was dark, his eyes and hair black, his body supple and strong. He had inherited the primitive skills of the Indian, the pride of the Spaniard, and combined the two with the natural simplicity of the poor, uneducated man. His heart could be callous and cruel, his actions savage, and yet he could be quickly warmed to friendship, was rarely dishonest, and believed implicitly in the religion of the Spaniards. The horse of the pampa was his greatest friend and highly esteemed but, at the same time, often suffered cruelly in his hands.

There were thirty such men to partake in the roundup and six more to guard the stockade and keep it prepared for the first onslaught of trampling, frightened horses. The thirty gauchos planned to ride in V formation, *boleadoras* at the ready to cut down any would-be escaper, dogs to help them where needed. They looked forward to the roundup with great excitement. There would be much hard riding, much killing, and much fighting with unbroken horses. What more could any gaucho desire?

2.

La Bruja was unaware of the danger which threatened. She grazed unconcernedly throughout the days, and there was nothing to bring fear to her. Perhaps if she had known of man and learned to fear him, she would have taken warning from the gaucho she had seen, but within a few hours she had not even a memory of him.

Other horses in that district were a little afraid. Most of them had had some experience of man, and in the last few days they had been aware of several men, who, though not touching them, filled them with a sense of foreboding. Stallions kept their mares in tight bunches, allowing no stragglers, so that their attention need never be diverted from the search for danger.

It was the birds that gave the first warnings. They swept across the sky in ever-increasing numbers, screeching down to the horses of what they had seen, disturbed from their ground nests by the hunters who advanced slowly but surely across the pampa.

Stallions, mares, and youngsters all looked up, alerted, and they began to follow the birds, uncertainly at first, not having yet seen the danger, but growing in confidence as other pampa creatures came in their wake.

A dozen frightened deer and a herd of loping guanacos intermingled with flustered rheas. Now the horses were certain of danger and from which direction it came.

They spent little time grazing but eagerly followed the stallions as they led the way to safety. Eventually, as the gauchos had carefully planned it, the various herds met, and at first there was bickering among the mares and fighting among the stallions until they realized their common danger and combined together to defeat it.

Five separate herds united into one swell of mares, colts, and stallions, keeping their individuality as much as was possible, all journeying unwittingly toward the stockade, thinking, as this was the only way open to them, that it must be the way to freedom.

La Bruja and Thamár came, too, mingling unnoticed among the others. La Bruja was reluctant to surrender her solitary state, but she felt safe among so many. There were young colts, not two years old, and several lone stallions, for the gauchos had spread over a wide area in order to draw so many into their trap.

The horses traveled with increasing fear, bewilderment, and speed, not knowing from what they fled but given no time to stop and puzzle things out. All they knew was that some mysterious power had forced them together against their will and that the birds warned that the power was fearsome, drawing closer each day.

Suddenly the enemy declared itself, on a morning sunny and fresh and seemingly calm. From every direction except in front of them came wildly screeching, whip-flapping, madly galloping gauchos, with baying dogs beside them. The astonished, petrified herd stared incredulously, whinnying, neighing, stricken with panic.

Of one accord the horses broke into a mad gallop, blundering into one another before deciding upon a general direction, then fleeing one behind the other blindly, recklessly, wherever the gauchos chose to drive them. When the first panic died, many of them realized that a trap awaited them, and sometimes individually, sometimes two or three together, they struggled out of the crush and tried to escape alone in a different direction.

What vain hope was this! Whips and savage dogs drove them back again, or cleverly thrown *boleadoras* entwined themselves about their legs and brought them headlong to the ground.

Not a single horse escaped, not even La Bruja and Thamár. Those that remained behind on the pampa were the perhaps fortunate dead, two or three that had fallen in the general stampede and had life crushed from them by trampling hoofs that could not swerve in time.

Apart from these, the horses swept unknowingly into the huge stockade, swirling round, crashing into one another, falling under one another's hoofs as they were abruptly brought to a standstill by a towering blockade on every side. The melee was wild, rough, and confused, and the gauchos watched with sparkling eyes and laughter, already picking out their favorites among the frightened brutes, consigning the rest to death.

After a while the struggling ceased. Exhaustion overcame them and desperation became dejection. With drooping heads they stood and panted, tongues lolling from parched mouths, legs weary almost to crumpling.

Thus the gauchos left them, glad to rest themselves, in no great hurry to begin the slaughter, for there was plenty of time in the days to come.

Chapter Six • IN THE STOCKADE

1.

La Bruja and Thamár stood together in one corner, pressed hard against the strongly built stockade wall by the many trembling, sweating bodies on every side. Like the rest, they were too dejected and overcome with exhaustion to care about captivity, and when the glaring sun had vanished and a soothing darkness filled the sky, some of La Bruja's fear faded. Nothing more had happened. Her youngling was unharmed and still beside her. There was the dreadful uncertainty of bewilderment, the hatred of captivity, the crush of bodies all about her, but apart from this, danger did not seem to threaten.

Unaware of man's power, unaware of man's brutality, unaware of his feelingless heart, La Bruja could not fear more than a little, could not grieve for more than the freedom she had lost. It was too soon for her to realize what freedom meant. Except for the last few hours, she had always been free and knew no other existence.

But when the morning came, La Bruja learned to fear and hate and grow violent against man, for not until the morning did she begin to comprehend the nature of her captors. Morning brought death to the stockade, a violent, lingering massacre, which nauseated and terrified the horses as they saw their companions die before them.

One by one the mares not considered fit for riding were captured and killed. While the second died the first was skinned, and so it went on all morning until the smell of death choked the clean air and the earth was red. Hawks clung to perches on the stockade, eyes greedily surveying the slaughter, flocking to each carcass as it was cast aside, fighting with screeches and flapping wings even though a feast was spread before them.

So the pampa was violated by man, and the spirit of each living horse was crushed by the sight, smell, and sound of its dying companions.

La Bruja, squashed in the corner behind terrified mares and stallions, inconspicuous in coloring, was somehow overlooked. To her section was designated every animal reprieved either for its looks or probable capabilities. They were mostly colts and stallions, for mares were commonplace, rarely ridden by gauchos, so that the few mares saved were young and beautiful, not like La Bruja, who should have died.

The slaughter stopped only when darkness came, but darkness could not destroy the smell of death. The living horses stood in terror and utter disgust, hearing the quarrelsome hawks, which slept with bloated bellies about the corral, as they rustled their feathers and sometimes pecked one another.

The night was peaceful, and the pampa outside the stockade, where the horses had dwelt so shortly since, was sweet and calm and quiet. The same moon that looked down upon the young, fresh grass looked down upon the signs of slaughter. It looked down upon the sleeping gauchos and the trembling horses, and it was impartial in its gaze upon horror and beauty.

Another day dawned, and with the coming of the sun the hawks began again to scavenge among the bodies that remained. Below the fresh, golden sky of morning, shadows faded from the pampa, and the slaughterers awoke to share the beauty of the sky before they returned to the work they had begun the day before.

To their knowledge they had killed all the horses they wanted to kill. The rest were to be broken to a rider and put to work. The stallions and colts would be gelded, the several mares considered carefully for breeding, and they would either be kept by the gauchos who broke them or sold to anyone interested.

So after a day of death came a day of fighting, and as they were skilled and heartless butchers, so were the gauchos skilled and brutal breakers.

The first stallion was chosen, and two men on horseback sorted him out from the others. This was no easy task, for when he divined their intentions, he dived into the center of the herd, creating chaos there. The horses milled and raced about, and the screeches of delight uttered by the gauchos only increased their fear and confusion. The stallion, a small, handsome red roan, was brought to the ground by cunning lassos, and while he struggled to all fours again, one of the ropes was whipped about a post in the center of the stockade and that around his hind leg was dragged over his back, pulling the captured hoof from the ground and leaving him helpless with only three legs to stand on.

A saddle of sheepskin was flung across his back and cinched tightly about him while he fell again, so that his flesh was puckered and squashed. He could not kick that saddle loose, no matter how hard he tried. A leather halter was fixed about his plunging head with a rein attached, and as the ropes were released and the stallion began to fight, a gaucho sprang on his back, and the battle was on.

The fight was furious. The stallion had only his strength and rage, while the gaucho had skill, cunning, and a pair of sharp spurs tied to his naked heels. The stallion reared and tossed, he twisted and bucked, eyes rolling, mouth open, and with every effort he made, the gaucho dug in his spurs and yelled like a savage, clinging to the roan as if he were a hair upon his back. The stallion tried to grab one of the legs that kicked and stung him, but as his head came round and his teeth snapped, a heavy slash from the gaucho's whip across his ear halted him, gasping and half stunned.

The gaucho won the battle, and the stallion was his, defeated, exhausted, but still beautiful and worth possessing. Now it was the turn of another man and horse, and a similar battle commenced.

So it went on all day. Sometimes the gauchos won, sometimes the horses, though the latter was rare, for if one man gave up, there was another to take his place. Sometimes neither won, for a proud, freedom-loving stallion would fight till his heart burst rather than submit himself to man. Then there would be another corpse to skin, another feast for the hawks, but no pity or compassion—never that.

La Bruja's sire, the handsome khaki-colored stallion with the white-starred forehead who so loved to race with the wind, was among the horses that died. He with all his mares had been ensnared, and he survived them but a day, preferring death to slavery.

Of all his herd only La Bruja remained, she and the foal which he had sired, and sooner or later her fate, too, must be decided. The colts and mares were broken one by one until only a few remained to be dealt with on the following day. Among them was La Bruja.

2.

The few horses that remained alive and unbroken in the corral to mope another long night through had been saved for sport on the following day. Now that the work was more or less completed, the gauchos had decided upon a fiesta to satisfy their appetite for fun and laughter. Those who had womenfolk nearby rode in haste to fetch them from their tiny, windowless homes on the pampa, dressed in all their finery; and a *payador* chanced to pass that way, his guitar slung across his shoulders, and he was begged to stay the night beside their fires and entertain them on the morrow.

There were but four horses unbroken in the stockade, excluding Thamár, and these four were ravenous with hunger and half crazed with thirst, for none had thought to feed and water them. The grass had been crushed beneath many sharp hoofs, and that which remained was rusty with dried blood, so that the horses could find no desire in all their hunger to eat it. Thamár, the only youngster, felt not the discomfort of her mother or the other three, for, though she had cropped grass for several weeks, the sweet milk of her dam was still her staple diet, and this satisfied both hunger and thirst. La Bruja's lean flanks grew leaner, and there was less milk for Thamár, as this was her third night in the stockade, and she had not tasted even a mouthful of grass or water in all the days between.

Hunger made her savage. The smell of death had brought fear to her, and fear became violent hatred against those who had wrought the slaughter all about her. She knew that her time must come to face her captors, and her heart swelled with savage intentions as she waited.

With so few horses in the large stockade the gauchos could no longer overlook La Bruja, and they saw her with astonishment. She was so ugly, so colorless, that some mistake must have been made. Surely no gaucho had claimed her. Then they saw her foal, the beautiful, almost golden-coated filly, with black points like her sire, and each man spoke in admiration of her.

La Bruja, for Thamár's sake, was reprieved again, so the mother and daughter spent their last night in the corral together, the last that they were ever to share.

With the dawning of the following day the gauchos killed two long-horned cows and a sheep, and as they fell, there were more moans of death to frighten the horses. Hastily skinned and prepared, they were slowly roasted over beds of burning dung, and from the early hours the savor of sweet, melting fat and browning flesh filled the air. Dogs yelped and whined and hopefully watched the several carcasses, jaws slavering with hunger. The wild horses grew restless at this new, strange smell, for they had an instinctive fear of fire, but no one noticed them.

The *payador* seated himself on the skull of a horse and surveyed the scene in solitude, shaded from the strength of the morning sun by his faithful mount, an old bay gelding who stood behind him with drooping head and twitching ears. The dark eyes of the *payador* lacked the wildness of the gauchos'; his face was kindly and full of understanding. The hair which flowed to his shoulders was hidden behind a handkerchief tied about his head beneath his tall sombrero, and his long gray beard and wrinkled skin gave him the appearance of a sage.

The *payador* was something of a sage, for he had lived long and had been made wise by the things he had seen, heard, and read. This man could read, and the stories he read he told to the gauchos in song and verse, often inspired to the use of beautiful words which his listeners, for all their ignorance, appreciated and understood. In his words was the song of the pampa, the sounds of spring and winter, birth and death, and all these things the gauchos knew.

The *payador* was respected and well loved by all who knew him, for he was gentle and kind, yet unobtrusively forceful. He told stories of the birds; he put words into the mouths of animals with understanding and yet with amusement. He could make the gauchos laugh; he could make them sit in silent thought, for the *payador* wielded great power with his words and the accompanying guitar.

While the gauchos prepared for the fiesta and worked in their several ways, some idling and chatting with the womenfolk, others loading the last of the half-dried skins into the huge ox-drawn wagons stationed near the stockade, still more guarding the roasts, the *payador* thought of the stories he would tell them. As well as old favorites they would expect something new, and the *payador* thought of the horses which had died in the corral. He made up a verse about them and plucked the strings of his guitar as words came into his head, for his mind and fingers worked as one.

The gauchos, hearing him, gathered about him and begged to be told of what he thought. The tune was sad, the strings hummed with mournful vibrations, and the *payador* waited until he had drawn a crowd before he began, conditioning them for the sadness of his song by the hollow sobs of the guitar, which throbbed its message to all of them.

The gauchos fell silent, and nearby horses turned with pricked ears to listen, also. The *payador* began his song, and in his ancient voice was all his wisdom, all his understanding, all his remembrance of sorrow and pain. The verses were short and the words simple, for it was among simple men that he dwelt. He sang:

> "Horse of the pampa, run to thy doom.
> The gaucho chases after thee and has no mercy
> in his heart.
> See the blue sky for the last time.
> Taste the green grass before dying.
>
> Horse of the pampa, race to thy doom.
> The birds call thee back, but in fear thou dost
> not hear them.
> Freedom thou hast lost forever,
> Excepting the freedom of death."

There was silence when he had sung his song, and the gauchos felt sorrow for the horses they had killed. They loved freedom, as did the horses; they dwelt upon the same land, shared the same sky, and slept upon the same grass. The horse of the pampa was their brother, helpmate, and friend, and for a while the gauchos were sad, thinking of the betrayal.

But as the day progressed, they forgot. They sliced themselves mouthfuls of meat from the smoking roasts, using the same long knives that had killed, and grew loud and gay in their merrymaking.

They remembered the four horses in the corral and rushed to release them one at a time, crowding gleefully about the gateway, and they agreed to save La Bruja until the last, for she was ugly enough to be made clown for the day.

The first horse dashing for freedom, a three-year-old colt of piebald coloring, was stopped suddenly in his flight by *boleadoras* twisting round his hoofs and dragging him to the ground. He sprang to all fours again, and a lasso fell over his head. In confusion he became aware of a man upon his back and, squealing with rage, did his utmost to fling him off. But all his strength was of no avail. The battle was like those of yesterday except that this colt had more freedom.

He dashed among the yelling gauchos and crushed several naked feet. He fled across the flaming beds of fire and made for the open pampa, but a gaucho on horseback turned him, and he galloped back again, all the while aware of the man astride him who laughed and hooted and dug in his spurs. The frantic fight went on until the colt fell down in exhaustion, defeated.

Out came the second horse, galloping to freedom as madly as she could, a dun-colored mare who had borne eight foals on the pampa. She put up only a token fight when a gaucho jumped astride her, for she had a ninth foal within her and was weak with hunger.

When she was defeated, the gauchos opened the gate again and let out the third, a filly in her second year who had little more energy than the mare. She was beautiful, a bay with a white streak down her face and black points, and the man who rode her was gentle, for he did not want to ruin her.

There remained only La Bruja and Thamár, and La Bruja shot out of the corral with such fantastic speed that the gauchos were astonished and forgot to bring her down. Thamár galloped valiantly behind her, and the gauchos laughed at the amusing spectacle of beautiful daughter trying so vainly to keep pace with her ugly dam.

Thamár fell with the *boleadoras* tangled about her legs, and when she had regained her footing, La Bruja was far out of reach, a fast vanishing shadow on the pampa. The gauchos brought the struggling foal to the *payador* and asked if he would accept her as payment for his song about the horse of the pampa.

The old poet gravely examined the trembling, fawnlike creature, who, too fearful of all the men about her, did not struggle to escape.

"She is very beautiful," said the poet. "Like a princess, and I shall call her Thamár for her beauty."

The gauchos put a rope about her neck and tied one foreleg beneath her chin so that she could not run away, and on three legs she stood and trembled until the day was over, fear, discomfort, and hunger her companions. With the coming of night the *payador* released her leg and tied her to a wagon wheel, saying her name again and again, and she fell asleep with the sound in her ears . . . Thamár.

Chapter Seven • FREEDOM AGAIN

1.

It was soon that La Bruja realized her loss, but such was her fear of mankind that she dared not return in search of her youngling. She turned back a little way to call her softly, not daring to raise her voice above a nicker for fear that some man would spring out of the grass to take her. In this land of flatness there could be no doubt that Thamár did not follow, for there was neither ridge nor tree to hide her if she came, nor even giant thistles.

Deeply mourned La Bruja for the foal. Never had she been so lonely as she was now, and she circled constantly about the place where she had been a prisoner, distant enough for safety but near enough, she believed, to hear any answering cry. But Thamár had gone. The *payador* stayed only one night more, and La Bruja called in vain, her cries stricken with grief and longing for her foal.

The gauchos heard and saw her. They recognized the lonely mother as she stood afar off, calling to Thamár, and they wondered at her audacity and her grief. They left her alone, for she was ugly and undesirable as either mount or brood mare, and they were preparing to leave the place, hitching oxen to the wagons, saddling up their horses, stamping out the fires they had made. Let her find new companions and forget Thamár. They had had enough of killing for a while and felt no desire to molest her.

The gauchos, ever nomads, moved away from the place of slaughter, and when La Bruja in her desperation came nearer, she saw that the place was deserted and decided to explore, though she kept well clear of the empty stockade, fearing it still. What scent there had been of Thamár had long since faded, borne away on the winds, and the lonely mother found nothing to tell her of the foal.

She stayed close to the place for some time, still calling to Thamár and listening with quivering ears for the foal's reply, but no answer came to ease her aching loss, only the passing of time, which heals all sorrows.

So La Bruja forgot Thamár, though for some time she missed the dancing shadow at her heels, the hungry lips searching for milk, the soft, warm body to caress. While she remembered, she moped and became more ugly; and even when she forgot, her life was empty and she could find no joy.

Winter came, and her hair grew thick in gingery patches. She cropped the grass and found a place to drink, but always she grazed alone, near the place of slaughter, for no other horses dwelled nearby.

The winter grass grew through the bloodstained earth, and the fat-bellied hawks left few remains. Skulls and ribs grew bleached in the sun and wind and rain, but La Bruja did not recognize them and had no fear of them. She grazed round them as if they were stones, never knowing them as the remains of her companions, and the earth no longer smelled of blood but was fresh with new grass and damp dew.

La Bruja saw no more of men, but she kept a wary watch for them. Although she forgot Thamár, she never forgot the brutalities of man, and her heart remained bitter toward him, rankling at what she had seen, heard, and smelled.

If La Bruja had been only ugly, she would have been completely forgotten by the gauchos, but she possessed the speed of her grandsire, and this had not gone unnoticed by one man at least. His name was Gregorio, and he had watched La Bruja's flight from the stockade without comment, appraising her with his sharp black eyes, but stolidly chewing a piece of meat. He listened to his companions as they laughed and joked about her and learned that they had only regarded her ugliness, perhaps excusing her speed for fear. They had not considered the length of her legs, the shape of her body, which told Gregorio of her different blood, and he decided he wanted La Bruja, for what is ugliness if the horse is faster than any other?

Gregorio had a job waiting for him at an *estancia* far distant and, with several companions, had been employed to drive a herd of cattle to the Brazilian borders. For this reason he could not chase after La Bruja now. But this did not trouble him. He felt certain that La Bruja would not have wandered far from the district in which she dwelt by the time he returned to capture her, and he was prepared to wait.

Gregorio, a tall, thin man of middle years, had learned patience, knowing that few things in life can be had at once. The money he earned from the cattle drive would suffice to pay for a good horse, and he would need a fast mount if he were to catch La Bruja. He remained silent about his plans, for fear that some other might claim La Bruja also, and while he jogged steadily across the pampa to Brazil, driving skinny, half-wild cattle before him, he kept a picture of the ugly mare in his mind and silently rejoiced with the thought that one day she would be his.

2.

Spring came again, the fourth that La Bruja had known, and this time there was no newborn foal at her heels, bleating for milk, for she had dwelt alone all this year. She felt the gladness of the season, and her moping heart grew bright again as the summer birds came flocking back to their grassy playground, crying and squawking their greetings as they flew, leaving the

Northern Hemisphere to the bitterness of coming winter. Thick mists enveloped the land each new day, and the sun shone through them like a brazen ball, glowing fiercely orange, almost red. La Bruja rejoiced in the freshness of the mornings, which were damp and clean and exhilarating. For the first time since the loss of Thamár she was glad again, and her spirit swelled within her as she smelled and tasted, felt and heard the hope with which spring came winging over the land.

She spent her newfound energy in racing about the pampa, kicking, twisting, tossing her head, a foal again in her delight. When she galloped, the wind blew against her; mane and tail streamed out behind her, and she felt the air rushing past her body, glorying in her speed and the thunder of her hoofs over the earth.

Her shaggy winter coat fell away, and glossy new hair replaced it, shining even in the dullness of its color. Her eyes grew warm and bright, and her angry heart was eased. Excitement filled her, and she roamed the pampa, restless in her loneliness, the turgid blood of winter no longer creeping through her veins. She drank in the wind with eagerness, searching she knew not what, and one day the scent of her own kind was in the wind.

This was what she wanted, company after so many long months alone. She galloped toward the place from whence the wind came, head high, heart excited, possessed by a spirit she did not understand. She came to new territory in her search, land she had never trod before, but she was aware of no strangeness, eager only to assuage the feeling within her and to find the horse whose scent she had followed for days.

She ate of the fast-growing thistles, becoming fat on their succulent leaves, and she rested but little, for she felt no tiredness. She came suddenly upon the horse whose scent she had followed, drawing back, startled, as she found him standing among the thistle thickets, watching and waiting for her, for he knew she came.

He was a young stallion with scarcely more than six springs behind him, and he surveyed La Bruja with eagerness, his bright eyes sparkling, his small, sharp ears straining toward her. Skewbald in color, he was almost completely white but for a chestnut patch across his rump and a chestnut head broken only by a triangular patch of whiteness on his muzzle. He had no herd of his own and, as yet, had fought few battles in order to possess mares for himself. He grazed alone without companions, and sometimes he followed the rheas or the guanacos when loneliness became overwhelming.

Thus it was with great eagerness that he surveyed the startled mare. He nickered a soft welcome, and La Bruja twitched her ears in acknowledgment, fearing too much friendliness. The stallion drew near to her, and she stood her ground, quivering as he approached and touched her with his soft, damp muzzle.

Then she returned his greeting, and, standing among the thistles, they discovered each other unhurriedly, the spring sun shining warm upon them, crickets chirping in the grass.

296

Chapter Eight • MAN WITHOUT PITY

1.

La Bruja and the stallion stayed together. Both lonely creatures, they grew to like each other's company and they grazed daily side by side, the stallion guarding La Bruja with tenderness and zeal. Sometimes he was overzealous, and La Bruja did not like him then, turning on him with bared teeth and flattened ears if he tried to drive her against her will. He learned to respect her independence, and each day passed in contentment for them both.

Sometimes they wandered alone in search of food, but they rarely strayed far apart. Together, with curiosity, they watched two stags fighting for possession of each other's hinds, and they jumped, involuntarily startled, as the angry antlers clashed again and again. The stags pushed each other back and forth, digging their dainty hoofs with firm force into the earth in order not to give way under pressure; but finally the power of the elder stag prevailed, and the young one limped, crest-fallen, away, leaving his hinds to the other.

Handsome cock birds preened their feathers before entranced hens but sped away startled at the heavy approach of La Bruja and the stallion. Baby guanacos ran beside their mothers with the same long necks and haughty stares, and their coats were soft and curly.

La Bruja and the stallion fed greedily upon the thistles and grass and clover. Summer was coming. The air grew hot and sultry, the freshness of the spring months faded, and dryness crept slowly over the land. The sap in the thistles began to evaporate; the flowers opened and let loose millions of floating seeds in a last desperate attempt for prolongation of life. The seeds sank to the ground, and here the two horses feasted upon them, snaffling them up with their soft upper lips, snorting as they found them in their nostrils, not noticing those which stuck in their manes and tails; and where the seeds remained uneaten, there grew thistles the following year.

The grass withered and grew brown. The thistles stood tall, rusty, and dead, and La Bruja and the stallion no longer fed so well. There were days of constant sunshine, weeks of heat when no wind blew, and then came a session of storms which softened the sun-baked ground and brought freshness once more to the pampa. During all this time La Bruja and the stallion grazed without coming upon another of their kind, for this part of the pampa was almost bereft of horses since the gauchos had done their slaughtering the year before.

There came a day, however, when the horses' sharp ears caught the trembling of hoofs upon the ground, and they looked up sharply, fear striking La Bruja, curiosity the stallion's only reaction. Upon the horizon they saw two horses, one of which carried a rider, and this sight was enough for La Bruja. She turned swiftly from where she stood and fled from the approaching traveler. The stallion did not follow, not understanding her fear.

He stared again at the horses and rider and viewed them with puzzlement, as innocent of man as La Bruja had once been. Then he turned to see where La Bruja had gone and found that she was far distant from him now, not even answering the plaintive cry he sent after her. He remained where he was for one moment more, curiosity and desire to stay with La Bruja struggling one against the other. Eventually he decided in favor of La Bruja and galloped after her, forgetting those who followed, for they had no meaning to him.

The man who followed was Gregorio. He had traveled back and forth across the pampa all that spring and summer searching for La Bruja, and at last he had found her. He did not hurry his horses, for he knew that La Bruja would tire herself in panic and then he could take her, for his horses would still be fresh. He smiled to himself as he saw how she ran, appreciating her even from such a distance, for she was soon far away from him in her fear. The horses he had bought were fleet, but with a fleetness not comparable to that of La Bruja. Therefore, Gregorio knew that he must use cunning to catch her, cunning and time.

2.

The days that followed filled La Bruja with constant fear, for always on the horizon was the man with his horses. She grew fretful and would not eat, never satisfied until the man was no longer within her sight, needing to run many miles in order to lose him. The stallion could not understand her fear, and he tired of her strange behavior. She was too swift for him, and one day he did not follow when she bolted again, gazing wistfully after her for a while but no longer prepared to spend each day in such a manner. Some fear of man she had communicated, so that he did not stand and wait for the gaucho's approach but made off in another direction, and for some days his heart was sad because he had lost La Bruja.

La Bruja, alone again, grew more anxious. She had taken comfort from the proximity of the stallion and felt safer when he was near. Now he had deserted her, and fear became panic as she realized that she could not escape the man who trailed her.

Southward she fled, and behind her came Gregorio, quietly certain of success. La Bruja could feel no security unless she put great distances between herself and him, and because of this she traveled constantly throughout the day, galloping until her strained heart stabbed with pain and her legs buckled.

On and on came Gregorio, no pity for the lone wild mare within him. She would be soon within his reach, for he saw how she half staggered at times and noticed that her pace had slowed. How proud he would be of her when she was his. Even her ugliness would be overlooked when his friends saw how she ran. It was a pity that she had not the beauty of her foal, but one could not have everything in this life, and animals, like humans, have usually at least one defect.

La Bruja knew she was beaten. For weeks the man had followed her, through sun and storm, and she had not outrun him. Her heart was overtaxed, her legs were tired, and her growing foal seemed like lead within her. She stared with wild eyes and flattened ears, flanks heaving in distress; and with hope dying in her heart, her spirit overwhelmed with fear and hatred, she saw the man draw near.

She turned again to flee and heard fast-pounding hoofs not far behind her. She strained with every muscle, fear giving her a strength which did not come from her body. She might have escaped the gaucho even then had he not swung his *boleadoras* after her and, with deadly aim, entwined them about her hoofs. She crashed to the ground in shock and confusion, not even realizing that the thing round her legs was an invention of man, and when she staggered upward once more, a lasso fell over her head and she was a prisoner.

Even now she would not give in. She fought against the rope which held her with all the fury her tired, shaken body could muster. She screamed and reared and savagely shook her head, but the rope grew tight about her throat and nearly choked her. Exhaustion defeated her eventually, and she suddenly dropped her hoofs

301

to the ground and stopped fighting, head hanging, tongue lolling from her jaws, swollen and dry.

Gregorio held her in his power, and he was confident that she would soon be docile. He could afford to feel kindly disposed toward her now, so he led her gently to a lake which was at some short distance, giving life to a solitary *ombú* tree, and there La Bruja gladly slaked her thirst, forgetting the man in her eagerness.

But she could not forget him for more than an instant, for he held the leather rope which clung to her throat and commanded her every movement. His shadow fell across her like the shadow of the *ombú*, and there was a shadow across her heart because she was his prisoner.

3.

La Bruja remained wakeful all the night. She stood by the lake, occasionally swallowing a mouthful of water, and the heaviness in her heart did not fade, because not far from her slept the man who had captured her. He had tied her hind legs together so that she could do no more than hobble when she moved, and his two bay geldings dozed not far from him, forgetting their new companion while they slept.

The sky was dark and the moon hidden in a sickly haze of pallid light. The pampa was alive with a multitude of tiny creatures, and La Bruja listened to them, pricking her ears as she stood beside the lake, involuntarily aware of them. The night seemed long to the waiting mare, and when the gaucho stirred in his sleep, her body trembled and sudden fear rose within her. Nocturnal insects and cicadas busied themselves beneath the branches of the *ombú* where the gaucho slept, and La Bruja was aware of them, too, aware of everything in that endless night.

How lonely she felt and afraid. She stared at the two geldings, wondering at their calm acceptance of man, their docility. They were completely incomprehensible to her, and even though she saw these two of her kind unafraid, she could not believe that the man would not hurt her. The fear and hatred she had learned in that stockade of death remained in her memory and returned to torment her now. The night was long while she awaited her fate, and she could not sleep for fear of it.

The sun rose, and it was a feeble sun, so that from early morning the sky was overcast with grayness, and a chill wind blew, tugging at La Bruja's ragged tail and mane, rustling among the thickly leaved branches of the tree. She nibbled without hunger at the grass and ignored the nickered greetings of the two geldings, fearing them, too, as creatures of man.

Gregorio awoke, and he let La Bruja see how he patted his mounts and spoke to them with kindness. She trembled for them when his hands touched their bodies, but they did not seem concerned, and one even pushed his head toward the gaucho as if begging more of his attention.

With the coming of dawn the rodents had vanished to their underground retreats, the insects had faded with the darkness, and apart from the birds which inhabited the lakeside, the three horses and Gregorio were alone on the pampa, which by its very drabness portended sadness or evil.

The weather did not disturb the gaucho. He felt the warmth of the shabby, gaily striped poncho, and he pulled his hat well down over the handkerchief round his head and neck. He wore new leather boots, the heels of which sparkled with silver spurs, and on these and the horses he had spent his money.

Gregorio had proved his patience by the way in which he had waited his time before setting out to capture La Bruja and by the way in which he trailed her once he had found her again. He had spent many, days in the chase, and his reward was the mare, which he knew he could never have captured by ordinary methods. But now that La Bruja was in his hands, his patience fled away. He was like a child who must play with his new toy at once, and on this drab and chilly morning he was determined to ride the mare until she accepted him, anxious to feel her power under his command, eager to race with her as she stretched her long legs in flight across the pampa.

Already La Bruja was trembling, divining his intentions, so Gregorio gave her time to calm herself while he prepared maté, the tealike herb so favored by the gaucho, which would sustain him until he had a proper meal. He carried his kettle slung beneath the belly of one of his horses, tied to its girth, and only a few minutes had passed by the time he had lighted a small fire, filled the kettle with water from the lake, and waited for it to boil.

La Bruja watched all these preparations with fear and bewilderment, translating everything the gaucho did into portending evil. She watched the steam rise from the kettle and disappear into the air; she saw the gaucho sit down beside the fire when he had made the maté, sucking it from a bowl through a thin metal tube; and Gregorio watched her, too. He saw that her trembling ceased, but he saw fear and hatred in her white-ringed eyes, and he did not underestimate his opponent.

The dullness of the day became more profound as time passed, and all the surrounding pampa lay under the same gray cloud. Beyond the other side of the lake there was little to be seen but occasional stalks of rushes which towered jaggedly above their fellows. The wild birds were strangely silent, perhaps subdued by the nearness of man. The breath of the three horses and the man hung upon the air, then vanished, and there was not a sound but the occasional rustle of a bird in the rushes or the impatient stamp of a hoof.

Gregorio's patience lasted no longer. Before, he had been all slowness, but now he showed a deceptive speed in the way he released La Bruja's hind legs and, a second later, flung himself upon her back, gathering up the lasso as he did so. Breaking a horse alone was a risky business, for if he should be thrown, La Bruja might escape him. He determined to hold fast upon the lasso about her neck, not intending to lose her after spending so much time in capturing her.

He was hardly upon her back when the fight began. The silence of the morning was crudely broken, for La Bruja was like any other wild horse in her fear of the body clinging suddenly to her. Her remembrance of the clinging puma came back to her, and it seemed to her that man must be akin to the lion, and she bucked and reared with savage fury, eyes rolling, ears flat, teeth bared.

Gregorio was no mean rider, and he bore with all La Bruja's tricks, encouraging her to fight more furiously and tire rapidly.

La Bruja that morning seemed tireless. She flung herself back and forth, squealing as her rage increased, rage mingled with desperation because she could not win.

Gregorio laughed and swore and urged her more, feeling tiredness creeping into her. She no longer flung her head so high, her bucks grew weaker, and her rearings were but feeble protestations. For all this, however, she would not give in, for the freedom of the pampa, which today was lost beneath a canopy of grayness, was in her blood, and her wild heart was strong within her.

The grief for her stolen foal, the sight and smell of slaughtered horses, the malice she had borne toward mankind ever since—all these things, forgotten in actuality, had become part of her instinct, and she fought now because violent instinct made her fight and the man upon her back was death to her if she could not defeat him.

Instinct died in weariness; trembling legs and beaten body could fight no more; savage spirit was quelled by gasping lungs and panting heart. La Bruja fell beneath the gaucho's weight and lay almost lifeless in the grass, jaws apart, eyes staring, legs stiff.

Gregorio, who had sprung aside as he felt her collapsing, looked down upon her with consternation. He put his hand upon her swollen neck, and a shudder passed through La Bruja's body. No, she was not dead, though her eyes were glazed and her tongue lolled out. Gregorio tied her legs again and left her to recover.

He made up the dead fire and sat beside it, needing himself to relax, for La Bruja's fight had been no mean one, and he was tired, too. His bay geldings returned to grazing, after watching fearfully the struggle between La Bruja and their master, and after a while, hunger overcoming all else, they forgot the exhausted mare.

Chapter Nine • *THE WILD HEART*

1.

Gregorio waited patiently until La Bruja stirred. She sat up slowly, struggling awhile before achieving this much, and for a long time she attempted no more than this, exhaustion still overcoming her. How ugly she looked in her weariness, her coloring in keeping with the funereal aspect of the daylight. Her tired head drooped to the grass, and she had not even the energy to snort when a few blades tickled her nostrils. She did not attempt to rise to all fours and for the rest of the day stayed as she was, ignoring the gaucho as if he did not exist.

Gregorio left her in peace. He took a horse and went in search of food, a deer, perhaps, which he could bring down with his *boleadoras*, sure that while he was gone La Bruja would make no attempt to escape him. Neither did she, and her heart was not even gladdened by his absence, for she was too weary to care.

The day and night passed, and the next dawn brought new light to the pampa, pushing away the grayness with warm, bright sunshine. La Bruja felt freshened, and she was on her feet before the gaucho woke, hunger driving her to eat greedily, although sadness had returned to her heart. Fear had died. The gaucho had done all he could, and she had survived him. Still she was a prisoner, but her sadness was broken by a rising spirit of anger as tiredness fell away and freshness came to her again.

Gregorio came a second time to ride her and was surprised by the fury with which she greeted him. He had considered her broken after yesterday's fight, but found her spirited and perhaps more bitter than before. The battle began again, and La Bruja learned trickery as she fought, turning with snapping teeth to grab at the gaucho's leg and rolling suddenly on the ground. But Gregorio was ready for all her tricks, and she did not take him unawares.

He thrashed her head severely when she tried to bite him; he jumped aside when she rolled but was upon her back again before she could rise and escape him. When she tried to crush his leg against the trunk of the *ombú*, he retaliated so severely that she did not try it again.

But La Bruja would not admit defeat, and again she fell down in exhaustion before Gregorio could break her. She lay as if dead, and the gaucho realized that he would never break her spirit, at least not in this way. While she recovered, he sat and thought, wanting to keep this mare alive, for he valued greatly the speed

309

she had shown. If he could not defeat her, he must either kill or release her, for she herself would accept no other alternative.

Another day's riding like this would kill her. Then all his long months of hoping would be wasted. There must be some other way to defeat her, but he did not know it. On the pampa a horse was tamed by brute force, by spur and whip and strength, and Gregorio knew no other way.

While he drank maté, ate meat, and slept in the afternoon sun, his saddle for a pillow, his poncho for a blanket, La Bruja gradually regained strength.

Through her blind, staring eyes the sun suddenly pierced. Scents returned to her nostrils, sounds came to her ears, and with this return to feeling came the ache of her weary body, bruised and cut by the weapons of man. The healing grazes of the day before were freshly opened, the bruises newly aggravated. What stiffness and what dizziness she felt as she lifted her head, feeling upon her the sun which beat down strongly.

She staggered to her feet and found it less difficult than on the previous occasion, for the gaucho had forgotten to hobble her. Her legs were free, but she had not the energy to run far, and run she must if she wished to escape, for there was no hiding place on this flat land, bereft of all camouflage.

The gaucho slept soundly, hat upon his face to keep the sun from his eyes, and he was unaware of La Bruja's recovery. The sun lulled him sweetly in its heat, and he knew nothing.

310

Seeing him lying there apparently helpless, for he was not upon his feet, all the bitterness and violence and pain surged into La Bruja's heart again; she hated the gaucho with unparalleled hatred and was filled with desire to destroy him. Unafraid now, reckless in her desperation, she approached the sleeping man, and the scent of him filled her with a madness and fear such as that which had struck her when the puma had attacked her so long ago.

She let out a wild scream of rage, and the gaucho woke with a start to find her naked front hoofs rearing over him. He gave a cry of fear and with the speed of a snake rolled from where he lay, but this time La Bruja was quicker. One hoof crashed upon the ground. The second landed heavily upon the softness of Gregorio's body, and he grunted with surprised pain as he felt it, too stunned for greater exclamation.

Again and again La Bruja attacked the gaucho, and he lay helpless beneath her vicious hoofs until all life was crushed from him and the violence that surged through La Bruja was satisfied.

For the second time in her life she had killed, but this time she had killed a man.

2.

La Bruja could not forget the killing of the man as she had forgotten the killing of the puma. Although she roamed far from the place of death, so that the *ombú* was not even within sight, the memory of what had occurred there rankled constantly within her. Perhaps it was because she had killed the puma with nothing but fear to spur her, whereas hatred had driven her to kill the man, even when he was not actually molesting her.

That hatred was with her still, smarting in her heart as the weals on her body smarted. The cuts of the spurs and the lashes of the rope healed upon her skin, but the soreness in her heart did not fade, so that she was constantly aware of a burning anger, even though she knew that the gaucho could harm her no more.

Although she had killed, still she had not completely freed herself from man's influence, for there was the lasso about her neck, and it trailed in the grass beside her while she grazed.

For many days she tried to rid herself of the rope. She shook her head from side to side; she stamped on it with her death-giving hoofs and grew wild with rage when everything she did was to no avail. As time passed, she grew accustomed to the feel of it about her neck and almost forgot it, but there were occasions when she trod on it while grazing, or when it tangled itself about her legs or about a clump of weeds, tugging at her as once the man had tugged, putting wild fear into her heart until she realized that it was not a man who held her.

The lasso greatly hampered her movements so that she could no longer gallop without fear of falling or being caught up in thistles or long grass, and after many

frustrations of this kind, she spent one entire afternoon chewing through a section of it, making it shorter but not removing it, the latter being her original intention. However, it was short enough after that not to trail on the ground, and though it swung constantly below her head, she ignored it and after a while accepted it as if it were part of her body.

The days passed by uneventfully. No more men came to molest La Bruja, and some of her wild anger faded. She grew more calm but never relaxed her vigilant watch of the horizon, and the slightest shadow was enough to set her racing in the opposite direction.

But La Bruja had few desires to hurry in these days, and it was only fear that pushed her to a gallop now and then. She had suffered much in the hands of Gregorio, and her body was still tired.

When the cold fingers of winter began to stretch across the pampa in gusts of wind and icy rain, La Bruja hunched her body and suffered the coldness, not having the energy to journey northward as she had done in previous years. With each succeeding day she felt more worn, and there came a morning when she knew that her foal would be born even though winter had hardly come and spring was far away.

She could find no shelter on the plain, for the new thistles had not grown and the old had fallen. She could muster no desire to search farther afield, so she stood where she was until the foal was born. The pampa was soggy with rain, and La Bruja's head drooped in misery.

The foal was born without life, and La Bruja did no more than sniff at it once before turning away, feeling nothing. She hurried away from the place of birth, as she had done the last time, but now there was no second Thamár to follow her, and she was lonely.

Throughout the whole winter La Bruja lacked strength and energy. She endured coldness and rain with surprising passivity, stirring only to graze and seeming not to feel the heavy showers upon her skinny body. She was gaunt and graceless in appearance, even more the scarecrow with the tattered rope dangling below her head and winter hair growing in rough, uneven patches.

With each succeeding day of winter, new grass came to the pampa, and with it came new energy to La Bruja. The first fresh grass was weak and tasteless, but as it grew in strength, covering the deserted pampa with new life, La Bruja ate more greedily until she had no need to search for fresh grass among the old. Then she settled down to leisurely grazing, and as the spring grew closer once again, her weakness faded, her old energy returned, and she was strong again.

Flesh came to her thin neck and ribby flanks. She lifted her head and gazed with brighter eyes upon her world, but now her eyes were marked with a bitterness which had not existed in the previous spring, and she had the look of vice. Her winter coat fell away, and a gloss came once more to her hide, a hide now marked with small, uneven scars where the spurs of the gaucho had cut her deep.

The sun grew warmer and came earlier every day, following fleecy clouds which glowed with touches of gold in a pale and silver sky. The warmth and the freshness of the new spring mornings gave La Bruja gladness once again, though she was not among the mares that gave new life to the earth, and for a second year she had no youngling to run beside her.

La Bruja listened to the pipits as they caroled in the sky; she heard the plovers and the lapwings chorusing the same message, and she felt again, as always, the excitement brought by spring. But this year, though she searched the grass and wind, she could find no scent of horses, and she wandered solitarily about the pampa, seeing groups of guanaco and deer, flocks of birds, but finding not a single horse for company.

When the first fever of spring passed away, La Bruja did not mind that she was without companions, and she felt no loneliness. The teasing gusts of wind were company enough, and she kicked up her heels in delight, tossed her head, and stretched out her legs to gallop once again, forgetting that she had been galloping in fear for so long, remembering only the thrill of the race.

Somehow for all her ugliness La Bruja seemed beautiful when she galloped thus. Her mane and tail flowed behind her; her long legs moved with grace and precision; her spirit soared like the flight of a bird into the blue sky, enhancing her ugly head as it gave a brilliance to her dark eyes, white-ringed though they were.

Left alone, La Bruja could have found contentment on the pampa, happiness in the grass, the sky, and the wind; and she would have forgotten the evil of man and her hatred of him. But in her destruction of man she had cut off her hope for happiness and a life unmolested, for now she was spoken of from place to place. Already a man had coveted her for the one thing that gave her happiness, and it would not be long before she should be coveted again.

Chapter Ten • FELIPE

1.

The death of Gregorio was discovered by two travelers who stopped for shelter at the solitary *ombú*. They journeyed that way only four days later, and the gaucho's geldings watched with pricked ears as the two riders cantered toward them, not understanding the events of the last few days but knowing that their master was dead. Trained in obedience, they had not wandered far from the lake and the *ombú*, and the sight of them grazing alone in the shadow of the tree was curious to the passing gauchos.

Dusk was gathering gloomily overhead as they reined in their weary horses, but it was not too dark for them to see the crumpled body which lay beside the saddle and the striped poncho, damp with the vapors of the earth. They uttered exclamations of surprise at the sight before them, hurriedly dismounting although they knew that they had come too late.

The way that Gregorio had died was not difficult to ascertain. The whole story was written in the trampled grass and broken ground, and the travelers, surveying the scene, soon understood what had happened.

They examined Gregorio's property—little enough, for all his wealth he carried in his saddlebags and belt like the travelers who found him. They admired his new, mud-streaked boots and fingered his silver spurs, for neither of them possessed boots, and their spurs were rusted iron. They discovered that there was no lasso among his property, a thing unusual, for the gaucho is a herder of cattle, and the lasso is the instrument of his trade. Because of this they assumed that the killer horse must still have the lasso about its neck and by this sign they should know it if they began a search.

The travelers that night felt no inclination to begin a search. The weather was very bad, and spending endless days searching a killer horse, which had probably fled far from the district, was not a tempting proposition. Instead they made a fire and slept beneath the tree, and when the morning dawned gray and cloudy, they tied the dead man to the back of one of his horses and continued their way to the town, speculating on the fury of the killer horse and on the man's identity.

In the town they discovered more, for it was there that Gregorio had bought his two bay geldings.

"He said he wanted two fleet-footed horses, for he was after the fastest horse he had ever seen."

This the horse dealer told to the travelers, and there was a quickening of interest in the eyes of all the listeners. Many heard his words, for they stood to-gether in the *pulpería*, a combination of tavern, store, and meeting place, and they leaned against barrels of flour or sat on sacks of potatoes, listening.

"Is that all he said?" questioned one of the trav-elers, a youth scarcely bearded but with eyes as sharp as the hawk.

"Little more. He did not seem eager to share his secret. All he would say was that the horse he sought was faster than any other and that he had waited a year to catch her."

"A mare!"

The exclamation was simultaneous upon every lip. None had thought that the killer could be a mare. There was a moment's silence while they digested this information. What kind of creature must she be that the gaucho waited a year to capture her and then died in his attempt to break her? It ill became any gaucho to ride a mare, so this one must be something special that he would sacrifice so much.

"Faster than any other," reiterated one at last.

"He waited a year to catch her," reminded another.

Then the man behind the counter spoke. He had listened unobtrusively to the conversation, counting money, checking off lists of goods; and when he chose, he was not conspicuous, for the lighting was bad in the *pulpería*, and there was a thick iron grill between him and the customers.

"I remember the man," he commented, and he was instantly the center of attention. "He was here a year ago after rounding up horses for the traders. I heard him say that he was going to Brazil. I didn't expect to find him here again like this."

"A year ago," repeated the young traveler thoughtfully. "Then he must have first seen the mare here. He waited a year to capture her. It adds up to that, does it not?"

"Perhaps he saw her at the roundup," added another.

"I was there, too, and not all the mares were killed. I recall one that escaped, an ugly brute. She looked like a witch. Strangely enough, she had a beautiful colt. We gave it to a *payador*, I remember."

"Then this must be the one."

The eyes of the young man gleamed. He drew closer to the gaucho who recalled so much and asked him, "Do you remember what she looked like?"

"Well, only that she was ugly and almost the color of the earth."

"Then that's enough," said the youth. "We know she's fast; we know she has a rope about her neck; we know she's ugly and dark in coloring. I am going to find her."

"And when you've found her?" questioned another.

"I'm going to ride her."

There was a snort of laughter at this, and the man spoke again.

"Son, you only came out of the cradle a year ago. You haven't the experience to ride a horse like that."

"You know nothing about me," returned the youth, and there was anger sparking in his dark eyes, so that the other, a fat barber of the town, decided to concede him the point.

"Very well," he retorted genially. "Go ahead and find her. Bring her back to town if you can. We'd all like to see this witch. If you succeed, I'll teach you how to shave."

The youth made no reply. He pulled a coin from his belt and slammed it down on the counter. He saluted his friend but no other, and left the *pulpería* with anger and hurt pride smarting within him. He left his own horse tied to the rail beside that of his friend, and he took the bay geldings of Gregorio, determined to seek La Bruja alone.

"I will find her, and I will ride her," he muttered as he slapped the horses into a gallop. He headed toward the *ombú* beside the lake where Gregorio had been killed, there intending to begin his quest.

2.

Daylight was failing as Felipe cantered toward the tree. Gray clouds clung together and were flecked with flames of red as the sun slowly faded behind them. The grass became dark, the tree lost its greenness, and the land was all one shadow beneath the reluctant glow of a feckless moon. The pampa seemed to be deserted, but Felipe knew that it was not so, for he had dwelt all of his sixteen years in this land and knew it, with all its moods and changes, better than he knew himself.

His naked feet had felt the damp coolness of the grass and had suffered the cruel stings of thistles lurking in its softness. With his own hands he had struggled vainly against the burrowing armadillo and learned that the smaller creature can have the greater strength. His face was brown from birth and his eyes black, for a fair skin would be scorched by the sun and wind; and he hardly remembered that the sky was not his natural roof nor the earth his bed, for he had been orphaned by Indians at an early age, and since then no one had offered him a home.

His first memories were of herding sheep for a rich man. He wore a jacket of sheepskin then and smelled like the animals he guarded, for he lived among them day and night, ate their flesh, and drank their milk. One day the man gave him money for his work. With this he bought a horse and took to herding cattle, but in all his life he could not remember a home nor the face of a kindly woman. He knew cattle and horses and sheep and the rough life of the men of the pampa, but he knew nothing of tenderness or a bed, for such things he had never encountered.

The sun vanished before Felipe reached his destination, but there was light enough by the moon to illuminate his path. The squat, widespread tree loomed ominously in its solitude, and the moonlight glinted upon the disturbed waters of the lake as night prowlers came to drink or swim.

Felipe dismounted beside the lake and unsaddled the horse, tying both geldings to a low-hanging branch before settling himself, with saddle and poncho, among the roots of the tree, wriggling and twisting until his position was comfortable. The ground below the tree was bare of grass, for many travelers stopped here to rest, and when they had gone, too little sunlight filtered through the heavy leaves, giving the grass no encouragement to grow again.

Felipe listened to the horses as they blew softly through their nostrils and moved about before sleeping. He heard rustlings in the grass beyond the shadow of the tree as pampa rodents went about their business, and a night bird cried sharply in sudden alarm, startling the boy although he had often heard the cry before. He gazed upon the spot where Gregorio had been found a week earlier and shuddered involuntarily at the memory. In his mind folklore, legend, and Christian religion were strangely mixed, and he believed in ghosts and spirits, thinking that perhaps the ghost of the dead man hung about the tree, for his manner of death had been brutal.

He turned his thoughts to La Bruja, for it was not good to think of ghosts when alone. He wondered where she was at this moment, far or near, what she did, and why she had killed Gregorio. He wished that La Bruja were a stallion, for then the glory of capturing her and defeating her would be far greater. Still, he would be proud enough if he caught her, so he let the wish pass.

She was ugly, one man said, like a witch. This was misfortune, too. For a moment Felipe doubted the wisdom of his decision. Surely it was folly for him to chase an ugly mare. Supposing her speed was but a fantasy? If it should be so, then he would have nothing to show for his pains. Then he remembered the scorn of the fat barber and was reassured. He would capture La Bruja if only to save his pride, and it was Felipe who first gave her this name.

Felipe was awakened by a spattering of raindrops upon his face. He started in surprise, for they were large and icy, and he suddenly remembered where he was and why as he saw the cavernlike branches above him, whose leaves bowed under weight of water. He scrambled up, stretched his cold and stiffened muscles, and wandered sleepily to the lakeside. The pampa was shrouded in a mist of grayness, and he felt the dampness of the morning clinging to him through his clothes.

It was no day to begin his search, for in such a mist as this the mare could easily elude him. He cursed and kicked the ground, for with the impetuosity of youth it seemed that a century must pass before he would find the trail of La Bruja, if a trail existed after so many days.

With one thought only he consoled himself. If the mare which escaped from the stockade and that which killed Gregorio were one and the same, she had obviously dwelt within this region for much of her life and looked upon it as her home. Therefore the chances were that she would still be within a few leagues of the lake, unless she had taken great fright at her actions and fled to another part.

The boy made himself believe the latter was not so. A man must have a certain amount of luck with everything, and he felt sure that he would be lucky enough to find La Bruja near within a week or two.

As he stood and thought these things, rain began to fall again. It hissed down finely all about him, and Felipe returned to the shelter of the *ombú*, whose branches were thick enough to guard him from all but an occasional trickle. He collected a few fallen twigs and added them to the remains of Gregorio's fire. Very soon he started a flame, and he crouched down beside it, warming himself, the gloom of the morning somewhat dispersing at this small comfort.

He would let the horses rest and shelter himself for the day. Perhaps on the morrow the sun would shine. He hoped so because, once he left the shade of the ancient *ombú*, there would be no more shelter on the pampa, and if it rained, he could not even light a fire to dry his sodden clothes. But the thought of La Bruja inspired him to take the risk. The dead gaucho had said that she was the fastest horse he had ever seen, and if this were so, she was worth chasing.

Chapter Eleven • *THE CAPTIVES*

1.

Felipe's quest appeared from the start to be doomed to failure, and bad luck followed him wherever he rode. The depression of the weather seemed interminable, and every dawn came weakly to the sky, hardly breaking through the blackness of the preceding night. The sun was without warmth or kindness, and the new winter grass grew long and heavy in its wealth of wetness, for there was hardly a day without rain.

While La Bruja gave birth to her lifeless foal, Felipe pulled his horses into the grass and sheltered between them, shivering with cold, no longer caring to wipe the rain from his face as it streamed down upon him. The geldings bowed their heads and bore the icy wind and rain, accustomed to obeying the whims of their master, though they would not have lain on the soggy ground from choice. Only will power kept Felipe to his hopeless task, for never in a single day did he sight La Bruja, and he suffered much for his pride.

There were days when hunger made him weak. The animals on the pampa saw him coming from a distance, and they fled from his reach before he could be among them. He caught a bird which he found fluttering feebly on the grass with a broken wing, and because he could light no fire, he had to eat the flesh raw. There were days when he was numb with cold and his naked feet were like marble. But never did he think of abandoning his quest, for he knew that La Bruja must be near and that only misfortune drove them to take paths in different directions.

Eventually the weather cleared. The sun shone with warmth as well as light, and the wet clothes began to dry upon Felipe's back as he rode. Warmth came to his body again; his frozen limbs began to feel and his spirits rose.

He came unawares upon a group of rheas and was among them before they realized his presence, fleeing in a mad panic to escape him, wings flapping, necks outstretched, ugly eyes bulging. He laughed and let them run for a moment, hastily unwinding the *boleadoras* about his waist. Then with a loud yell he set his horse at a gallop and raced after them, whirling the *boleadoras* above his head. Sure of his prey, a scraggy brown female that lagged behind, he let his weapon fly, and she collapsed in a heap as it entangled her legs, doomed in a moment to death.

Felipe made a fire that day and fed well upon the rhea. What flesh he did not eat he crudely smoked and packed away in his saddlebags for another day.

Then he began again his search for the elusive mare, hopes high and stomach filled, certain that one day he would find her.

Spring came. Felipe shared the gladness that was in the air and all about him, for he loved the song of the birds and the colors of the butterflies, although he led a life so rough. He was as aware as a poet might be of the beauties of nature, and his heart sang in tune with the rhythm of spring, putting a sparkle into his eyes and a grin upon his lips.

One day he saw La Bruja. There was no doubt as to her identity, for she was ugly as the man had said; she looked almost black in the distance, and a fraying rope swung below the level of her breast. She saw him in the same instant, and simultaneously they broke into a gallop, La Bruja flooded with fear, Felipe rejoicing.

The boy rejoiced too soon. Ill luck was his companion still, and as he urged the gelding to greater speed with spurs and whip, he was suddenly thrown forward, the horse collapsed beneath him, and Felipe spun dizzily to the ground, gasping with pain and surprise as he hit the earth.

The horse scrambled up first, but Felipe saw with dismay that he lifted one foot from the ground and rubbed his nose against it. Felipe was shaken and bruised but otherwise unhurt. He picked himself up and looked about, seeing at less than a length's distance the rodent hole over which the gelding had fallen.

The horse was timid in his pain and shied away when Felipe approached to examine him, but after a while he submitted to the touch of expert hands, uttering short nickers of pain. There was no doubt that the fetlock was broken, and Felipe cursed his misfortune.

He unharnessed the gelding, transferring saddle and bridle to the other horse, glad that he still had the two. He stroked the lame horse for a moment, then mounted again and looked about for La Bruja. By now she was no more than a speck of darkness on the horizon, but at least she was still within sight.

He kicked the second gelding to a gallop and called back to the other, "Good-by, old friend, and good luck."

The horse pricked his ears and watched him go, bewildered and not understanding. He was free of the trappings of servitude, but he could remember no other life and had no desire for freedom. He began to follow Felipe, cantering awkwardly until pain forced him to halt. He whinnied shrilly after his fast-fleeing companions, and it was a cry of longing to be with them.

For a long time he watched them, half expecting them to turn back. They did not return, and Felipe called no more. The pricked ears of the gelding drooped, and he touched his broken fetlock once again, but it was not within his power to heal it. He dropped his head to graze, holding his hoof from the ground, and eventually he forgot Felipe and the other gelding, waiting on the pampa until fate should resolve his future.

The nightmare in La Bruja's life began again. Followed always by Felipe, she knew no peace, no rest, and though he never drew near enough to threaten her, he was constantly there. She grazed scantily, snatching mouthfuls of grass and clover with flattened ears and gleaming eyes, pausing in her stride for no more than ten minutes at a time. She watched the boy on horseback with bitter hatred, but although she ranged far from his sight, she could not lose him.

He was not insistent like Gregorio. With only one horse to bear him, Felipe was held back and could not press the pace, for the gelding tired more quickly than La Bruja, who carried no extra weight. Therefore he could do no more than follow her as the moon follows the sun, day in, day out, never narrowing the gap between them but never losing ground, either.

Following her thus, watching her fear and desperation, Felipe began to develop a feeling of friendship toward her. He had searched for her long and constantly, his mind filled with thoughts of her from dawn till dusk, and now that he saw her every day, his desire to capture her faded, and he held only a desire to gain her confidence.

He saw how she watched him while she ate, head held high as her jaws worked hungrily, and as he slowly closed in upon her, she would shake her head as if in anger, turn about, and race away. As time passed, her reactions became slower. She allowed him closer and did not run so far. Either she was gaining in confidence toward him, or she was growing reckless because he had not harmed her. Whatever the cause, Felipe's heart was glad. With patience he might one day draw near enough to rope her, and then she would be his.

Following her thus, his every thought concentrated in gaining the trust of this ugly, elusive mare, Felipe lost count of the days he traveled and the direction in which La Bruja led him. The sun was warm upon his back, and he was aware only of the blueness of the sky, the growing thistles, and the canebrakes. He felt no lack of human companionship, and when he needed to give voice, he spoke to his horse and sometimes called to La Bruja. The sound of his voice was enough to set her off again with shaking head and tossing mane, and Felipe laughed to see her fear, for the chase had become almost a game to him. He forgot that he had once been in earnest and that La Bruja had killed a man.

La Bruja led him southward. Her native land seemed no longer safe to her, and fear drove her to search new pastures. She trod strange ground, but she could not shake off her follower. She ate new grasses and sometimes searched for days in thirst for water in these new lands, not knowing where lakes or rivers were. The ground became more undulating, and the horizons were no longer empty but shadowed by vague, blue hills. Wherever she trod, the grass was green and plentiful, for spring was over all the land and there was no lack of pasturage.

Apart from La Bruja, the gelding, and Felipe, the pampa was almost deserted. At times they passed herds of guanacos, bunches of deer, and several straying cattle, but they came across no human habitations, for La Bruja kept well clear of these. If she saw distant smoke or smelled the scent of man on the wind, she changed direction instantly, and the more she hurried southward, the less inhabited the land became.

But La Bruja could not escape Felipe, though now, after so many days and nights, his presence worried her less, for he seemed not eager to molest her. At times she almost forgot that he followed her, but when she heard his voice or saw him spur his gelding to a gallop, she fled before him, filled with fear and hatred once again. She could not forget Gregorio.

2.

One day both Felipe and La Bruja were startled. The morning had been quiet, broken only by the chirping of birds and the sound of the horses as they cropped the grass, when suddenly there was a pounding of hoofs to the west of them where the ground sloped steeply away, as if it were a plateau on which La Bruja grazed. Even as their attention was drawn, three wild horsemen topped the rise in the ground and with loud, inhuman screeches bore down upon them, waving fronded spears and whirling *boleadoras*.

They were Indians, with black hair to their shoulders and half-naked bodies gleaming. One glance sufficed Felipe. Fear leapt into his heart as he jerked his gelding round and thudded its flanks with his spurs. The gelding caught his fear and needed no urging. The fiendish screams of the half-naked savages were enough to drive him to an extent beyond Felipe's capabilities, and even La Bruja, trapped between the two, chose the evil she knew and followed the boy. She soon overtook him, flinging out her long legs with grace and incredible speed, and as the thundering hoofs and fearsome screams grew louder, Felipe longed to be astride her, for she ran like the wind far ahead of him.

The Indian ponies, fresh and wild, soon overtook the gelding, and Felipe was jerked roughly from the saddle by a lasso about his body. The Indians, too, had seen the speed of La Bruja, and they uttered excited words while they galloped along, still dragging the boy behind them, agreeing to capture her, too. The savage who had ensnared Felipe drew his pony to a halt, and his two companions raced after La Bruja, their *boleadoras* whistling above their heads as they prepared to let them fly.

La Bruja, galloping with open mouth and flecked with foam, dodged the first flung *boleadoras*, but the second, following swiftly, caught her about the fetlocks, and she turned a somersault as she fell. The Indians gave a cry of delight as she struggled to all fours. They both swung a lasso about her, and for the third time she was a prisoner.

Felipe saw what happened. Though racked with pain and breathless, he watched the progress of his mare, for he thought of La Bruja as his mare. The Indian, short, flat-nosed, and ugly, saw his interest; staring at him with unfeeling eyes, he made signs for Felipe to mount his horse again, pointing with his long spear to the saddle.

Stiffly Felipe did as he was commanded, and strangely enough some of his fear had faded. He was more sad than afraid, angry that the Indians should steal his horse after he had followed her for so long. He watched while the other Indians returned to their companion, La Bruja struggling vainly between them, and he hated them for the triumphant grins on their ugly faces, because it was his triumph that they had stolen.

The night was sultry and dark. Heavy clouds banked themselves in front of the moon, glowing with eerie light, blue and yellow and silver. The stars seemed distant, hardly visible with no moon to illuminate them, and the Indian encampment was a mass of obscurity, black and shadowless.

Felipe, lying prostrate on the ground, had feigned unconsciousness for hours. His arms and legs were knotted with cramps, and only fear of what the Indians might do, once they discovered him conscious, had kept him from crying out. Now all was silent. He had listened without moving until voices died, fires were extinguished, and footsteps faded. He knew only that he was on the outskirts of this village of tents and that horses were corraled nearby. The one thing which had been burning in his mind all this time, making each hour drag into days, was the knowledge that La Bruja was among these horses, for he had seen the Indians put her there.

While he lay in the dirt for hours, his body unmoving, his mind worked speedily, making and rejecting plans of escape. In his heart he knew that he was doomed, for the Indian could be likened to a cat with a mouse, playing with retracted claws until the game grew boring. Then—Felipe shuddered. The Indians were experts when it came to inflicting a lingering death.

So he thought of escape, and he thought of La Bruja, and soon he thought of escape *with* La Bruja. He needed a horse with wings to outrun a horde of Indians, and La Bruja was his only hope. He knew that she was wild, untamed, unridable, but if fate were on his side, she might tolerate him upon her back in the gladness of being free from the corral. He remembered how he had told the barber he would ride her, and even in his present plight he felt a surge of pride that the opportunity had come at last for him to try.

He judged the clouds and the moon behind them, deciding that he must act soon if darkness were to be his cover. Slowly, agonizingly, he pulled his throbbing body into action, wriggling toward the corral with wildly thumping heart. The horses stirred and snorted. Felipe halted. He slowly raised his head and searched for La Bruja, seeing with relief that she stood with drooping head beside the bars, the old lasso still about her.

Still wriggling snakelike on the ground, he found the entrance to the corral, and he risked raising himself enough to open the gate. The horses grew more restless, their sharp ears picking up every sound as Felipe crawled about the corral. Now that the gate was open, there was nothing more for him to do but run to La Bruja, jump astride her, and hope that she would carry him to freedom.

For a moment he held back, as if in that instant he realized all that he would lose if his actions failed. In his short sixteen years his life had been hard, but he had known contentment, and his pampa home was a place he loved. He could choose another horse, one already accustomed to a rider, and his chances of escape would be even.

Some instinct made him choose La Bruja, the wild mare for whom he felt great affection. Strange circumstances had led him to follow her so far, and he would not forsake her now. If he could not have her, no man would, and he dashed suddenly to her, vaulted onto her back, and whispered urgently, "Let's go."

La Bruja went. Startled, she fled through the open gateway, followed by four or five others, and the noise they made as they whinnied surprise and pounded away from the encampment with galloping hoofs brought half a dozen Indians from their tents, shouting and gesticulating. One, more alert than the rest, threw himself upon an escaping pony, grabbed a spear which leaned against his tent, and followed in angry pursuit.

At that moment, after struggling long to probe a pathway through the clouds, the moon shone out in all its brilliance, illuminating the pampa with sudden light, the final ill luck of Felipe.

The Indian grunted with satisfaction as he raised his spear, and within a second it had left his practiced hand and found its target, toppling Felipe soundlessly from La Bruja. The mare, suddenly free of the unaccustomed body, pricked her flattened ears and increased her speed. She faded into the darkness of the night, and the Indian let her go.

He jumped from the pony to find Felipe in the grass. The boy looked up, and their black eyes met for an instant.

"Well, I rode her and I said I would. She didn't fail me, either."

These words were in Felipe's mind, though he had not the strength to utter them. He smiled at these last fleeting thoughts, and then he died, the second man to do so who coveted La Bruja.

Understanding Life on a Pampa

1. After the death of her mother, why did La Bruja stay by herself even when she was part of a herd?
2. In the beginning La Bruja was not afraid of men. Why did she grow to hate them so intensely?
3. Which of the many tragic experiences in La Bruja's life was most responsible for her becoming a fugitive horse?
4. Why did the gauchos name her "The Witch"?
5. What did the book tell about the life of the gauchos? In what ways did the gauchos seem as wild and free as the animals of the pampa?
6. Give your impressions of the *payador,* the poet who was given Thamár. What did you learn about the gauchos through their feeling for him?
7. When Gregorio decided to capture La Bruja, he knew that it would take "cunning and time." What was his plan? In what way did his plan succeed and in what way did it fail?
8. What difference in motive was there between La Bruja's killing of the puma and her trampling of Gregorio?
9. On page 316 the author writes, "She lifted her head and gazed with brighter eyes upon her world, but now her eyes were marked with a bitterness which had not existed in the previous spring, and she had the look of vice." What events had taken place in this year of La Bruja's life that brought about this change in her?

10. What clues did the men who found Gregorio get about the identity of the killer horse? Why did Felipe want to capture La Bruja? What change came over him as he followed the horse?

11. What kinds of things do the words *wild heart* make you think of when you associate them with La Bruja? Now that you have read the first half of the book, tell how you feel about the author's choice of a title.

12. Compare this story with "Wild Pony," in Unit One of *Vistas*. Think about the settings, chief human and animal characters, and outcomes before writing the likenesses and differences that you found.

Ángel, whom you met on the first pages of *The Wild Heart,* reënters the story in the last half of the book. You will want to get Miss Griffith's book and read of the terrible decision that faced Ángel concerning La Bruja's future.

Sharing a Book with a Friend

Before you can tell a story well, you must be sure of the order in which the main events occurred. To tell a friend about *The Wild Heart,* you would want to remember the main points of La Bruja's life in the part of the book that you have read.

The outline on page 341 may serve as a guide for you. Sometimes chapter titles serve well as main headings. If you choose to use them, follow the pattern of the outline on that page. The first heading and the events that might be listed below it are given as an example. Chapters One and Two have been combined under this first heading because of the few important events occurring in these chapters. Some of you may prefer to use main headings different from those below. Your outline may also have more or fewer points under each heading. Arranging important events in their proper sequence will help make the story clearer in your mind.

I. Scarecrow Filly and *Pampero*
   A. La Bruja is born.
   B. The mother of La Bruja is killed.
   C. La Bruja becomes an outcast.

II. Second Spring
   A.
   B.
   C.

III. The Mother
   A.
   B.
   C.

IV. The Roundup
   A.
   B.
   C.

V. In the Stockade
   A.
   B.
   C.

VI. Freedom Again
   A.
   B.
   C.

VII. Man Without Pity
   A.
   B.
   C.

VIII. The Wild Heart
   A.
   B.
   C.

IX. Felipe
   A.
   B.
   C.

X. The Captives
   A.
   B.
   C.

Work for Word Detectives

The following words from *The Wild Heart* are Spanish or of Spanish origin, but the author makes their meaning clear in the story. Write your own definition of each word, and then check back to the pages given to see how well you remembered the meanings.

1. Trapalanda   (page 235)
2. Pegaso   (page 235)
3. pampa   (page 236)
4. *criollo*   (page 240)
5. vizcachas   (page 246)
6. gauchos   (pages 246 and 276)
7. *pampero*   (page 246)
8. guanacos   (page 255)
9. *payador*   (page 265)
10. poncho   (page 275)
11. *boleadoras*   (pages 276 and 279)
12. fiesta   (page 284)
13. *estancia*   (page 294)
14. *ombú*   (page 302)
15. maté   (page 304)
16. *pulpería*   (page 320)

As the following collection shows, the horse has been a
favorite subject of poets from Biblical times to the present.

Then the Lord answered Job out of the whirlwind . . .
Do you give the horse his might?
    Do you clothe his neck with strength?
Do you make him leap like the locust?
    His majestic snorting is terrible.
He paws in the valley, and exults in his strength;
    he goes out to meet the weapons.
He laughs at fear, and is not dismayed;
    he does not turn back from the sword.
Upon him rattle the quiver,
    the flashing spear and the javelin.
With fierceness and rage he swallows the ground;
    he cannot stand still at the sound of the trumpet.
When the trumpet sounds, he says "Aha!"
    He smells the battle from afar,
    the thunder of the captains, and the shouting.

The BIBLE, Revised Standard Version
(from the Book of Job 39: 19-25)

I will not change my horse with any that treads . . .
When I bestride him, I soar, I am a hawk.
He trots the air; the earth sings when he touches it.
The basest horn of his hoof is more musical than the pipe
   of Hermes . . .
He's of the color of the nutmeg and of the heat of the
   ginger . . .
He is pure air and fire, and the dull elements
Of earth and water never appear in him,
But only in patient stillness while his rider mounts him . . .
It is the prince of palfreys. His neigh is like
The bidding of a monarch, and his countenance
Enforces homage.

WILLIAM SHAKESPEARE
(from King Henry V, Act III, scene 6)

A gigantic beauty of a stallion, fresh and responsive to
   my caresses.
Head high in the forehead, wide between the ears,
Limbs glossy and supple, tail dusting the ground,
Eyes full of sparkling wickedness, ears finely cut,
   flexibly moving.
His nostrils dilate as my heels embrace him,
His well-built limbs tremble with pleasure as we race
   around and return.

WALT WHITMAN
(from "Song of Myself")

344

The Prayer of the Foal

by CARMEN BERNOS DE GASZTOLD

O God! the grass is so young!
My hooves are full of capers.
Then
why does this terror start up in me?
I race
and Your scents beat on my heart.
I race,
falling over my own feet in my joy,
because my eyes are too big
and I am their prisoner:
eyes too quick to seize
on the uneasiness that runs through the whole world.
Dear God,
when the strange night
prowls round the edge of day,
let Yourself be moved by my plaintive whinny;
set a star to watch over me
and hush my fear.

Amen

Foal

by MARY BRITTON MILLER

Come trotting up
Beside your mother,
Little skinny.

Lay your neck across
Her back, and whinny,
Little foal.

You think you're a horse
Because you can trot—
But you're not.

Your eyes are so wild,
And each leg is as tall
As a pole;

And you're only a skittish
Child, after all,
Little foal.

Reprinted from *Menagerie* by Mary Britton Miller. Published by The Macmillan Company.

More Books to Read

BALL, ZACHARY. *Bristle Face.*
New York: Holiday House, 1962.
The lively story of Jase, a fourteen-year-old orphan, and his large and peculiar dog, Bristle Face.

BIXBY, WILLIAM. *The Impossible Journey of Sir Ernest Shackleton.*
Boston: Little, Brown and Company, 1960.
An exciting adventure story of a group of men and their attempt to cross the Antarctic Continent.

DE TREVINO, ELIZABETH B. *Nacar, the White Deer.*
New York: Farrar, Straus and Co., 1963.
A magical understanding of animals earns Lalo, a mute boy of Mexico, the task of nursing back to health a pure-white deer with pink eyes and horns like pearl that is to be a gift to the King of Spain.

GRIFFITHS, HELEN. *Horse in the Clouds.*
New York: Holt, Rinehart and Winston, Inc., 1958.
The story of a thirteen-year-old Argentine boy and his love for a wild colt. Interesting comparisons may be drawn between *The Wild Heart* and this earlier book by the same author.

KRAENZEL, MARGARET. *Rain Cloud the Wild Mustang.*
New York: Lothrop, Lee and Shepard Co., Inc., 1962.
Dave Stoner's loneliness was lightened by his discovery of a wild stallion that he hoped one day to have for his own. When the stallion was accused of luring his father's horses away from their herd, Dave knew that he had to find the real thief or give up his dream.

Johanna Johnston, born and educated in Chicago, Illinois, now lives and works in New York City.

Because of Miss Johnston's particular interest in American history, most of her books for children and adults have a historical basis. However, she also writes books for very young children and for several years wrote for the radio. She specialized in children's programs, and her favorite was the popular "Let's Pretend" fairytale theater. Her daughter, Abby, is rapidly becoming as interested as her mother in creating books for young readers.

In 1961, Miss Johnston's *Thomas Jefferson, His Many Talents* won the Thomas Alva Edison Mass Media Award for Special Excellence in Portraying America's Past.

Thomas Jefferson,

His Many Talents

by Johanna Johnston
Illustrated by Richard Bergere

DODD, MEAD & COMPANY—NEW YORK ·

"A mind always employed is always happy."

Thomas Jefferson

Chapters One and Two of *Thomas Jefferson, His Many Talents*
by Johanna Johnston. Illustrations by Richard Bergere.
Copyright © 1961 by Johanna Johnston
Reprinted by permission of Dodd, Mead & Company, Inc.

AUTHOR'S NOTE

From the very first wheel to the outer-space rocket, from cave-homes to skyscrapers, the people who have changed the world and helped mankind to a better life have had one thing in common—inquiring minds.

Thomas Jefferson had this kind of mind to a unique degree. Nothing was so ordinary or taken-for-granted that it could escape his scrutiny and his questioning. And because he was extraordinarily talented in dozens of different ways—one of the most versatile geniuses who ever lived—this tireless interest in everything led him to accomplish surprising things.

Book after book after book has been written about his achievements as a political philosopher and statesman, and about the way he helped move the world to a new concept of democracy.

This book does not tell that story again, except as a background to all the other things he did. The variety of these other things is staggering, and in their very range, they show a truly inquiring mind in action.

They show, in fact, a man who could not help looking at the way men governed themselves and thinking of a better system, because this was how he looked at everything in life—with eyes that saw and a mind that asked "Why?" and "How can it be better?"

It is a way of looking at things we all can strive for and, as heirs of the better world he helped make for us, do our part toward making it still better in the future.

—JOHANNA JOHNSTON

Th Jefferson

ARCHITECT AND BUILDER

1.

He had a way of looking at everything as though it were brand-new. And a way of asking questions about everything, too—of himself and anyone who was around.

A plow, for instance.

What is a plow?

He stared at the plowshare, driving deep into the hard, red earth of his father's lands in the hill country of western Virginia. He saw it breaking the earth and lifting it so that it fell again, crumbled and loosened.

A plow, he realized, is a simple and wonderful tool, the purpose of which is to break the hard crust of the earth and make it ready for the planting of seeds. He looked at the plow and saw how it had been designed to achieve this purpose—the slanted V of the plowshare held and balanced and thrust forward by the beam, so that pushed or pulled across a field, it could not fail to dig and lift the earth as it went.

It seemed very beautiful to him in its simple efficiency, a real magic wand for turning the wilderness into a fertile garden—the most useful of man's tools.

He was just a young, redheaded boy then, with bright hazel eyes. It would be a good many years until, an experienced farmer himself, he would see a way in which that simple, beautiful design might be improved to serve its purpose even better.

But that intent way of looking at things, which was his even as a boy, was what helped make Thomas Jefferson all the things he became—a man who would invent an improved moldboard for a plow one day, as well as write the Declaration of Independence; a man who would become an architect, a furniture designer, a scientist, and half a dozen other things, as well as a statesman and President of the United States.

He grew up in a time and place where there was much to encourage such an inquiring mind. It was 1743 when he was born—April 13th, to be exact. And in the middle of the eighteenth century, America was still a new world, even on the coast where the first settlements had been built. Inland, no farther than a hundred or a hundred and fifty miles, there was still real wilderness, where everything was strange and unfamiliar to all men but the Indians.

The real wilderness rose just beyond the cleared fields of Shadwell, the farm in western Virginia where Thomas Jefferson was born and where he spent most of his boyhood.

And the wilderness fascinated young Thomas almost as much as the plow that tamed it.

How old must those trees be, to grow so tall?

What was that animal peering from the thicket? Or that one whisking away through the trees?

What sort of life did the Indians live in these forest deeps? Why were they always roaming, never settling down as the white men did?

He was fortunate, this curious boy with the eager eyes and the outthrust, stubborn chin. There was a whole, bright new world spread out around him. And he had a father who welcomed all his questions about it, answering the questions when he could, urging the boy on to answer them for himself whenever possible.

In many ways that father, Peter Jefferson, set the course for young Thomas' life.

Peter Jefferson was truly one of the strong men of early America, a pioneer who broke the wilderness and carved out a vast and profitable estate for himself and his family and, at the same time, a man who was constantly seeking to educate and improve himself intellectually, a man always ready to serve his friends and neighbors in any way he could.

He was a giant of a man physically and had personally helped clear a thousand acres of virgin forest to create the cleared fields of Shadwell and build a home. He was so strong that Thomas would watch and marvel as he flexed his muscles and pushed upright two 1000-pound hogsheads of tobacco at one time. Another time Thomas saw his father give a mighty tug at a rope with which three strong slaves had been trying to pull down a shed, and bring down the shed in a heap.

Of course Thomas wanted to be as strong as his father. His eyes intent, his chin set, he threw himself into learning all the physical skills his father was eager to teach him. He learned how to ride a horse, how to handle a gun and hunt, how to paddle a canoe on the swift, rock-strewn waters of the little Rivanna River that ran through the Shadwell lands.

And year by year, as Thomas grew taller and taller, he did grow lean and strong, with a physical endurance that would last all through a long, long life.

"Never," Peter Jefferson told his son, "never ask anyone else to do for you what you can do for yourself."

So Thomas learned the habit of doing all sorts of things for himself. He learned how to do things which, perhaps, there was no need for him to do, since there were slaves aplenty at Shadwell. But somehow that advice of his father's came also to mean, "Never ask another to do what you are not willing and able to do yourself."

The plow was not just a tool for others to handle. Thomas himself had to learn how to use that tool, driving a straight furrow across the field. And because a farm at the edge of the wilderness in the eighteenth century was a little world in itself, Thomas learned dozens of other skills as well.

He learned about spinning and weaving and dyeing. He learned about wagon-making, brick-making, and nail-making. He learned about distilling, caning chairs, and shoeing horses. All these activities were part of the busy life of Shadwell, carried on in sheds and outbuildings clustered all about the main house; and so they were part of Thomas' life, too.

But his father, who had found for himself the world of books, his father, who loved Shakespeare and Swift and Pope, wanted more for his son than a knowledge of physical skills. Thomas was still very young when his father taught him how to read and write and keep accounts. Soon he was exploring the library at Shadwell.

Books were one thing that could not be produced on even the most self-sustaining of farms. Books were treasures, brought from the coast, where they had been imported from Europe. Books were the first thing one thought of buying when it came to a question of spending cash for something.

Books first, and then perhaps musical instruments. People had to make their own music in those days, and Thomas, who loved it, soon learned to play on the fiddle. It was an accomplishment that would bring him pleasure all his life.

Indoors, outdoors, there was always something to learn. But above and beyond everything else in those years, there was something more Thomas was gaining as he watched his father. It was a vision of man as a builder—man clearing the wilderness to build a useful, productive farm; man using and sharpening all his talents to banish chaos and confusion and create order.

He was only six when his father, a self-taught surveyor, rode off with a professor from William and Mary College, which was over on the seaboard, to survey and map the still uncharted areas of western Virginia. His father and the professor came back with the first map ever compiled of "The Inhabited Parts of Virginia."

So Thomas saw that beyond the reach of the ax and the plow, man could still push back the unknown by exploration and observation, laying the foundation for future building by others.

Order—finding it in nature, creating it where it did not exist—this was man's goal in life. In order, there was room for his own talents to increase and expand, for everyone's talents to have their fullest scope.

And what was the way to that kind of order? For Thomas, the first step would always be asking questions.

358

Latin School

Shadwell bordered the wilderness, but there were a few neighboring farms, all the same. There was a tiny town nearby called Charlottesville. And there was a little Latin School near Shadwell, held in a small log house and presided over by an elderly clergyman.

Here, when he was thirteen or so, Thomas began to learn Latin and Greek and higher mathematics. Here he also met a friend, Dabney Carr, almost as curious about everything as he was.

Now, when school was out and Thomas went off hunting or exploring in the forest, Dabney Carr often went with him. Together they would spy a fox or a bird. Where was its den? Where was its nest?

Silently, trying to walk like Indians, they would track the fox or bird, find the den or the nest, study it, and ask themselves why and how it had been built just so.

Then one day as they were wandering on one of the hills that lay across the Rivanna, they made a wonderful discovery. They had climbed a long, rough way through virgin forest, and at last they came out on the top of the hill. And both of them stopped and stared.

It was not the highest hill anywhere about, but somehow from this hilltop they had a view like none they had seen before. The whole world seemed spread out below them, hills and valleys rolling endlessly to the horizon both east and west.

They were silent a moment, looking. Then the majesty of it all so overwhelmed young Dabney he could think of only one response grand enough. He told Thomas that here, on this hilltop, was where he wanted to be buried when he died.

Solemnly Thomas nodded in agreement. He wanted to be buried there, too.

Then Thomas had a less somber thought. This was more than a place to be buried. This was a spot on which to live.

"This is where I am going to build my house one day," he said.

Dabney looked at him. "A house—here? On a hill-top?" Nobody built houses on hilltops. Houses were built in the lowlands, by rivers or streams, so that crops of cotton, corn, or tobacco would have easy transport.

But "Why not?" asked Thomas. His father had built a house in the wilderness, where no man had built before. Why should he not build on a hilltop? There would be ways to solve the problems. He would figure out ways. Because as he stared out over the rolling hills, he felt sure that no one could ever be or think anything mean or small up here. Every thought must surely be tempered by this great vista into goodness and beauty.

"Yes, this is where I will build my house," said Thomas.

2.

And so, what is a house? As the days and weeks and months went by, this was a new question turning itself over and over in Thomas' mind.

First of all, of course, a house is a shelter of wood or stone or brick, to keep a man and his family warm and dry against the elements.

But Thomas knew already that a good house was more than that. A good house provided comfort and convenience as well as shelter. A good house held the people within it in friendliness, offering them rooms in which they might enjoy themselves together, other rooms where they might be alone. He looked at his own home and knew Shadwell was a good house in that sense, full of affection and activity, its doors always open to guests.

But somehow Thomas wanted something even more for his hilltop. A good house should be beautiful, too, he thought. It should fit the land on which it was built and express the dreams of the person who lived in it.

Where had this idea come from? Partly, perhaps, from the books he read, but mostly from his own heart. For Thomas was already that unusual combination—a practical person, methodically concerned with how everything worked, yet full of a passionate sensitivity that saw beyond all those details to some great ideal of beauty.

He wanted a *beautiful* house. But where, Thomas wondered, would he ever find a house beautiful enough for his hilltop? Or one that would express all that he felt when he stood there?

The days of his boyhood went on.

And then, when he was fourteen, his father died. That mighty man, the polestar of his youth, was gone.

Thomas was head of the family now, responsible for his mother, his younger brother, his six sisters.

Because he was the oldest son, all of Shadwell was his, too, including the hill where he meant to build his house. His younger brother was willed other farms from Peter Jefferson's holdings—for Peter Jefferson had not held with the general custom of those days in Virginia whereby a man left all his land for his oldest son. He did not believe in this, and one day Thomas himself, spurred as always by his father's example, would take real steps to abolish the custom in Virginia completely.

Right now there was nothing to do but accept his inheritance, go on with his studies, and try to carry on the Shadwell pattern as his father had established it.

Two guardians had been appointed to advise him till he came of age, but in actual fact, it was Thomas who had to supervise the day-to-day activity of the farm and give orders to the overseer. It was Thomas who had to carry on his father's tradition of lavish hospitality. Guests were always being entertained at Shadwell—neighboring squires and farmers, any travelers or hunters who might be passing by, Indians, too, with whom Peter Jefferson had always been friendly.

Young Thomas enjoyed the guests, and the Indians were his friends. He talked with them all, eager to find out everything he could about their customs and laws and habits. Already he was interested in learning the Indian language.

"What is your word for that?" he would ask a bronzed guest in buckskin, pointing up to the sun. Or he would ask the word for rain or snow or clouds.

He knew quite a few words of Cherokee, but different tribes spoke different languages. He was curious to learn the different words that referred to the basic, natural elements. Perhaps there might be some similarity in them that indicated they were all just variations of some common language. Or perhaps, way, way back, they were all based on some known language.

There was a theory about in those days—Thomas heard some of his neighbors discussing it—that the Indians were originally the ten lost tribes of Israel, and had wandered to America, somehow, by way of Asia. This did not seem very likely to Thomas, but a study of all the Indian languages might give one some clue.

All sorts of questions were piling up in his mind these days, dozens of questions for which no one seemed to have any answers.

He was seventeen when it came to him that if he ever hoped to answer all of them, he needed more learning than he could get from the old clergyman, or even from reading by himself. Besides, all the activity of the farm, with the guests coming and going, kept him from studying as much as he would have liked.

He decided to leave home and go to college.

There was not much doubt about where he would go. William and Mary, one of the three colleges in existence in the colonies, was only a little more than a hundred miles away, in Williamsburg. It was so well thought of that students came from faraway New England to attend it, as well as from all over the South.

So young Thomas packed up his clothes and his fiddle and some of his books, and with his eyes brighter than ever, his chin tilted happily, he mounted his horse and rode off to Williamsburg.

What is a house?

In the rich and civilized little city he came to now, he saw many beautiful homes. There was the Governor's Palace, stately and dignified in red brick. There were other fine homes—George Wythe's, for instance. George Wythe was a lawyer, renowned throughout the colonies, and his house, though simpler than the Governor's Palace, was large and gracious and well proportioned.

Soon Thomas came to know both those houses well. A professor at the college, impressed by Thomas' eager

George Wythe's house

Governor's Palace, Williamsburg

intelligence, took Thomas under his wing and introduced him to both the Royal Governor and the famous lawyer. Soon Thomas, young as he was, was a close friend of the witty and able Governor Fauquier, the wise and thoughtful George Wythe. The Governor, the lawyer, the professor, and young Thomas were a foursome who met often for dinner at the Governor's Palace.

But the Palace, rich as it was, answered no dream for Thomas of what his own house should be. Neither did George Wythe's house.

Thomas was as popular with the young people in Williamsburg as he was with the older men. He flung himself at his studies as he had once flung himself at learning to ride and hunt. Sometimes he studied as much as fifteen hours a day and then, for exercise, ran a mile out of town and back again. With all that application and his own natural quickness, he was, of course, outstanding. No one had ever seen a student who could master so many different subjects so rapidly and so well —Greek and physics, calculus and Spanish, early Anglo-Saxon and Latin.

Still, none of his fellow students could bring themselves to resent his hard work or his success. When he put down his books, he flung himself just as eagerly into gaiety and liveliness.

His fiddle came out sometimes as he played for his friends to sing or dance. He liked going to the theater when traveling players appeared in Williamsburg. He tried his hand at gambling. And he liked dancing and flirting with the girls. He did not make many jokes himself, but everyone liked hearing his quick laughter when someone else said something amusing. His conversation was still full of questions, but his voice was so soft and mild, it was so obvious he really wanted to know whatever he was asking about, that nobody minded his endless curiosity.

Naturally his popularity took him to balls and parties at all the fine houses in town, parties at nearby country houses, too. But none of these houses answered his dream, either.

Two years Thomas persevered in college. Then he decided to take no more courses at William and Mary. He had made up his mind to be a lawyer. He would quit college and study law with his friend George Wythe.

The law, he soon found, was nowhere near so much to his taste as some other subjects. But spurred by the example of his teacher, unable to do anything by half measure, he flung himself at his law books. Of all the professions he might choose, he felt the law offered the most opportunities. So he would be a lawyer, and a good one.

Politics began to concern him. Sooner or later everyone in Williamsburg was caught up in them. The House of Burgesses, to which his father had once been a delegate, met in Williamsburg, and Thomas often stopped in to listen to the debates when the House was in session.

The atmosphere was tenser now than in his father's day. Men were troubled by England's ever-increasing harshness in the rule of her colonies. A few tried to defend King George and his taxes, but more and more men were growing angry and defiant.

One day in 1765 Thomas was standing in the back of the hall when his old friend Patrick Henry rose to make the most violent attack yet on the King. "If this be treason," he concluded, "make the most of it."

Was it treason?

Of course Thomas asked himself that question. Was it treason to suggest that if George III continued his despotic way, he might meet the same fate as other tyrants?

Asking himself that question simply led to other questions.

What were England's rights over her American colonies? What were the rights of any governing body over the people it governed?

Thomas pondered. He talked and argued with his friends. He read and he thought some more. And gradually, along with many other men all over the colonies, he began to evolve answers for himself—answers that would one day startle the world.

Still, with all of this, the dream of the house was not forgotten. Summers, on vacation back in Shadwell, he would study all day, and then at sunset he would paddle his canoe across the Rivanna to the foot of his own special hill. Then he would climb to the top and gaze out at the world that was visible from there.

He set some of the slaves he had inherited from his father to clearing the hilltop and leveling it off in preparation for the house he would someday build.

But still he did not know what that house would be like.

Then one evening back in Williamsburg he found out. It was his friend Governor Fauquier who helped give him the answer. Thomas was one of a group at the Governor's Palace, and the Governor had some new books to show. One of them was a big, beautiful book of designs by a famous Italian architect of the previous century, Andrea Palladio.

Thomas took one look at the simple, classic lines of the buildings Palladio had designed and knew he had found the kind of beauty he was searching for. It was a house designed in this style that he wanted for his hilltop.

How would he achieve it?

Jefferson's sketch of Palladio drawing

3.

There were no architects, as we know them, in the colonies in those days—no one who could interpret those designs for Thomas into the kind of home he wanted.

Very well. Thomas recalled that his father had taught himself to be a surveyor. He, Thomas, would teach himself to be an architect.

He had learned some skill with a draftsman's tools from his father. Using Palladio's book as a guide, learning from every other book on architecture that he could find, he would design his own home in the Palladian style.

In the next few years, that is just what he did. He searched out every book on architecture in Williamsburg and hunted eagerly for more in every shipment from England. He sharpened his quill pen, tacked down paper on a drafting board, and made copy after copy of the precise and beautiful plates in Palladio's book. Finally, when it seemed to him he really understood the meaning and the reasoning behind the proportions and arrangements Palladio had used, he began to modify one of the plans and draw his own design.

It was 1767 when he finished his law studies and was admitted to the bar. He was ready to return to Shadwell and begin the practice of law in his home county of Albemarle. He was ready, also, with his carefully drawn, carefully thought-out plan for a long low, colonnaded mansion to be built on the crest of his hill. Monticello, he called that hill now, from the Italian for "Little Mountain."

There it was, his Little Mountain, rising green against the sky whenever he rode out from Shadwell or rode back again. But a young lawyer with a name and a living to make had little time to start on any project so grand as a mansion. One after another the cases came in. They took him all around Virginia to various county courthouses.

Still, he set the slaves to building a road through the forest up to the mountaintop. And he began talking to everyone about a project that would certainly benefit a future house on the hill, just as it would benefit Shadwell and other farms along the Rivanna.

It was a project that had occurred to him a year or so before, on one of his vacations at home. Paddling up the little river, he began wondering if it were possible to clear it of the rocks which made any sort of transport so difficult. He had gone further and surveyed the river and decided that although it would be quite an engineering feat, it *was* possible.

So now he went from courthouse to courthouse with his cases, and from one person to another with his scheme for clearing the Rivanna. By the time a year and a half had passed, he had succeeded so well, both in his legal arguments and his river-clearance zeal, that he was elected to the House of Burgesses.

The first bill he introduced, however, had nothing to do with the river. It was a bill that proposed to give slave owners the right to manumit, or free, their slaves.

He had grown up with slavery; it was part of the Southern way of life, where vast tracts of land had to be kept in cultivation if the farmer was to see any profit. Still, almost as soon as he had started to ask questions, he had wondered how one man could *own* another.

Because a Negro's skin was a different color from the white man's, because he had been forcibly transported from his homeland to a strange country, did this mean he was not a human being with the same rights as any other man?

He introduced the bill, the first of many he was to propose in the same cause, and it was defeated.

He had better luck with the river-clearance plan. Legislative approval was granted, and soon the work was started that made it possible to send cargo craft, loaded with tobacco and other crops, down the Rivanna.

And what of his hilltop all this time? Was any progress being made at all toward fulfilling the dream?

There were some signs that someone planned to build there someday. And Thomas' memorandum book had these notations:

> four good fellows, a lad & two girls of about 16 each, in 8½ hours dug in my cellar of mountain clay a place 3 ft. deep, 8 ft. wide and 16½ f. long=14⅔ cubic yds . . .

And:

> in digging my dry well . . . they dug and drew out 8 cubical yds in a day.

And:

> Minor's sawyers left off work. They have sawed (as they say) 2500 pales, 220 rails. 650 f. of inch chestnut plank & 250 of 2¼ inch do.

And:

> A bed of mortar which makes 2000 bricks takes 6 hhds of water.

In other words, he had the start of a cellar and a well, timber had been cut and left to season, and he was beginning some sort of building.

But more and more legal cases were coming in. For all that he found the law cut-and-dried, Thomas was a success as a lawyer. He had twice as many cases the second year as the first, and his practice doubled again during the third year.

Yet the work on the hilltop went on. Thomas set out fruit trees to start an orchard for Monticello. He planted a few fields in various crops. A row of sheds was built on the hilltop, utility sheds to accommodate all the activities needed for building a house.

Finally, three years after he had come back to Shadwell, one small brick building was completed. In the grand overall design of Thomas' plan, it would ultimately be a small pavilion at the southeast end of one of the long wings stretching out from the central portion of the house. Thomas planned it for his office.

Then, in 1770, disaster struck at Shadwell. The main house burned to the ground. All Thomas' precious books were lost, the library he had inherited from his father and all the books he had collected so lovingly at Williamsburg. He would have to start buying books all over again, for life was no good without them.

But the fire left him in no doubt about where he should live. His mother and his sisters went to live in the overseer's house, but Thomas—Thomas went right straight up to Monticello.

I have here but one room, he wrote to a friend, *which like the cobblers, serves me for parlor, for kitchen, and hall. I may add for bedchamber and study, too. My friends sometimes take a temperate dinner with me and then retire to look for beds elsewhere.*

He had but one room, but at last he was living where he had vowed he would live, on his hilltop, with all the hills of Virginia spread out below him.

Two years more—two busy years as a lawyer with several months every winter and spring in Williamsburg when the House of Burgesses was meeting—and still there was only that one small building completed. Even so, Thomas was bringing a bride to live on the hilltop, too. He had found the love of his life, and on New Year's Day, 1772, he was married to the young and beautiful Martha Skelton.

Two weeks after the wedding Thomas and his bride left her home near Williamsburg and set out for

the Little Mountain. It turned out to be a dreadful day for the journey. One of Virginia's rare snowstorms had blown itself into a blizzard. Still, the new Mr. and Mrs. Jefferson struggled on. Before they reached Charlottesville, they had to give up their snowbound carriage for horses. Then, as the horses floundered in the snow on the slopes of Monticello, they gave up the horses, too, and fought the last distance up the hill on foot.

What is a house?

That night, when they were finally safe in the snug little red brick building, that one small room fulfilled the first requirement, giving them warmth and shelter against the storm. And with a fire in the fireplace, candles lighted, and wine on the table, it was more than that, too—a good house, however small, full of love and happiness and wonderful dreams for the future.

4.

It was thirty years and more before all Thomas Jefferson's dreams for his house on the hilltop came true. But in the next few years he did at least complete the main outlines of Monticello.

And in every part of it, it reflected the mind of its designer and builder, the man who saw everything as though it were brand-new, and asked himself how it worked and if it could be made to work better.

The house consisted of a central pavilion, fronted by a portico, and extended on either side in two long ells. When it was finally completed, it looked only one story high from the outside, and this was by design. Jefferson had never wanted a towering house on his hill, but a house that looked as though it clung to the land, growing up from it like another long, low crest. Still, when one entered the main doors, the central hall rose in spacious two-story height.

The look of uncluttered space in this hall was no accident, either. Jefferson had thought a long time about the problems of this main hall, asking himself first of all what its chief purpose was, then the other ways in which it would be used and how it could best be designed to serve those ends.

It was, of course, the room visitors would enter to gain their first impression of the house. It was also the room from which one went right and left to all the other rooms in the house, the room from which, most usually, a stairway would ascend to the rooms on the floor above.

But before Jefferson built his stairway, he remembered one of the chief uses of every central stairway he had ever seen. The occupants of the house used it. But even more than they, the servants were forced to use it in an unending parade of activity. Firewood had to be carried to the fireplaces on the second story; ashes had to be brought down again. Hot water for bathing, cold water for drinking, food and dishes had to be carried up; jugs of water and dishes had to be brought down again.

Surely all the beauty of a wide, sweeping stairway was lost in the confusion of such traffic.

How, Jefferson wondered, could he do away with this nuisance, banishing all that needful but distracting activity out of sight?

The answer he worked out was two small, sharply turning stairways on either side of the main hall, hidden away, leaving the hall itself free, open, and beautiful.

He looked at other housekeeping problems and studied them as if no one had ever attempted to solve them before. The kitchen, for a large house like Monticello, was almost always in a small separate building near the main house. As a matter of fact, all the workshops of a large plantation were usually clustered about the main building in a random, haphazard fashion.

Jefferson had already banished these unsightly shops, offices, and sheds, hiding them along the rear of the house, under a terrace. The kitchen was there, too. Even so, the food still had to be carried along an open walk to a warming kitchen and serving pantry inside the house.

Surely there was something that could be improved on here. Hot food lost its heat on this journey, and the servants were still exposed to all sorts of weather.

Jefferson decided to build an underground passage from the kitchen to the main house.

But this decision brought new problems. A tunnel would be damp. In the dampness, would the usual mortar hold the stones, or would it soon crumble away?

He began to experiment with mortar, using various proportions of lime and ash. Finally, after a dozen or more experiments, he hit upon a recipe which seemed to solve the problem perfectly.

He jotted down the proportions in his notebook:

1 bushel each of lime, wood ashes, and pulverized brick, brought to the proper consistency, will harden in water.

Actually, what he had arrived at in those homely experiments on the hilltop was an almost exact chemical foreshadowing of our modern formula for cement.

And so the underground passage was built, and it is solid and dry to this day, almost two hundred years later.

The underground passage was not the only innovation he thought of to make the serving of food more convenient. Before Monticello was finally completed, he had designed and built a service door to hang between the serving pantry and dining room. The door had shelves on the side turned to the pantry, which could be loaded with dishes and food. Then the door swung on a central pivot to bring the shelves into the dining room, where they could be unloaded by the servants there. Naturally it worked just as well in reverse when it was time to clear the table.

Still another convenience was a small dumbwaiter concealed in the fireplace in the dining room. This dumbwaiter went down to the wine cellar below, so that wine could be placed on it and then drawn up into the dining room when needed. And, of course, the empty bottles could be returned the same way.

Other rooms in the house received his attention. There were large double glass doors between the main hall

and the drawing room, and Jefferson worked out an intricate mechanism, concealed in the paneling, which caused one panel to open or shut automatically in harmony with the other as it was opened or closed.

He gave some thought to his own room and how it might best be arranged for his own habits and needs. He liked to rise early in the morning and, after a cold bath, get to work at once on his notebooks or accounts. He liked to read at night or answer letters before he went to bed. His room, in other words, was as much a study and a workroom as it was a bedroom.

Was it necessary to have a bed, used only at night, taking up space all day in a room that was really a study?

He decided it was not, and designed a sort of double room with an alcove between the two halves. In this alcove, he had a bed hung on one wall, so arranged that it could be lowered at night, then hauled up and fastened against the ceiling during the day. The alcove passage became free when this was done, uniting the dressing-room half of his room with the study in one airy unity.

And still he thought of more ways to make his house functional.

Years before real plumbing systems were invented, he evolved a plumbing system for Monticello, a way by which indoor privies could be emptied and the waste carried away, out of the house, and deposited underground in a central tank out on the grounds.

He achieved this by means of buckets, placed under the privy seats, which could be removed by a manually operated pulley, carried along an underground tunnel to the spot for emptying, and then returned, by pulley, the way they had come.

How does it work? How—if it has never been done before—can it be made to work? Asking himself these questions, Thomas Jefferson seemed to find no end to the improvements he could make in his home.

And there was always another question, too. How may it all be made as beautiful as possible, worthy of the hilltop?

Tall, graceful windows opened every downstairs room to the lovely views on every side, and opened the whole house to the cool airiness of hilltop breezes. Cornices, moldings, and fireplaces were carved in simple, classic designs, and none was too hidden to be worked with meticulous care.

Every door was solid mahogany, every sash of solid walnut. The handwrought hardware was delicate and ingenious at the same time. Many doors had catches which, as the door swung open, engaged automatically and held it in place.

He had wonderful plans for the grounds surrounding the house—plans for formal gardens and a small Gothic temple, plans for wildlife.

Keep it, he wrote while he was still planning, *"in deer, rabbits, peacocks, guinea poultry, pigeons, etc. Let it be an asylum for hares, squirrels, pheasants, partridges, and every other wild animal (except those of prey). Court them to it by laying food for them in proper places. Procure a buck elk, to be, as it were, monarch of the wood; but keep him shy, that his appearance may not lose its effect by too much familiarity.*

Oh, yes, he had hundreds of plans, and as the years went on, he kept thinking of new plans.

In the 1780's a distinguished Frenchman came to America and visited Monticello, and when he went home, he wrote a description of the house which he ended by saying, . . . *we may safely aver that Mr. Jefferson is the first American who has consulted the fine arts to know how he should shelter himself from the weather.*

But long before that visit was made or those words written, long before all the comforts and beauties just described were achieved, Jefferson had to stop his happy labors on the hilltop and leave his home for longer and longer periods.

The questions that had begun to agitate the American colonists back in the '60's were burning for answers now.

What *were* Great Britain's rights in the American colonies? Could the colonists win the King and Parliament to a less oppressive attitude by reason, or was there no alternative but revolt?

In 1774, men from all over the colonies were assembling to discuss those questions in Continental Congress. Jefferson was only thirty-one, but he had made enough of a reputation both as a lawyer and in the House of Burgesses to be named one of the delegates from Virginia.

At the last moment illness forced him to stay home at Monticello. But he had written a paper outlining his own answer to one of the questions: "A Summary View of British Rights in America." The paper was read in the Continental Congress, and after that no one thought of Jefferson as an obscure young Virginian any more. He was a young man who obviously had ideas and knew how to express them.

In 1775, when the Second Continental Congress was assembling, Jefferson was again named a delegate.

He quit his house-building, said good-by to his wife and baby daughter, got into his carriage, and started off. For the next few years he would be helping to design and build something even more basic and important than a house—a new kind of government that would try to take account of all the needs and desires of men as they had never been considered before, and then try to answer them in a better, more logical way than they had ever before been answered.

SCIENTIST AND NATURALIST

1.

All his life he was busy taking notes. His father, who taught him so many things, started him on that habit also, and naturally, to anyone as engrossed as young Thomas in the how, the why, and the what of things, the habit was soon almost as automatic as asking questions.

There was always a notebook in one of his pockets. There were notebooks piled on his desk at home, and bundles of loose notes were tucked here, there, and everywhere. He had an expense book from the time he first had money to spend. Later he began keeping a Farm Book, with notes on his planting activities and experiments and all his building projects. He kept a Garden Book, with more notes on planting. And along with all these he had begun a Weather Memorandum Book, back in the Williamsburg days, in which he made regular entries on the weather.

Now, on his way to the Congress in Philadelphia, what else should he be doing during the long, slow journeying, day after day, but taking notes?

He sat in his light, open coach, jolting along over the rough country roads, down from the hills of Virginia out onto the flat, seaboard country of Maryland and Delaware and, finally, on across inlets and rivers to Pennsylvania. He propped a box on his lap to give him a writing surface and scratched away with his quill pen, taking notes on everything he saw.

As always, he was interested in the natural life all about him, the birds, the animals, the flowers, the trees. As always, he did more than note he had seen such a deer or such an oak. He recorded the approximate size of the animal or tree, its coloring, its habitat, and every other distinguishing characteristic he could observe. He noted how the natural life changed with the changing countryside, how certain trees, familiar in the hills, were seen less and less in the lowlands, and how the same changes took place in animal life.

It was not a very comfortable way to write, sitting in an open phaeton with the wind blowing his paper and the inkstand always about to overturn. But he kept on.

The changing weather from hill country to lowlands was something else to record. Weather study was a long way from being a science in those days, but all over the colonies men of a scientific turn of mind were making observations on the weather where they lived, slowly charting some pattern for the climate of this great new continent.

The Fahrenheit thermometer was a recent invention, delighting men like Benjamin Franklin and Jefferson's old friend Governor Fauquier. Jefferson had long since resolved to buy himself a new thermometer in Philadelphia. Meantime, he made notes on the clouds and rainfall, the sunshine and wind.

At night the stars interested him. Astronomical observation was something else in which Governor Fauquier had encouraged him.

And at night, stopping in various inns along the way, he found things to observe indoors as well. He paid for his supper and his bed, for lodging his servant and his horse—and one night the price was quoted in shillings, the next night in guineas, the next night in pistareens. There was no standard money system in use anywhere, and the logical, methodical Jefferson began to be annoyed.

Was a man supposed to carry a bagful of coins of every conceivable kind wherever he went?

He knew how the confusion had come about, of course. Men settled a new community and continued to use whatever money had been standard in their European homeland. Then, as they moved about from settlement to settlement and men from different countries met, there was soon a hodgepodge mixture of a dozen kinds of coinage. It was understandable, but the whole thing was now ridiculous.

Just to show how very ridiculous it was, Jefferson listed all the coins he had seen in use in his notebook. Then, of course, being Jefferson, he began asking himself questions.

How can the confusion be ended? What kind of coinage system would be best to set up as a standard everywhere?

In one corner of his mind he began thinking about answers to those questions right then. And the notes he took that spring of 1775 were seeds that flowered eight years later, when he became one of the Virginia delegates to a Congress of the newly independent states. By then he had a better money system all worked out and ready to present in a bill. The decimal system, based on units of ten, had finally seemed to him the simplest, most logical way in which to measure money values. He proposed a dollar unit in his bill, and a coinage system derived from that. And so he fathered the whole coinage system that we use in the United States today.

The notes he made on money were not the only seeds that flowered from the observations of that one particular trip.

Six years later, the notes he had made on flora and fauna, stars and soil, were to be of great value, too, when he embarked on a book describing the natural characteristics of Virginia. It became a book that won him fame both in America and abroad, and made him, as well, one of the pioneers of North American geography.

And that was still not the only consequence of his ten days' journeying from Monticello to Philadelphia. The inconvenience of his makeshift writing desk made him think how pleasant it would be to have a really well-designed traveling writing desk.

He sketched out a design—a compact box, not much larger than a big book, with a drawer to hold an inkstand and paper and quills, and atop it, a folding shelf which could be lifted and tilted as a reading stand or opened out to use as a surface for writing.

It was a nice coincidence, after he had arrived in Philadelphia and found lodgings, to discover that his landlord, a certain Ben Randall, was a skilled cabinetmaker. Jefferson gave Ben Randall the sketches for the desk and asked if he could make up such a contrivance for him.

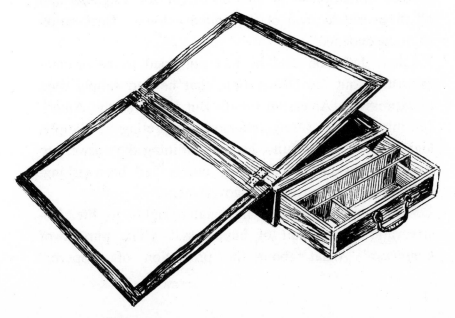

And so it happened that when he went home to Monticello in August, he carried with him a handsome and convenient writing desk on which to take his notes.

Nothing had been finally settled in that Second Continental Congress. The conflict between England and her colonies had exploded into real fighting, at Concord and at Bunker Hill, but war had not been declared. New proposals from the King's chief minister had to be answered.

But a second session of the Congress was called for the next June. And, again a delegate, Jefferson returned to Philadelphia, bringing with him the little desk—a desk that would soon be used for a most important writing assignment.

In this summer of 1776 the delegates were ready to make up their minds. They chose the tall, red-headed young Virginian to write out the announcement of their intentions—an announcement for England and all the world to read of the united colonies' Declaration of Independence.

Later, Jefferson said he had not tried to be original in writing out the Declaration, that he had simply tried to express the American mind. But if it was the American mind, it was surely Jefferson interpreting it. Simply, logically, and beautifully, he was outlining the answers to the questions he and so many others had been asking.

What is the purpose of government?

"To secure men their inalienable rights to life, liberty, and the pursuit of happiness." (The pursuit of *happiness?* What about the protection of property?

There were many who felt this was the duty of government. But Jefferson had a vision of a government that protected all men, not just the lucky few. Every man had the right to pursue happiness, and a good government would protect that right.)

How does any government derive its just right to power?

In the Declaration, Jefferson spelled out the simple answer. A government derives its right to power "from the consent of the governed."

After he had written out his draft of the document on the little writing desk, he took it to the Congress. The delegates read it over and then began criticizing various passages.

Jefferson sat in silence, his firm jaw set. Criticism had always hurt him. Now, when it seemed to him he had weighed and pondered every phrase to make sure it was both exact and necessary, these arguments and disagreements over what he had written were like physical blows.

Worst of all was the disagreement about his words condemning the slave trade. Surely a document proclaiming every man's right to liberty should take a stand against an institution that denied liberty to some men because of their color!

So why? Why were some of the delegates who hated slavery as much as he did still insisting that that passage be removed?

Deep in his heart Jefferson knew why—knew why he himself kept the slaves he had inherited even though the idea of slavery appalled him. The Southern way of farming was based on slave labor. Some new system for working vast plantations would have to be evolved before men would feel they could free their slaves.

Still, slave *trading* could surely be condemned.

But no. The delegates crossed it out.

Wounded and unhappy, Jefferson still sat quietly and went on taking notes on the proceedings—and on other things as well.

On July 4, 1776, for instance, when the debating finally drew to a close, he noted in his expense book that he had spent 3.15 pounds for a Fahrenheit thermometer. And he also made a note of the temperature readings at various hours of the day. At 1 P.M. it was 76 degrees, a very pleasant and temperate day for the delegates finally to sign a document as explosive as the Declaration of Independence turned out to be.

2.

What once had been colonies were states now. And men from thirteen states were fighting a war against the English in an effort to make good the independence they had declared.

As the two armies battled, Jefferson was fighting in another way. The states were free from Great Britain's rule in name only if their laws and institutions remained exactly the same. So back in Virginia he was working in the House of Delegates to make the changes in Virginia's laws and Constitution which would really put the principles of democracy into action.

Years before, inspired by his father, he had begun to be troubled by the old English law which provided that if a man died without a will, his estate be passed on, undivided, to his oldest son. Another old English system, called entail, allowed one estate to remain undivided and owned by the oldest male heir forever. Now Jefferson realized that this system of entail and primogeniture created an aristocracy of landowners.

At last he had an opportunity to change this. He drafted and introduced and fought for the passage of two bills which abolished the two systems entirely. One allowed a landowner to will his estate to whomever he wished. The other amplified that freedom by giving him the further right to divide his lands however he wished and sell them to any purchaser he pleased.

Two more bills seemed equally important to him. One was aimed at distributing as widely as possible something even more vital than land. It was a bill providing for free public education. The other bill, which gave him the most satisfaction of all, guaranteed religious freedom to everyone in Virginia.

He was Jefferson the Builder, laying the foundations of democracy in those days. He was Jefferson, the man who looked at everything to see how it might be made to work more efficiently, as he labored with his old friend and teacher George Wythe to revise Virginia's legal code.

But he was still Jefferson the Scientist, taking notes on all sorts of natural phenomena—the first blooming of the fruit trees at Monticello, the total eclipse of the sun in 1778, the uses of the orrery, a sort of planetarium which had just recently been invented.

In 1779 he was elected governor, and during his two years in that office there were troubles everywhere. The war was going badly both in the North and South; Richmond, the new capital of the state, was invaded, after which he himself was bitterly criticized by many people because the city had been so ill prepared.

Wounded as only he could be by this criticism, he was delighted when his term was over in 1781 and he could retire to Monticello to recover his serenity with all sorts of farming experiments.

For several years now, he had had a stimulating new neighbor, a certain Italian gentleman of many talents. Jefferson himself had induced him to settle nearby and experiment with growing grapes for wine. Phillip Mazzei was his name, and soon Mazzei was not only growing grapes but had imported olive trees and sour-orange trees as well.

Jefferson was growing some of these at Monticello, making careful notes on their progress. There were all sorts of other experiments under way as well.

And then came a scientific project that was really made to measure for him.

What was the state of Virginia like? What were its natural resources, its climate, its flora and fauna?

The French government wanted to know. A representative in the French legation in Philadelphia had forwarded the request for information to Jefferson.

Eagerly Jefferson flung himself at the task of compiling the answers. Out came the bundled notes of years —all those notes he had taken on the journey to Philadelphia in 1775, notes he had taken on all of his journeys around the state and on rambles over his own land— hundreds and hundreds of notes on trees and flowers, animals and weather, hills, rivers, rocks, and stars.

For the next year he was working at arranging and editing all these notes and writing letters here, there, and everywhere for still more facts and statistics.

Some old bones had been dug up far inland, along the Ohio River. They were huge in size, and the men who studied them had decided they belonged to some large quadruped they named a "mammoth."

Jefferson had been fascinated by the reports on those bones from the first moment he heard of them. Now he was busy collecting all the data he could get on them to prove that the creature was indeed a mammoth and not an elephant as some far-off European scientists had tried to insist.

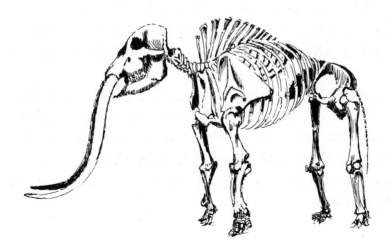

A patient pursuit of facts, and cautious combination and comparison of them, is the drudgery to which man is subjected by his Maker if he wishes to obtain sure knowledge, he once wrote to a friend.

He called it drudgery, but he loved it all the same. This was a book he had always wanted to write. More than that, it was a unique opportunity to set European scientists right, not only on the mammoth but on all sorts of facts about America about which they were misinformed.

Notes on Virginia, he called it when it was finally finished and ready to send off to France. And in years to come it would become a classic.

But even as he was finishing the book, it seemed for a while as though all his interest in life were ending, too. It was the summer of 1782, and each day his wife, Martha, grew frailer and seemed less likely to recover from the birth of her last child. In September she died, and for months after that Jefferson was sunk in grief, roaming and riding the woods, speaking to no one.

At last it was his family that called him back to life again. He had three little daughters to raise. And there was a cluster of relatives living at Monticello, among them his sister, who had married Dabney Carr, and her children. (Dabney himself had died, and, true to his boyhood promise, Jefferson had buried him on the hilltop.)

Suddenly all these relatives and friends, and all the slaves on the plantation as well, were threatened by an outbreak of smallpox, one of the most dreaded diseases of the time.

Smallpox! Now it was well indeed that Jefferson had always loved science, read about it, talked about it, corresponded about it with friends everywhere. Like a few other people in America, he knew about inoculation against the disease. In fact, he had, himself, been vaccinated some years before in Philadelphia.

But there were no doctors around Monticello who understood the process or had any faith in it. If his family and friends were to be inoculated, Jefferson himself would have to do it!

He reviewed all he knew about the process, remembering his own inoculation. He thought back over the letters he had received on the subject from scientists in England and France. And he got out all the medical books in his library and studied them.

Then one by one he inoculated each of his daughters, lightly scratching their small arms, rubbing in the fearful smallpox germs. One after another he inoculated the others, too. Then he waited for the reactions, hoping they would be no worse than headaches for a few days and sore arms.

It was all right! No one was really ill at all. Everyone had been saved from smallpox.

Later, when he was President, Jefferson was to throw all the prestige and authority of his office behind a movement to create general acceptance for an improved method of smallpox vaccination by means of cowpox. He did it with a conviction and enthusiasm that had been confirmed that fall of 1782, when he made his own pioneering effort in medical science.

3.

"A mind always employed is always happy." Gradually now, with all sorts of mental employment, Jefferson began to be happy again.

He was a delegate from Virginia to the first Congress of the newly independent states, and among other bills, he was able at last to introduce his long-pondered bill to reform the coinage system. He proposed that weights and measures also be standardized to the decimal system, but this measure was defeated. Only his plan for standardizing the coinage was accepted.

Then, after just a few months, Congress asked him to go to France as a minister plenipotentiary to assist John Adams and Benjamin Franklin in creating treaties with various European countries.

And so he went to France, where he was to remain five years, first in the original post, later succeeding Benjamin Franklin as ambassador to that country.

He went, of course, on affairs of state for the United States, as a politician and a diplomat. But being Thomas Jefferson, he could not help going as a scientist and naturalist, and a farmer and an architect as well.

In all these roles he had one chief goal—to observe and take notes and bring back as much information as possible about everything in the Old World that would be of value in the New.

But he had another aim, also. He not only wanted to learn. As an American, there were a few things he wanted to teach Europeans, too.

All sorts of strange ideas about America were widespread in Europe in those days. Jefferson had done his best to correct them with facts and figures in his *Notes on Virginia,* which was just about to be published in France. But surely, going in person, he could do even more as he talked to people face to face.

There was one French scientist in particular whom Jefferson wanted to meet, a certain Comte de Buffon, pride of the French Academy and one of the most respected authorities on natural history in the world. But celebrated as he was, Buffon held one theory that irked all Americans almost past enduring.

He believed, and published it for the world to read, that all animals in the New World were smaller in size than the animals in the Old World, that there were fewer species there, and that animal and human life in general tended to grow weak and feeble there.

Why were things in such a sorry state in America? Well, Buffon blamed the climate, of which he knew very little also. He said America's huge mountains and great forests held an undue amount of moisture in the air, that vast areas of the continent were covered with noxious vapors, and, as a result, all animal life suffered. He believed, along with many other Europeans, that America really was a new continent, just recently heaved up from the bottom of the ocean, and that nature had not had time to finish the job there.

Even before he left America, Jefferson had been thinking of ways to fight these fantasies. In Philadelphia he saw a huge panther skin at the door of a hatter's shop, and bought it at once and put it with his luggage. Here was proof, even more tangible than the facts and figures in his book, that animals were anything but small in America.

And, of course, he was going to talk a good deal about that wonder of America, the mammoth. White men had only seen its bones, but Indians claimed the huge creature still roamed at large in the wild northern parts of the country.

Oh, Jefferson had many things to tell French scientists, as well as many problems of state to help solve for his country.

At last, after he had been in France several months, he met M. Buffon. The scientist was amiable enough, but Jefferson found it very difficult to shake any of his convictions. "Read my book," the Frenchman said blandly, "and you will be satisfied that I am right."

Jefferson, his voice as mild as ever but his stubborn jaw set, persevered. He showed M. Buffon the panther's skin, and that made some impression. Then he discovered that M. Buffon was convinced no American deer had horns more than a foot long.

At once Jefferson was writing to a friend in America with an urgent request. Please, would he obtain the largest pair of buck's horns possible and ship them to him in France? Would he also send the skeleton and skin of an elk?

Some months later he received the horns, "a most precious present," but in the meantime he had been led into boasting to Buffon that the European reindeer could walk under the belly of an American moose. It was necessary to send a call back to America for the antlers, bones, and skin of a moose.

It turned out that the order was not such an easy one to fill. In the snows of a New England winter his friend went moose hunting, and after many misadventures, finally bagged one. Then there were endless problems in cleaning and arranging for the preservation of the skin. There were problems in transporting it to the coast, problems in getting it on board a ship for France.

At last the dismantled moose arrived in Paris. Jefferson winced as he paid $150 in shipping charges, but soon he felt it had been money well spent. When M. Buffon saw the moose, he was visibly shaken.

"I should have consulted you, Mr. Jefferson, before I wrote my *Natural History*," he said, and he promised to make various changes in the revised edition.

Buffon, of course, was not the only scientist with whom Jefferson talked or corresponded. His scientific missionary work ran through all his busy days that were filled with ambassadorial duties and other political responsibilities.

Back home in the United States, an earnest group of men was laboring to write a constitution for the new nation. Jefferson could not help wishing desperately that he were there with them, helping to create this uniquely important document. Next best to being there was to write constantly to his friends in the constitutional convention, filling his letters with all sorts of suggestions about ways in which to ensure a truly democratic constitution. He scoured the Paris bookstores for books on government and shipped them back to his friends.

Still, he always found time for letters correcting misstatements about America which he found in foreign encyclopedias and books. He always found time to meet with foreign scientists or write to them on the subject of the American climate or American wildlife. Whatever immediate effect all his efforts had, he undoubtedly played a part in bringing European scientists a truer picture of America than they had had before.

And meantime, of course, he was always taking notes —notes on all sorts of European advances in the fields of science or invention or agriculture, notes on everything he thought would be of value back home.

One of the most exciting advances of the day was man's first conquest of the air, by means of balloons. In

1783, just before Jefferson went to Paris, the Montgolfier brothers had given the first public demonstration of the lifting and flying properties of a balloon.

By the time Jefferson was living in France, ballooning was the rage, and he wrote many detailed reports on the balloon demonstrations he witnessed. Of course, being Jefferson, he also speculated on the future usefulness of ballooning to mankind—the way in which air travel could transport commodities over difficult or enemy territory, the way in which ballooning could be used to throw new light on atmospheric phenomena. He even suggested that the Pole might be discovered by air flight, a project that ice had always made impossible by land.

He made a visit to England and took notes on factories and steam mills there. "A peck and half of coal," he noted, would do "exactly as much as a horse" could in a day. He speculated that the steam-engine principle applied to boats would "lay open all the streams to navigation," and he felt a surge of satisfaction that America had so much coal.

Back in Paris he watched a demonstration on the Seine of a boat crossing the river, propelled by a screw turning in the air. He wrote home about this invention and suggested that it might work even better if the screw were in the water.

All the latest scientific publications intrigued him. He bought them and sent many of them back home to friends at William and Mary, at Yale, and at Harvard. And he wrote to other friends about the latest discoveries in astronomy.

In the midst of all this, he fell and broke his wrist. It was a painful fracture, and it was not set properly. Worst of all, it was his right wrist. Slowly, painfully, his jaw firm, he learned to write with his left hand.

Then in 1787 he took a three-month tour of southern France and northern Italy. Never mind the difficulty in writing now! A positive blizzard of notes flew from his pen as he jotted down facts and figures about bridges, gardens, pumps, plants, forges, and everything else he saw that seemed as though it might be useful in America.

During this trip Thomas Jefferson, Architect, appeared again, too. From the beginning of his stay in Europe he had delighted in seeing for himself the architectural beauties of the past which had been known to him only through books before. Now, in Nîmes, the site of many Roman ruins, he fell in love with a beautiful classic building known as the Maison Quarrée. He spent hours gazing at it and sketching it.

Maison Quarrée, Nîmes

Capitol building, Richmond

Ultimately those sketches of the Maison Quarrée became the basis of his second big architectural project, a project he carried out while still in Europe. Friends in Virginia wrote him and asked him to find an architect to design a new state capitol for Richmond. He found an architect, all right, but what that other architect did is hard to know. It was Jefferson's design, based on the Maison Quarrée, which was sent back to Virginia and which was used to create Richmond's beautiful new capitol building.

But all the while, wherever he went, it was every aspect of farming that interested him most. He thought of America as a country which would always depend more on her farms than on any kind of industry, and he was sure that farming was the happiest way of life there was, both for a man and for a country.

The greatest service which can be rendered any country, he wrote, *is to add an useful plant to its culture; especially, a bread grain; next in value to bread is oil.*

So he took notes on dozens and dozens of European plants that he thought might be adapted for American culture, but he felt his greatest enthusiasm for the olive tree and a certain kind of rice that grew in Italy.

He had already experimented with the olive tree back in Monticello, thanks to his friend Mazzei. But there were new varieties to observe in southern France. He arranged for some of these to be sent to America. Perhaps they would do better than the ones already there.

As for the rice, he had read of a species growing in northern Italy which was supposed to be far superior to the American Carolinian variety. He wondered if that superiority might be due to an improved cleaning machine, but naturally he had to see for himself.

Jefferson began asking questions about rice as soon as he arrived in northern Italy. Finally, in the area of Vercelli, he found the grain he was looking for.

He studied the cleaning machine. It was identical with the ones used in America. Plainly it was the rice itself which was better. Plainly this rice must be tried in America.

But then came a horrid discovery! There was a law against exporting any of this rice from the Piedmont region of Italy. It was, in fact, a crime punishable by death.

Thomas Jefferson reflected awhile. He had a great respect for the law but an even greater respect for reason. It had never seemed reasonable to him for a few men to keep for their own exclusive pleasure or profit something that would benefit all men, whether it was land or freedom or education—or rice.

He decided to break the law.

Quietly he looked about until he found an obliging muleteer who agreed to carry two bags of the rice over the Apennine Mountains to Genoa, where Jefferson would soon be going himself.

Then, just in case, Jefferson filled his coat pockets with some more of the rice and pleasantly took his leave.

It was a good thing he took that last precaution. In Genoa he waited vainly for the muleteer to arrive. So it was the rice he had taken in his pockets that was sent back to America, where, incidentally, it grew very well indeed.

As for Thomas Jefferson, Smuggler, when he looked back on the whole business he felt nothing but satisfaction. In fact, he sometimes felt his importation of the Italian dry rice to America ranked with his authorship of the Declaration of Independence as a contribution to his country.

1787. 1788. The years in Europe were going by, and for Thomas Jefferson, the scientist, the farmer, the architect, the art lover, and the book lover, they were full of all sorts of discoveries. But still he was growing homesick for his hilltop in Virginia. Only two daughters were left to him—Martha, called Patsy, and Maria, known as Polly—and both of them were with him. Still, he yearned for home.

The arts and sciences of Europe intrigued him, but the tyranny of almost every government in Europe was appalling to him. Nowhere but in America, Jefferson found, did men have any voice at all in how they would be governed.

1788—and he beguiled the spring with another trip, this time through the Low Countries and western Germany. Again there was a storm of note-taking, sketching, and letter-writing. In Holland he saw a new sort of plow, which he studied and sketched. He made notes of a machine for drawing empty boats over a dam. He admired and sketched various bridges.

Various household conveniences in Holland impressed him. There were windows designed to open so as to admit air and not rain. There were tables which would let down "with single or double leaves so as to take the room of their thickness only with a single leaf when open." These he sketched, too. And in Germany he was impressed by an invention which would one day become a household institution in his own country, central heating.

But the longing to be home kept growing.

1789. In Paris, Jefferson heard that the new Constitution of the United States was going into effect in March. In April, George Washington was being inaugurated as the nation's first President. The revolution which had begun to rack America in the 1770's was over, and a new government was born.

From Paris, Jefferson wrote to his old friend, the new President, and begged for a leave of absence from his post to visit home for a while.

The answer was slow in coming. Before it arrived, France's own revolution had begun its terrible course with the storming of the Bastille. Thomas Jefferson, Democrat, who had been observing the wretchedness of the poor French people for years now, might recoil at the horror, but he could only sympathize with the desperate need of these people for a better life.

The Marquis de Lafayette and other French friends came to him asking his help in framing a new Constitution for France which might help avert further disaster. But Jefferson was a foreigner, in a delicate diplomatic post. Once again he could only sympathize and offer his ardent wishes for their success.

And then, at last, word came from President Washington granting him a six-month leave of absence from his duties in France.

In October, he and his daughters set sail for America, along with eighty-six packing boxes, fifteen of them filled with books. Others held art objects, paintings, sculpture, models, and, of course, scientific instruments and curiosities of all kinds. He was taking back also the seedling of a cork tree, various other seeds, plants, and cuttings—and to round out the luggage, there were a couple of shepherd dogs as well.

Discovering Keys to Greatness

1. Immediately preceding the story and again on page 400 is Jefferson's quotation "A mind always employed is always happy." In what ways was Jefferson a distinguished example of this?

2. Miss Johnston refers to Thomas' father as "That mighty man, the polestar of his youth . . ." What is a polestar? In what ways had Peter Jefferson been a polestar to his young son?

3. Why were books especially important to a boy growing up in Jefferson's time? In what way did Thomas' father contribute to his love of them?

4. Thomas took his clothes, his fiddle, and some of his books when he left for college. These things he considered necessary. What does the inclusion of his fiddle in this list tell you about the personality of Jefferson?

5. What inspired Jefferson to devise a new money system for the newly independent states?

6. What was Jefferson's purpose in fighting for bills to abolish the systems of *entail* and *primogeniture*?

7. What particular quality or qualities in Jefferson's character led to his involvement in so many endeavors?

8. Contrast the picture of George III presented in this story with that in the play "Franklin and the King" (*Vistas*).

9. How did Jefferson's lifelong habit of note-taking benefit his country and mankind in general? List some of the notebooks he kept and tell how he later used them.

10. What were Jefferson's requirements for a house? If you had lived in Jefferson's time, would you have liked to live at Monticello? What would you have liked most about it? Least?

11. A well-known proverb states: *Necessity is the mother of invention.* How would you explain this in your own words? Name several of Jefferson's own inventions that he created to fill a specific need.

Going Beyond the Book

1. In "Up Periscopes!" you remember that the late President Kennedy paid tribute to the rare and exceptional talent of Thomas Jefferson. Another man, Leonardo da Vinci, of another country and another age, calls forth the same acknowledgment of "universal genius." If you would like to read of his life and contributions to the world and compare them with Jefferson's, the Landmark book, *Leonardo da Vinci,* by Emily Hahn, will provide you with the opportunity. Many very interesting parallels can be drawn from their lives.

2. Round-table discussions bring out many good ideas that would otherwise go unspoken. An interesting topic for discussion among those of you who have read of Jefferson's many talents would be: Is the present as likely to produce men of "many talents" such as Jefferson and da Vinci, as the past?

3. Have you ever found yourself wishing someone would invent something because you needed it? Did you do

anything about a solution to your problem? Describe the thing you improvised to do the work you needed done. If you haven't yet "invented" anything, try to think of something you have needed that hasn't yet been invented. Plan a solution and draw a design for the tool that would fill your need. You may prefer to improve something you have that has one thing about it that has always bothered you when you used it. The following examples may remind you of one:

    something to help in a job you do around home

    something to improve a game or your bicycle

    something you'd like on your desk at school

       or in it

Remember to ask the questions Jefferson asked when he approached a problem for which he sought a solution: "Why not? What is its purpose?" When preparing to make an improvement in something, remember the questions he asked before tackling problems in his own home and furnishings: "How, if it has never been done before, can it be made to work? How can it be made pleasing to the eye?"

4. Name some inventions since Jefferson's time in which you think he would have been particularly interested. Which of his inventions do we enjoy the use of today?

5. If you could have been a student in Williamsburg at the time of Jefferson, what would you have liked to talk about with him? Would you have enjoyed stopping in to hear debates when the House of Burgesses was in session? What opportunities to watch lawmakers or statesmen in action are available today?

414

What might be some of the topics under discussion among lawmakers today?

Appreciating Genius

Column I below lists important roles Jefferson played in his lifetime of service to his country. Column II lists the contributions that resulted from those various roles. Copy the titles from Column I. After them write the letters that stand for the contributions (one or more) that correspond.

Column I	Column II
1. Father of present United States coinage system	a. Worked for passage of bills abolishing systems of entail and primogeniture.
2. Member of Virginia's House of Delegates	b. Planned and designed his home, Monticello, as well as many conveniences and devices.
3. Author of the Declaration of Independence	c. Introduced and saw passed bills granting religious freedom to everyone and free public education.
4. Representative to France from the United States	d. Gave the United States a money standard that was based on the dollar unit.

5. Member of Virginia's House of Burgesses

6. Architect and inventor

e. Worked to bring about treaties with various European countries.

f. Expressed in writing the American colonies' desire for freedom from British rule.

g. Introduced and saw passed a bill requiring clearance of the Rivanna River.

Daily Life

by WALT WHITMAN

The commonplace I sing:
How cheap is health! How cheap nobility!
The open air I sing; freedom, toleration:
The common day and night, the common earth and waters,
Your farm, your work, life, occupation—
The democratic wisdom underneath, like solid ground for all.

BROWN, MARION MARSH, and RUTH CRONE. *The Silent Storm.*

New York: Abingdon Press, 1963.

Orphaned and quite blind herself as a child, Annie Sullivan knew the terrors of darkness and the unknown. This understanding was the source of the courage required to take on her task as teacher of Helen Keller.

DOWNER, MARION. *Discovering Design.*

New York: Lothrop, Lee and Shepard Co., 1947.

An eye-opening adventure into the world of nature. Photographs and brief explanations reveal the elements of design as they are part of our everyday lives—in nature and in man-made objects. An Honor Book, Children's Spring Book Festival, 1947.

JOHNSTON, JOHANNA. *The Story of Hannibal.*

New York: Doubleday and Company, Inc., 1960.

An account of the long fight of Hannibal, Carthaginian general, against Rome. Hannibal emerges as the skillful general who disliked destruction and whose strategy for overcoming the powers of Rome was built upon preserving the city.

JUDSON, CLARA INGRAM. *Mr. Justice Holmes.*

Chicago: Follett Publishing Company, 1956.

Oliver Wendell Holmes (1841-1935) was one of the great Americans whose life inspires pride and patriotism. Here, his life story is told from his boyhood through his many years as United States Supreme Court Justice.

LATHAM, JEAN LEE. *Carry On, Mr. Bowditch.*

Boston: Houghton Mifflin Company, 1955.

The story of Nathaniel Bowditch, who, with little formal education, became an expert navigator. His book, *The American Practical Navigator,* is a standard text at the U.S. Naval Academy.

STROUSSE, FLORA. *John Fitzgerald Kennedy, Man of Courage.*

New York: P. J. Kenedy and Sons, 1964.

An inspiring biography of an inspiring man.

WIBBERLEY, LEONARD. *Young Man from the Piedmont: The Youth of Thomas Jefferson.*

New York: Farrar, Straus and Company, 1963.

The boyhood of Thomas Jefferson began in the British colony of Virginia in 1743. This book carries the reader through his spirited youth up to the signing of the Declaration of Independence in 1776.

———. *A Dawn in the Trees: Thomas Jefferson, the Years 1776-1789.*

New York: Farrar, Straus and Company, 1964.

This second volume covers Jefferson's work up to the end of his mission as ambassador to France.

———. *The Gales of Spring.*

New York: Farrar, Straus and Company, 1965.

Jefferson's biography is continued in this third book of the series.

Erik Christian Haugaard was born and grew up in a country with a typical seacoast atmosphere, Denmark. His feeling for the sea and his enthusiasm for Nordic mythology seem to be natural outgrowths of his background. To write the story of Hakon, he poured over volumes of Icelandic sagas and talked to people of the Norwegian fiords. Their descriptions of Viking heroes gave him inspiration as well as information. The result is a powerful capturing of the mood of the land and of the people he knows so well.

As a young man, Erik Haugaard traveled extensively in the United States, Canada, England, Italy, and Spain. During these years he was a farm laborer, carpenter, shepherd, air gunner in the Royal Canadian Air Force, and, he writes, "before, after, and in between: vagabond and poet."

At present he, his wife, and their two children live in Denmark. In addition to *Hakon of Rogen's Saga*, he has written a book of poems and a play, *The Heroes*, which was first presented in the United States.

hakon of rogen's saga
by erik christian haugaard

Long before modern nations came into being, the Vikings were found all over Europe. They were an adventurous and seafaring people. *Hakon of Rogen's Saga* is the story of a boy who lived at the end of the Viking period.

At the time this story begins, the island of Rogen, just off the coast of Norway, has been ruled for many years by the Viking chief Olaf and by his family before him. Olaf's wife is dead, but he has a twelve-year-old son, Hakon, who expects one day to take his father's place as ruler of the island's people. But as you are introduced to Hakon in the part of the story presented here, his future is uncertain.

As a result of Olaf's theft of a rival king's daughter for his second wife, a battle has taken place between the men of Rogen and those of another small Viking kingdom. The men of Rogen were badly outnumbered, and when Olaf's brother, Sigurd, refused to help him, the battle was lost. Olaf was killed, and the enemy forces recaptured his new wife and departed, leaving Rogen without a ruler.

Hakon feels he is still too young to rule, but fears for his birthright if Sigurd takes hold of the leaderless island. As Hakon watches the enemy sail away, he wonders: What tempest is waiting to rip my sail, to break my slender mast?

HAKON OF ROGEN'S SAGA

ERIK CHRISTIAN HAUGAARD

Illustrated by Leo and Diane Dillon

HOUGHTON MIFFLIN COMPANY   BOSTON

The Riverside Press Cambridge

PREFACE

"Your dog, your horse, your friends, and you, yourself:
all shall die. Eternally live only your deeds and man's
judgment over them." This was the credo of the Vikings
—the lonely heroes ever watched by the future, ever
composing their own sagas. From manhood unto death,
they were players upon a public stage that stretched from
the northern tip of Norway west to Greenland, east to
Nizhni-Novgorod, and south to Constantinople, which
they called Mikkelgard.

They were not a nation; Norway had more kings than
all of the countries of Europe have today. They were
a group of poets who, according to their own taste and
ability, were composing epic poems out of their lives.

Their gods fitted them: Odin and Thor, father and son,
Gods of Battle and Brutality. Freya, the Goddess of
Love; and Frig, who guarded the apples from which the
gods ate to keep their youth eternally. The Vikings had
many gods, for their poems were long and well written.

Loki, the God of Evil: the God of the Broken Promise, whose symbol was the fire; and Balder, the God of Goodness, who, swordless, was to inherit the world when all the other gods had died.

They were not romantic heroes, for the romantic hero is but a dream—a paper doll cut with a pair of embroidery scissors. They were intensely alive; their minds and bodies were linked together, as Achilles' and Hector's were.

In *Hakon of Rogen's Saga*, I have attempted to tell the story of a boy who lived at the end of the Viking period. It was not written for "youth," in the sense that I have blunted my pen before I started. I abhor those writers who have not the skill to keep the attention of adults, and therefore think themselves equipped to write for children. I have done my best, and I leave you to be my critic.

—ERIK CHRISTIAN HAUGAARD

9

The song of the sea is always pleasant to the ear; only the shipwrecked or the starving fisherman will curse it as the storm-whipped ocean laughs at his misery. From my childhood on, it has ever been my friend. I have listened to its gay song in summer, and my heart has followed its beat when the winds have whipped it to anger in the fall storms. The song of the sea is nature's greatest song. It is, I believe, the voices of the gods, for in the laughter of the sea there are hidden tears, and in its anger, laughter. The bird's song in spring has no promise of winter in its melody, and the cry of the sea gull in winter, no promise of spring. Only the voice of the sea says, "I am eternal. I am eternal." And that blessing makes it laugh when the hot sun fondles it, and that curse makes it sigh when the storm-torn, white moon of winter kisses it.

At dawn—while we were still sleeping—the day after the enemy had left, my uncle and his men came. They were all armed, and my uncle was on horseback. Sigurd Sigurdson flung open the door with such force that it banged against the wall, awakening all of us.

With sleep-matted eyes we stared at him. He was wearing his finest clothes, and his right hand rested on his sword hilt. "Awake and dress yourselves," he cried, assuming what he must have thought to be a masterful pose.

"You are late, Sigurd," one of my father's old comrades spoke from his bench. "We are tired from work. We have earned a bit of sleep. Go sing your song somewhere else."

My uncle had little courage but much pride. He drew his sword and walked over to Bjorn, who was lying motionless on his bench, as if he intended to return to sleep. "Get up, Bjorn."

Bjorn smiled and said, "I think I hear a fly buzzing, a carrion fly."

"I warned you!" screamed my uncle, his face contorted with anger. Then swiftly, before anyone could stop him, he thrust his sword through Bjorn.

"Brave man," Bjorn muttered; then sighing, he spoke his last words, "Now I shall sleep." Blood flowed from his mouth, and his body twisted and fell with a dull thud from his bench to the floor.

Rogen, that had first been ruled by my father's justice and later by my stepmother's love, now would know how it felt to be ruled by the sword. Like many weak people's, my uncle's cruelty was dictated by his fears.

Ruled by fear himself, he could not conceive that man could be governed by love and respect. Several of the men in the hall gladly would have killed him, but behind him stood his men with swords drawn.

We were a sad-looking group that stood outside the hall in the yellow light of the early autumn morning. My uncle climbed back upon his horse, feeling, no doubt, that he could impress us more speaking from that position.

"My brother harvested the crop that grows from the seeds of folly. The gods have meant people to be ruled and have given them kings and earls and chieftains to obey. My brother thought himself mightier than Magnus Thorsen and paid the price of disobedience, as Bjorn has just paid it."

Some men mumbled something about not being slaves, but none dared to speak aloud.

"I am now the ruler of Rogen, and those who serve me well shall be fittingly rewarded. And so"—here my uncle laughed—"shall those who serve me ill."

To our surprise, two of Sigurd's men now entered the hall and came back with the body of Bjorn.

"For those who disobey me there will be shame, and their death shall be like the death of an animal." Turning to his men, he ordered, "Go, throw his body into the sea, and let the fishes eat it."

I thought the murder of Bjorn a shameful deed, but his last resting place not an unfit one for a hero.

Each of us had to swear allegiance to Sigurd. When my turn came, my uncle said, "I need not the word of a child. I shall be in your father's stead, and I shall teach you humility. Go among the women, and give me that sword."

I would have rushed at him, but Harold the Bow-bender took my sword from me, and whispered in my ear, "The wind cannot break a blade of grass, but it can fell an oak."

I believe that my uncle was disappointed when I did not attack him; for if I had, he could have killed me in self-defense, and no one could ever have disputed his right to my father's property.

My uncle decided to make his home in my father's house. His own he gave to Eirik the Fox, one of his companions—a lying, deceitful man who knew well that his power depended upon my uncle's good will. The men whom my uncle suspected of not being loyal to him were divided between the two houses. Two of my father's old friends disappeared shortly afterwards; my uncle claimed that they had been drowned while fishing, but others thought that they had been mur-dered. With their death the last hope of an open revolt was gone. Backs were bent under the whip of the des-pot, the weak taking pleasure in it, the strong growing sullen and dull.

Rark and little Helga* reappeared. They had been hiding in a cave in the Mountain of the Sun. But Rark, whom my father even before he made him a freeman had treated almost as if he were one, now learned the wages of slavery. All heavy work fell to him, and curses and kicks were his only rewards. The man who

430

*Helga is the daughter of the slave woman, Gunhild, who had cared for Hakon after his mother died. Gunhild had been taken away from Rogen by Ulv Erikson, an enemy warrior sometimes known as Ulv Hunger.

lives in the present and has no plans for the future will sink in his own misery, but there are those who will ever invent hope when only despair is present. I knew that Rark was planning his escape, although he did not speak of it, fearing—no doubt—that although my ears were old enough for his secrets, my tongue might not be.

Also I learned to work, woman's work—lighting and tending the fires, scrubbing pots, turning the spit the meat was roasted on. My bow and arrows were taken from me as my sword had been; even the little knife my father had given me the summer I was six, I was not allowed to keep. My uncle wanted me to appear like a slave to the other men. The clothes I wore were the meanest rags; my sleeping place, among the children. With many of the men he succeeded. Some of them took a pleasure in ordering me—their former chieftain's son—to do the work of a slave. The drink of a slave is bitter water; but from that, too, there is a lesson to be learned. Those who abuse slaves have themselves slaves' souls. They are so foolish that they cannot see the difference between the respect given by a freeman to another freeman and the fawning flattery of a slave. They fill their purses with pebbles and think themselves rich. Foolborn, they strut around like geese in the farmyard, who think their fate will be better than that of the hens.

Little Helga suffered even more than I did from my father's defeat. Used to kindness from my father and love from her mother, Gunhild, she was doubly robbed.

Helga was given to Eirik the Fox to be his slave. Although my uncle was mean, his ambitions were too great for him to spend much of his time tyrannizing a child; but Eirik the Fox was not above such pettiness.

How did Helga bear his mistreatment? She never cried, even when he beat her, but her face grew older, and it was strange to see this little child with the face of an old woman.

All this I was told by the other children, for I saw Helga only once during that first winter after my father's death. My uncle suspected me of plotting against him and did not allow me to walk far from the hall. The one time I did meet Helga was on a wet, dismal fall day. We were both gathering brushwood on the side of Thor's Mountain.

When I saw how thin she had grown, tears came into my eyes; and when she saw my rags, she wept. "Oh, Hakon, Father Olaf has left us!"

I touched her dirty, matted hair (Eirik had taken her comb from her, and he did not even allow her to wash). "Little Helga . . . little sister, I shall take care of you."

She shook her head and looked down at the ground; and at that moment the idea that had been so vague in my mind became a certainty.

"We shall run away!" I exclaimed, and pointed out toward the sea. "We shall sail away. We will steal a boat next summer—you, Rark, and me."

When I mentioned Rark's name, a little smile flew over her face; and in that moment it became a child's face again. "They will be expecting me soon, and if I haven't gathered enough wood, Eirik will beat me."

I took all my wood and gave it to her. The heavy bundle on her back made her look like a dwarf, like one of the ones that live in the mountains.

"I will die if you leave without me," she whispered earnestly.

"I shall never leave alone. I swear it!"

She took a few steps. Then she turned around to stare at me. Without another word, a moment later she was running down the mountainside.

Now I had no wood for myself, and probably would be scolded and made to appear the fool by Sigurd's wife, who was now mistress of my father's hall. But all concern about my own situation had vanished from my mind. I decided that instead of gathering wood, I would climb to the top of the mountain to visit my father's grave.

The wind blew a fierce dance on the plateau. I ran into the storehouse, but it was roofless now and gave little protection. My father's grave had been covered with big boulders. I kneeled by its side, and my blue lips murmured, "I shall avenge you, Father." It was not Magnus Thorsen that I was thinking about when I spoke of vengeance, but my Uncle Sigurd.

A gull screamed near my head. It startled me, and I thought that it might be one of Odin's ravens until I saw its white wings. I glanced up into the cloud-filled sky and spoke loudly: "By Odin, by Thor, I shall avenge myself!"

The winds blew my words out over the sea, and no one heard them; but then, most words spoken to the gods are merely conversations we hold with ourselves.

The day after my visit to my father's grave I was feverish, and by night I was unconscious. I shivered with cold, though my body was burning like fire under the bearskin that covered me. Had it not been for Rark, I would have died before the Midwinter Feast. He fed me when my hand was too helpless to hold a bowl, and sat by my side during the long nights when the fever brought monsters to my dreams.

10

Winter came late that year. It arrived at the time of the Midwinter Feast, and like a hungry guest it did not like to depart. We learned that year that the bark of trees could be eaten, and there was no animal—no matter how small—that was not hunted. We grew gaunt, and our bellies swelled, and the least bit of work made us tired. Seven people died that winter, and we were hardly able to dig their graves. How I survived, who had been sick all fall, must have been by the grace of the gods.

Rark had fed me seaweed, which the others had refused to eat. But I think there must have been magic in it, for in spring when so many were sick, Rark and I were not. Maybe this is the food of the God of Fishes. Some say that there is a god who has a castle on the bottom of the sea—so far down that the light of the sun doesn't reach it.

Finally spring came, and the sound of a thousand streams was heard again on Rogen. Nature rose from its winter bed, and the song of tomorrow began. Each little blade popping up from the ground declared that it soon would be a flower. Even the gulls sang of love, though their voices did not grow any sweeter from it. Spring green, tender green, stood on the sides of Thor's Mountain, and all the bushes and shrubtrees were sapswelled, bending complacently to the southern winds and saying, "We knew you would come. We knew you would come."

Most of the human beings on Rogen were too weak to welcome spring. They had gone past hope and despair, and the newborn sun found their eyes a poor place for reflecting its strength. Thanks to Rark, I felt much better than the others, and the coming warmth made me more determined than ever to escape. If we were not able to flee that summer, we would have to spend another winter on Rogen. And would I survive that long? My Uncle Sigurd's face was not a pleasant place to read my future. So many foul deeds had my uncle committed that my murder would not weigh heavily on his conscience.

At present I felt safe, for the battle of survival was not won and a hungry man thinks more about food than revenge. Of animals, only two horses—my father's mare and a stallion—had survived our hunger.

As soon as the ice on the fjords in Norway had broken and floated out to sea, my uncle set sail for a village called Odin's Cove. Rark and I were ordered to sail with him. It took us five days to reach Odin's Cove —although it was common to do the trip in two—because we were only fourteen men and we could not row the big boat against the waves.

The chieftain of the village, a man named Lief the Lonesome, gave us a friendly welcome. Lief was the only surviving son of Bjorn the Tall, who had been famous for his ability with a sword and for his quick temper. Lief was a peaceful man, having learned from the example of his father that the sword is a poor judge of a grievance.

My uncle bought three pigs, two calves, and a young bull, besides ten yearling sheep and four cows. He paid for the livestock with two gold rings and some silver armbands. I noticed that one of the rings was one he used to wear on his finger, but the others I had never seen before. I realized that they must have constituted part of his private treasure, and recalled with bitterness how the invaders had stripped my father's hall.

We did not stay more than a few days in Odin's Cove. On the second day we feasted on one of the pigs that my uncle had bought. This was the first time in many months that any of us had had as much to eat as he wanted. Several of the men were too greedy, and they paid for their greed with a painful night.

For Rark the voyage was an ordeal. My uncle tied him to the mast while we were in Odin's Cove. The men grumbled about it, for most of them liked Rark, and several of them knew that my father had given him his freedom.

This was my first trip, and though the world outside was not that much different from the one I knew, there was enough for me to wonder at. The mountains rose much higher than on Rogen, and for the first time I saw full-grown trees. I was treated most kindly by Lief the Lonesome, and while the rest of the men ate near the boat, he invited me as well as my uncle to sit at his table. This did not please Sigurd Sigurdson, and when Lief praised my father, my uncle's eyes dwelled upon me with such hatred that I could not look at him. The thought of running away occurred to me. But then I thought of Rark bound to the mast—it would not be an easy task to free him. At night all the men slept on the boats, and we would be heard. By daylight any attempt would undoubtedly be seen. There was always someone down by the boats, if not one of Sigurd's men, then one of his host's. Ships are to men as infants are to women; they cannot pass one by without examining it—one eye filled with tenderness, the other looking sharply, ready to criticize.

Even if I could free Rark, where would we go? To us this was an unknown land. Certainly the people of Odin's Cove would not help us, for they did not know what kind of man my Uncle Sigurd was.

Lief the Lonesome asked my uncle if I was to be chieftain of Rogen when I came of an age to shoulder such a task. Lief had four daughters, and a marriage into our family would not have displeased him.

Suddenly, in the midst of this conversation, I remembered little Helga—how I had considered escaping without giving her a thought—and my cheeks grew red with shame.

My uncle had two sons, whom I have not as yet mentioned because they were very young. I suspected that he was thinking of them when he replied to Lief's question. "Rogen is Hakon's birthright. He is the oldest—and only son—of my older brother. If it is the gods' will that he shall live to be a man, then Rogen will be his."

Lief smiled at me and said, "Oh, Hakon is a strong lad."

Now my uncle turned to me. While the ghost of a smile—which did not have laughter as a mother—played around his lips, he answered, "Against the will of the gods, none of us can protect ourselves."

The loading of the animals was difficult; especially the bull and the ram gave us trouble. With their legs tied and their eyes turned in protest against the heavens, they mooed and mayed at us from midship during most of the journey. On the return voyage we had lucky winds and were home in two days.

One of the sheep had broken its leg during the trip. It was slaughtered and its meat roasted. It was not much meat for so many people, and even with the smoked ham that my uncle had received as a gift from Lief the Lonesome, few left the table with filled stomachs. But to the people of Rogen it was a feast. I noticed with disgust that many looked at my uncle with gratitude and admiration, as though the gift of the food had showed him to be their natural leader. Those who had been abroad jested and told tall tales of the feasts we had had in Odin's Cove.

We had milk again for the children, and to make cheese. Three of the cows were excellent milkers, but the fourth had something the matter with its udder; its milk dried up. My uncle had it slaughtered and the meat divided among the households.

My uncle had also managed to buy onions from Lief the Lonesome. It was our luck that the people of Odin's Cove had had a good harvest the year before, for few people can boast of being able to sell onions in the spring. All men who stay at sea for more than a few days must eat a large raw onion daily, or their stomachs will bloat and their gums bleed. Finally, their teeth will fall out, leaving them as ugly as Loki's wife. Many on Rogen had had these complaints that winter and spring; even the women had felt the sailors' sickness. The only two who totally escaped were Rark and myself.

As spring glided into summer and food was no longer the subject of everyone's conversation, my uncle's plans for me became more and more apparent. In the horror of that winter the seed of murder had lain dormant in my uncle's mind. He spoke to everyone of my foolishness and pretended to pity me for not having inherited my father's intelligence. He spoke well of my father and ill of me, and soon some forgot how Sigurd had betrayed his brother. A bird in the hand is worth two in the bush—my uncle had the power and I the birthright. Legal rights are very much like the birds in the bush.

There were a few men on Rogen whom I trusted, but to ask them to help me was the same as to ask them to die. One of them, Erik Longbeard, suggested that I offer to share the island with my uncle.

I retorted angrily, "The only part of my birthright that Sigurd Sigurdson is willing to give me is a plot of land beside my father's grave on Thor's Mountain!"

II

I was surprised and suspicious when my uncle, who had taken all my weapons from me, gave me back my bow and quiver of arrows and suggested that I should go hunting. Still, the pleasure of a day away from the hall was too attractive to be spurned, and I set out for the Mountain of the Sun, hoping that I might see little Helga along the way. I did not go directly to the other hall (the one which used to be my uncle's home), because I had no wish to meet Eirik the Fox—between us no love was lost. But in my search for Helga I passed very near the outer buildings which surrounded the hall. Helga was nowhere to be seen, but a man who was busy mending a fence greeted me by my name, Hakon Olafson, and I took this to be a good omen. It was a sign of respect, for Sigurd and his men never called me anything but Hakon the Orphan.

To be alone in nature, to be an animal among other animals, to feel the sun baking on your back and smell the earth and the grass. I forgot the past and had no thought for the future. I was the first man on earth, ageless as the gods.

I wanted to find the cave that Rark and Helga had hidden in when they had been hunted by Ulv Erikson.* Rark had described it to me. It was located halfway up the southwestern slope of the Mountain of the Sun. Its entrance was narrow, almost blocked by a large boulder. Near the boulder grew two small birch trees.

There are many boulders and many birch trees on the Mountain of the Sun, and it was late when I finally found the cave. The dark opening was so narrow that I had to squeeze myself through, but once inside, the cave was huge—as big as my father's hall, if not bigger.

The light was very dim, but near the entrance, under some branches, I found a bow and some arrows and a sword. Rark had told me that he had hidden these weapons in the cave. The sword was a fine one. It had belonged to Thorkild the Mute, who had been killed by Ulv Erikson.

A cave attracts and repels at the same time. It is an opening into the unknown—into a sunless and moonless world, where you might meet your most bitter dreams.

There are often deep holes in the floor of a cave. I had no fire, and I did not dare to explore it without light.

On the way home I hunted for hares, but my luck was not with me. By the foot of the Mountain of the Sun I hid among some bushes, hoping that the hares

443

*Ulv Erikson, the enemy warrior who had carried away Helga's mother, had also hoped to claim Rark and Helga as his slaves.

would be tempted by the good grazing in front of my hiding place.

No hares came. It was growing late. The shadow of the mountain stretched out over the valley, and the evening breeze was chilly. I stood up, and at that moment I realized that I was not the only hunter on the Mountain of the Sun that day. An arrow sang past my ear. I threw myself upon the ground, expecting a second arrow to follow the first, but none came. I looked toward the mountain, for the arrow had come from behind, but I could see no one. I leaped over the bushes and threw myself down along the other side of them, so that I would be protected from the view of my hunter. That I was the hare for whom that arrow had been intended, I did not doubt. A little less than an arrow's shot above me a pile of boulders made a perfect shelter for a hunter. I put an arrow in my bow and pointed it in that direction.

How long I lay clutching the bent bow, I do not know, but my hands began to tremble. Finally, when the ache in my arms became unbearable, I turned my gaze away from the boulders and, to my amazement, saw the hunter.

It was Eirik the Fox. He had retreated from the boulders by following a dried-out riverbed. He was now below me. He must have thought that I had fled when I jumped over the bushes, for he was walking confidently, making no effort to conceal himself.

Not far away I found the arrow that had missed me. The arrow told me nothing; it could have been anyone's

arrow. I put it in my quiver—that arrow that had destroyed my childhood world. I looked at my shadow—the only companion that I dared trust—and laughed.

On the way back, a thousand plans occurred to me, but none satisfied me. When I entered the hall, I found my uncle seated at the table with Eirik. They both looked up, and Eirik scowled.

"Well, Hakon, how many hares do you bring us?" My uncle's voice was jovial, but his face stern.

"None . . . I saw a fox, though. If it had been within arrow's shot, I would have killed it."

Neither my uncle nor Eirik responded. I placed my weapons at my sleeping place; then, taking Eirik's arrow from the quiver, I walked back to the table. "I found an arrow—an ill-made arrow, a crooked arrow, an arrow like the one Loki killed the god Balder with." I threw the arrow down in front of them, and kept my glance on Eirik's face.

"Where did you find it?" my uncle asked.

"It came flying like a bird—like a crow."

My uncle took the arrow into his hands, and breaking it in two, he said, "Yes, it is an ill-made arrow." He rose and flung the broken arrow into the fire and watched it burn. "And you are an ill-natured boy."

At my uncle's words, a shiver passed through me, and I knew that I had been a vain fool. We were not alone in the hall. Sigurd's wife, Signe, a stupid woman who worshiped her husband as a dog its master, was stirring the soup kettle, which hung over the hearth.

"Pack your things," my uncle ordered. "You are to go with Eirik and stay at his house."

"So long as my father's house stands, I need not work for strangers."

In a few quick strides my uncle crossed that part of the hall that separated us. His arm was lifted and his hand clenched.

I knew what was to come, but I did not stir. The fifth time my uncle hit me, I fell to the ground, and a loud scream opened my tightly closed lips. Blood ran from my nose and mouth. It tasted salty, like the waters of the sea. Twice my uncle kicked me; then my memory stopped. My last thought was, "Now I die."

I did not die. Some of the men had come when they heard my screams, and this saved me. My side ached, and my nose swelled to almost double its normal size; but in a few days I was up and around again.

If I breathed deeply, it felt as though a knife were being stuck in my side, and I could lift nothing. My uncle acted as if I didn't exist, and I knew that he was making plans for my murder. I was too weak to attempt to escape; besides, there was my promise to little Helga. All I could do to save myself was keep close to the hall and to other people.

Seven days after my beating, my aunt told me to go to Thor's Mountain to gather wood. I went to my sleeping place to get my bow and arrows, but she took them from me, saying, "I told you to gather wood, not to hunt."

I thought of appealing to her, but she was not clever enough to respect the rights of any but the strong. Besides, the thought of what her sons would inherit if I were killed made her a willing accomplice to my murder, though I doubt if she herself could have delivered the death blow.

As I looked at Thor's Mountain from the yard in front of the hall, it struck me as being as good a place as any to die. I was so tired, so weak. The yard was empty, for all the men had been sent out to fish. I looked about me and whispered, "I shall never see this again." Here I had played when a child. A cat came out of one of the storehouses, blinked its eyes at the sun, and sat down to wash itself. Tears of self-pity formed in my eyes and rolled down my cheeks. It is hard to die, especially when you are only thirteen years old.

As I passed one of the haystacks, a pebble hit me on my shoulder. I turned, and there was Rark. He beckoned me to come. I ran to obey him, my heart beating with newfound hope at the sight of his face.

"Your uncle and Eirik the Fox, with three of his men, are on Thor's Mountain. They are going to kill you."

I nodded wearily.

"Go to the cave."

Again I nodded.

Rark took me by the shoulders and shook me gently. "Hakon, are you a child that a beating can break you?"

I could not explain to him that it was not the beating, for, to be perfectly truthful, I did not know what had broken my spirit.

"I have a plan. I shall come to you soon. Be brave, little Hakon."

My uncle's blows had not made me weep, but Rark's kindness did. When he called me "little Hakon," the tears came running like a spring rain. Rark let me cry, holding me close to him without speaking.

When my tears had finally stopped, I felt much better, and Rark laughed. "Will you go to the cave?"

"Yes," I answered firmly, and turning my face defiantly toward Thor's Mountain, I decided that it was too early to hunt for my grave.

"You will need a fire and some skins. Stay here by the haystack until I come back."

I sat down on the ground at a spot where the haystack would protect me from view, both from the hall and the mountain. The spirit of life, which so mysteriously had been drained from me, came back now like a tide. The idea of living alone in a cave in the Mountain of the Sun appealed to me. It seemed to be the pleasantest house a boy of thirteen could have.

When Rark returned, he had with him a bearskin and a clay pot filled with embers and ashes. From one ear of the pot to the other, he had tied a piece of rope, so that I could carry it without burning my hands.

"Now run, Hakon. But don't build too large a fire."

I threw the bearskin over my back and picked up the pot. When I turned to say good-by to Rark, he had disappeared.

I took the path which followed the sea until I was near Eirik's hall; then I crossed the island, thinking it better to approach the mountain from the more deserted western shore.

449

It was almost midnight when I came to the cave. The sun had disappeared under the horizon, but a strong red glow burned over the dark sea. I entered my cave and built a fire. The flames' flickering light illuminated the cave's high loft. It was a huge cave and even now, at midsummer, very cold. I wrapped myself in the bear-skin and fell asleep. I dreamed about my father and Thora; but my father had Rark's features, and Thora's face was tear-stained.

12

If you have learned to be alone without fear, then no man can call you weak, though your arms be unfit to wield a sword or an ax. Many a strong man trembles when night has made him a small island in the ocean of darkness and the hooting owl is heard. But the man who is hunted learns that the most lonely place is the friendliest, and that night is better than day.

When I awoke from my first sleep in my new home, I was thirsty. The fire had burned down; in the gray ashes only a few red embers glowed. I rekindled the fire but kept it burning low, for fear that the smoke, which streamed out of the small crevice in the rocks above the entrance, might lead my enemies to the cave. I took my bow and arrows and the earthen pot, and went in search of a spring.

The Mountain of the Sun was much more barren than Thor's Mountain; little soil clung to its sides, and the trees were hardly more than bushes. I was long in finding a spring of clear water. My hunter's luck, however, was with me.

In a tiny valley I saw two hares busy eating. They were not as frightened as the hares that live near the halls, and I was very close to them before I shot my arrow. One of the hares was pierced in the neck and died instantly, leaping only once and then lying still. The other hare looked with surprise at its comrade but did not run away as I had expected.

Quickly I took a second arrow from my quiver and shot again. Being excited, my aim was faulty, and instead of hitting the forepart of the animal, my arrow lodged itself in one of the rear legs. With an arrow protruding from its leg and blood trailing it, the hare ran away.

I had only four arrows. The loss of one was serious to me; but more than this, I did not like the thought of the wounded animal dying a painful and slow death. I spent the rest of the day trailing the poor hare. Finally I found it. The arrow had gotten caught between two branches, and the animal, having only one thought—to push forward—was trapped. A second arrow killed it, and I returned to the cave.

I cleaned both hares and skinned one of them; its rear leg I pierced with a stick and broiled over the fire. The meat of the freshly killed hare is tough; it should hang several days before it is fit for a meal. But hunger made my teeth sharp.

What concerned me most was that the spring was so far away, for my little pot could not hold a day's ration of water; but I gave no more than a few moments' thought to this problem before I was deeply asleep.

My fire and bedding lay near the opening of the cave. How far back the cave stretched, I did not know, but I was determined to find out. The next morning I gathered more wood and built a second fire farther back. From its light I could see that by an ever-narrowing passage the cave went deeper and deeper into the mountain.

Returning to the entrance for more wood, I noticed that it was less smoky there than where my fire was. Excitedly I realized that this meant that there must be another exit to the cave for the smoke to disappear through.

The wood was not dry enough to make decent torches. I had only walked a few steps when the flames died. I crawled to what I judged to be the end of the cave and built a third fire there. At this point the loft of the cave was just above my head, and the smoke made my eyes water, but the mystery of where the smoke went was solved. In the light of the flames I saw a large hole—big enough for me to attempt to crawl into it. But the smoke was too heavy—my eyes were smarting. I retreated from the cave, out into the fresh air.

I thought I might find a second entrance to my cave farther up the mountain, but I looked in vain for signs of smoke from the fires. Far below me stretched the never-ending sea; looking down at it, I saw a small beach. I did not know that there were any beaches on the southern shore of Rogen. The white sand gleamed friendlily up at me, and I started to climb down the mountain, forgetting my search for the smoke. But very soon the mountainside became too steep, and I grew frightened of falling. I was keeping my eyes on the beach—trying to find the best way to descend—when suddenly my feet no longer had rock beneath them. I had fallen into a hole. It was not very deep, and I was more frightened than hurt.

The hole was as deep as I was tall, and my nose tip was level with the ground. I had lost my bow and quiver of arrows in the fall. The bow I found lying at my feet, at the bottom of the hole. As I bent down to pick it up, I smelled smoke!

The rock that formed the floor of the hole was filled with small crevices—the largest being so big that I could push my hand through it—and out of all these was pouring smoke. I had hoped to find a second entrance that I could use to escape through, should my uncle and his men discover the cave. This exit could only be of use to a lizard. Disappointed, I climbed out of the hole.

I looked for my arrows near the place where I had stumbled, but to my surprise, they were not to be seen. The mountain fell sharply away at this point, and carefully, lying on my stomach, I leaned over the edge. Below me, hanging from the branches of a small bush, was my quiver of arrows. The distance was no greater than I could have jumped, had the plateau not been so tiny that I feared falling over the edge.

Without my arrows I would starve, so necessity made me choiceless. Grabbing hold of a protruding rock with both my hands, I slowly edged my body over the side of the mountain. When I had lowered myself as far as my arms could stretch, I let go and fell!

When my feet hit the ground, I bent my knees and fell forward. Except for a scraped knee I was unhurt, and there, facing me, was the second entrance to my cave! A large, gaping hollow in the mountain!

That it was an opening to my cave, there was no doubt, for I could smell smoke. I had to bend my head to enter, but once inside, I could stand upright.

It was a small cave, and from the innermost part of it a tunnel led into the mountain. I started crawling. The first reaches were well lighted. From the tiny openings that I had discovered in the bottom of the hole into which I had fallen such a short time before, shafts of sharp light played upon the floor. I climbed on, upward and deeper into the mountain. Soon my body blocked the lights from the tiny crevices, and the darkest of nights engulfed me.

Several times I bumped my head. The roof of the tunnel became so low that I had to squeeze myself through like a snake. I crawled on and on blindly—my hands were now my eyes. I was frightened and tired, my breath came in short gasps, and had the tunnel been wide enough for me to turn around, I probably would have.

The passage was becoming narrower and narrower, and there was smoke. What if it weren't the smoke from my own fire I was smelling? In the mountains live the dwarfs. They were Odin's friends, but were they mine? I called Odin's name, but no one answered. The tunnel curved slightly. I flung my hand above my head. I touched nothing. Forward, my arm could reach freely in all directions. I saw two eyes of fire staring at me. I gave a cry of fear!

Was this the cave where the Fenris Wolf was tied? And were those his eyes I was staring into? I buried my head in my hands and dared not look up, while I kept saying, "Odin! Odin! Odin!"

Only stillness greeted my cries. I lifted my head. The eyes were still there, but now there were not two, but many. I scrambled forward, my fear gone. The eyes of the Fenris Wolf were the brilliant embers from my fire. I was back in the big cave. I ran to the entrance and out into the sunlight.

I had been only a short time inside the mountain, but now I understood the horror of Hades—of that shadow world for those who do not die in battle.

456

Soon the passage between the two caves became very familiar to me. I moved all my belongings into the smaller cave, since it was safer and less frightening.

I quickly discovered that it was a short climb from the plateau to the beach, and halfway down I found a spring. The beach itself served me with as much driftwood for my fire as I could use. The hearth in the new cave was my special pride. I built my fire in the back of the cave, and the smoke passed through the tunnel and out of the small crevices. Even the biggest of fires caused no tears to come to my eyes, and should anyone find the big cave and discover the passage, he would have to pass through the smoke-filled tunnel and jump over my fire, in order to reach me. I was contented and proud of myself, but soon the wish to see Rark overcame me, and I started to plan a nocturnal visit to my uncle's hall.

13

I planned to visit my uncle during the night, that is to say, during that part of our summer day when the sun for a short time withdraws its face beneath the horizon. As day and night become one in common darkness at midwinter, so does day reign uninterrupted over Rogen in summer. Winter is night and black; summer is day and white. Still, man must sleep. We are not like bears, who can hunt all summer and sleep all winter.

I left the cave while the sun was still above the horizon, walking along the western and most deserted shore of the island. When I reached the foothills of Thor's Mountain, the sun had set. The low clouds that hung over the sea were on fire; the sky above was not blue but white. I was armed only with my bow and arrows. Rark's sword was too long and heavy for me to have taken it along.

I had decided to approach the hall from Thor's Mountain instead of from the sea, because to make one's way from the water's edge to the house, at any hour, was to risk being seen. I believe men's hearts must belong to the sea, for, whether they wish to be consoled in their grief or have their happiness enhanced, they walk to its shore.

I sat down and rested. I needed many things. I had only two arrows left and the scantiest of rags for clothing. But first and foremost I had come in order to find Rark. In the winter he usually slept in the cowshed, but in summer he often slept outside. Before me lay the woods, "the forest" as we called it—though there was not a tree that was taller than a full-grown man. Between the forest and the house stretched a meadow where the cows grazed; the sheep, who were not allowed there in summer, were given the poorer grazing farther inland. I walked through the forest to the edge of the meadow. Now I could clearly see a thin streak of blue smoke coming from the opening in the roof of the hall. I waited in the shadow of the trees until I was certain that no guard had been posted; then I darted forth and ran across the meadow, not stopping until I reached the haystack where I had seen Rark last. I had had an idea that he might be sleeping there, but he was not. Next I searched the cowshed and the smaller storehouses.

The entrance to the large storehouse was directly opposite the entrance to the hall, and I was afraid that someone might hear me when I opened the door. The storehouse was empty, or almost empty, for in the corner were some sheepskins, rope, and ship's tackle.

I was just about to leave when I heard a noise outside the door. I hesitated and then ran toward the sheepskins, burying myself among them. My hiding place had a most unpleasant smell, for the skins had not been cured.

The door opened, and I heard my uncle say, "A flea will make a giant scratch."

Eirik the Fox's voice was high like a woman's, and a shiver ran down my back when I recognized it. "When you want to catch a wolf, you tie a lamb to a pole and hide nearby."

"Maybe he is already dead." But I was sure from the tone of my uncle's voice that he did not believe his own words.

"Why should he be?" Eirik was quarrelsome.

"What is your plan?" My uncle's feigned indifference was obviously an attempt to guard his purse.

"The slave girl Helga, whom you gave me as a present, we will send to the Mountain of the Sun——"

My uncle interrupted Eirik. "I didn't give you the girl."

A curse flew from Eirik's lips, and then some words I could not hear, but they must have angered my uncle, for he said threateningly, "Few men keep a fox as a pet. Beware, Eirik!"

When Eirik spoke again, his tone was as humble as his words. "Sigurd Sigurdson, I have sworn to serve you, and so I shall. All that I own is yours."

"Then what is your plan? Be quick. It is getting chilly."

"My plan——" Here Eirik paused, as though he had wanted to say something else and then thought better of it. "My plan is to post men on the Mountain of the Sun and send Helga to gather wood there. When Hakon sees her, he will come out, and we shall catch him."

"I don't want him alive. I want him dead."

What madness is it that makes a man want power, that makes him wish to rule others with such passion that he will sacrifice all his virtues to achieve it?

"You have my permission to try your plan. And if you bring me his head, I shall reward you for it." With these words my uncle left the storehouse. Eirik followed him and closed the door behind them.

I stuck my head out from under the skins. I was nearly suffocating from the smell. With my fingers I touched my face, and for a moment I saw my own head being exchanged for a gold ring.

My uncle's mentioning that he had felt chilly made me certain that he had returned to the hall, but where had Eirik gone? I opened the door cautiously and peeped out. No one seemed to be about. Quickly I flung the door open and dived round the storehouse and out of sight of the hall.

My heart was beating so loudly in my breast that it seemed to echo in my ears. A dog started to bark. It was my father's dog Trold. (It was my luck that most of the dogs had died during the winter; usually we had ten or more dogs around the hall.) Trold came up to me wagging his tail, much more pleased to see me than I was to see him. I scratched him behind the ears, and he whined gently with pleasure, his tail banging against the wall of the house behind which I was hiding.

I realized that I would have to give up trying to find Rark; it was too dangerous. There seemed nothing else for me to do but return to my cave. No one saw me run across the meadow except a lone cow that with a loud *moo* greeted me as I ran past. Trold had followed me and would not return to the hall; now I was pleased to have his company.

Taking the same path back along the western shore that I had followed on the way out, I thought about my situation. I would have to free little Helga as soon as possible, for I feared that if Eirik the Fox's first plan failed, he might get the idea of torturing little Helga to make me do something rash. Suddenly it struck me that perhaps this was a good time to visit Eirik's hall. I crossed the island to the south of my destination and then turned north.

Surrounding the beach close by Eirik's hall were large boulders, which made very fine hiding places. I ran from behind one to behind another, until I was near enough to the buildings to see if anybody was about. There were seven buildings in all, two halls—the largest being the one my uncle had given to Eirik—and five storage houses. There was no one in sight. Somewhere in one of these silent buildings little Helga slept, but to try to discover which one might be to risk my life.

Drawn up on the narrow beach was an eight-oared boat. It was almost new; the oars and the mast were in it, but not the sails. I put my shoulder to the side of the boat, but I could not budge it. Inside it were some fishing lines and hooks, and these I took. There was also a smaller boat anchored by a big rock, in the shallow water.

Suddenly I heard Trold growl. I glanced up toward the buildings, taking an arrow from my quiver at the same time. A man was coming out of Eirik's hall.

I threw myself to the ground alongside the boat.

It was Harold the Bowbender. He looked up at the sky and then out over the sea. I watched him. He had been a friend to my father and had been along on that unhappy trip to Tronhjem. I remembered, too, that he had followed me out of the hall on that terrible day when I had brought the message to my Uncle Sigurd of the invaders coming, and that he and his sons were the only ones among my uncle's men who had fought to defend Rogen. Harold was now walking down toward the boat. He was unarmed.

With my hand I muzzled Trold, fearing that he would bark. Harold didn't see me, though he passed only a few steps away. Leaning against the other side of the beached boat, he stood motionless, contemplating the sea. I rose and drew the bowstring tight; then, pointing the arrow at his back, I spoke:

> "The tide of luck
> Ran out to sea,
> The hammer struck
> But killed not me."

Harold looked at me with such wonder in his face that I could not help smiling. Then he answered:

> "The grave will speak
> Where a strong man lies,
> Only the weak
> With his fortune dies."

I lowered my bow, and he took me in his arms and embraced me, as is the custom among friends.

We talked much, and I told Harold about the conversation I had overheard between Eirik the Fox and my uncle. Harold promised that he would protect little Helga and that he would—if need be—die for my cause. With Harold, his two sons, Rark, and myself, there were enough of us to handle one of the smaller boats and escape from the island. Harold brought me some clothes, gave me ten more arrows and a pair of shoes. I returned to the cave, where I roasted some hare, and Trold and I had a feast.

14

Tomorrow, that for so long had meant added fear, now was a word of comfort to me. So foolish was my uncle's and Eirik's rule over Rogen that the movement of the sun—time itself—worked in our favor. The tyrant falls, not because he is too weak, but because he is too strong; each injustice that seemingly strengthens his position actually hastens his downfall. The dead body of Bjorn was more dangerous to Sigurd than Bjorn alive would have been. It was a symbol to the weak and the downtrodden, and when they would begin to fear for their own lives, their very cowardice would lead them to perform deeds that a brave man would never stoop to.

The tyrant lives in fear of poison, the knife in the shadow, and the witch's brew. The brave and the just know their enemies as well as they know their friends. The tyrant can only guess at the fear that lives in the hearts of his subjects and, by ever increasing it, hope to escape their vengeance.

Harold the Bowbender had told me that he would come to the cave with Rark when the sun had sunk into the sea for the fourth time after our meeting. During these four days I stayed in the cave, and Trold was a great comfort to me. I imagined poor Helga walking the mountainside looking for me, probably not knowing herself that she was a bait in Eirik the Fox's trap. I kept repeating to myself, "Harold will protect her." But I did not dare ask myself how.

It was Trold's growl that told me of the arrival of Harold and Rark. I had retreated to the back of the big cave, while at the entrance I had built a fire, so that I could see anyone who might enter without being seen myself.

"Hakon!" Rark called.

I ran from my hiding place to embrace my friend. Rark was smiling, and his eyes were moist. Tears are funny guests, as fond of arriving when you are happy as when you are unhappy. Harold's news was better than I had hoped for. For two days Eirik and his men had followed little Helga as she scoured the northern and eastern sides of the Mountain of the Sun. The steeper western and southern faces of the mountain she had avoided, complaining that they were too difficult to climb.

When we heard this, Rark and I nodded our heads in amazement and admiration. Helga must have guessed Eirik the Fox's plot and suspected that I might be hiding in the same cave to which Rark had taken her, when Ulv Erikson was hunting them.

466

Poor Helga was tired, but no one hurt her. My uncle himself called off the search for me and declared me dead. My birthright he claimed for his own elder son. Few believed my uncle's assertion, and seven of the best warriors on Rogen told Harold the Bowbender that if I were alive, they would come to my aid as soon as I unfurled my banner. My old plan of escaping by boat was now discarded, and a new plan was formed —the retaking of Rogen.

It would have been best for us if we could have waited at least as long as it takes the moon to wane and grow full again—but we did not dare. Eirik the Fox had a sharp nose and a coward's heart. He was trying to convince my uncle to ban Harold and four other men from the island. They were to be given a small boat and enough food to reach the mainland. In this way Eirik hoped to get rid of his most troublesome subjects without creating new enemies. Apparently none but Rark and myself needed to fear for his life, for Eirik and my uncle had finally realized how much hate the murdering of freemen aroused.

I thought it best that Rark should stay with me, but he refused, explaining that his escape might spoil our plot. We had decided that we would attack Eirik's hall on the first night of the dark moon. We were to meet at sunset, by those rocks which Eirik hid behind when he shot an arrow at me.

It was sad to say good-by to my friends, for though my dog Trold was good company, I missed the sound of human voices. Once they had left, I returned to my own cave—the smaller one—to sleep, but I could not rest. Dreams and reality turned in my head as if I had a fever. I walked down to the beach and threw sticks into the water for Trold to retrieve—a game he never tired of.

15

A plan should be whole and tight like a cooking pot, and ours seemed to me to resemble a fishing net. Ifs and ifs piled on top of each other make a poor house, but luck always favors the young.

The day following our meeting I stayed in the cave. By night I grew restless and decided to test my luck by hunting. I took my bow and arrows and walked in the direction of Eirik's hall.

A half-moon shone in the light summer sky. I saw no one by the houses, but I dared not go too near. About ten spear-lengths from the main hall, I hid behind a bush. In the pale twilight the houses looked filled with mystery, more as if they were the habitations of elves or trolls than of human beings. The door to the hall opened. A man stepped out and glanced with sleepy eyes up toward the sky. It was Eirik the Fox!

Without thinking, I put an arrow on my bowstring, pulled it back, and with my full strength let the arrow

fly. It struck in the door a little above Eirik's shoulder. He turned in my direction, and I saw the shock and terror in his expression before he fled to safety inside. I sprang up and ran back toward the Mountain of the Sun.

All that night and the next day I worried about my foolish deed. Harold had told me to stay in the cave, so that no one would see me. And what about Rark? Would the arrow that missed Eirik be his death? A man that is governed by his temper is a fool, a piece of driftwood that is at the mercy of the currents and cannot steer its own course.

When the sun rose for the second time after my foolish attempt to kill Eirik the Fox, I could no longer stand being confined in the cave. To my conscience I used the excuse that I had no more food. I climbed to the top of the mountain. From there I could see the big hall, and as I stood there watching it, I dreamed that it was still my father's house and that he still lived there.

Suddenly I saw far below me an army of men— probably all of the men on Rogen—walking toward the Mountain of the Sun. I knew that they had come to hunt, and I knew the name of the hare—Hakon Long-Ears!

I hurried back to the cave and put out the fire; I feared that the smoke might be detected. I waited long, my arm around Trold's neck. At last I heard people calling to each other, and I feared that the dog might bark. But Trold seemed to understand his master's danger, and with that sorrow mirrored in his eyes that only animals seem to know, he looked up at me. I climbed over the hearth, with Trold following, and in through the tunnel. The narrow passage held no fear for me any more, and soon I was in the big cave. Squatting by the opening of the tunnel, in the recesses of the cave, I waited—for what I wasn't sure.

My legs fell asleep, and I stretched them in order to make myself more comfortable. Time passed slowly. Trold kept trying to lick my face, and I—in order to avoid his wet kisses—scratched his ears.

I was just about to return to the smaller cave when something moved at the entrance. I felt all the muscles in Trold's body stiffen, and the hair on his neck rose.

"Why should he be there? We are wasting our time. I think Eirik dreamed that arrow." The voice of Harold the Bowbender was very loud, and I guessed that he had spoken to warn me.

"You can't dream an arrow!" Eirik returned irritably.

"Have you so few enemies that no one but that boy should wish you dead?" The shock of hearing my uncle speak made me tremble.

"Olaf, go inside the cave," Eirik commanded.

Olaf, who was called Olaf the Toothless, for he had lost his front teeth in a fight, replied, "Go yourself, Eirik!" Olaf was quarrelsome; everyone knew that he had no liking for the dark.

"Olaf the Brave!" my uncle said sarcastically.

"And do you know where the cave leads to? Who knows what spirits live in its darkness!" Olaf's voice was shaking, partly from anger, partly from fear.

"Eirik, why don't you go? You are a brave man."

I did not recognize the voice, but its tone must have made Eirik wince, and he made a noise as an animal does when it feels itself being menaced.

"I will go." It was Harold who had spoken, and I drew a sigh of relief, for even though I might manage to escape—by crawling through the tunnel into the smaller cave—the ashes of my fire would make anyone who saw them suspect that this was my dwelling place.

"No, Harold, Eirik will go." My uncle's tone was commanding, not asking.

I saw Eirik very plainly when he entered; then he was lost in the shadows. "It is very big." The tremor in his voice indicated that he would have preferred the cave to have been small.

472

"Walk to the very bottom of it," my uncle demanded very sternly from without.

I could judge from his footfalls that Eirik was moving very slowly toward the middle of the cave. At that moment when he had gained the very center, Trold —who had been so quiet that I had forgotten him— howled. A long, low groan that echoed throughout the cave and sounded like the wailings of the spirits in Hades. A scream of terror answered Trold's howl.

I did not wait to hear what effect this had had on my pursuers. I pushed Trold in front of me into the tunnel, and I returned to the little cave.

Later I was told by Harold the Bowbender that when Eirik came out of the cave, he was so frightened he was speechless. When they returned to Sigurd's hall and Eirik was able to talk, he insisted that he had seen the Fenris Wolf—its eyes as big as shields and burning like fires. Like the fool he was, he kept repeating the story and by that gained many converts for my cause.

The people whispered that the gods had taken pity upon the orphan, and it was said that the Fenris Wolf suckled me to keep me from starving. Harold and Rark were quick to take advantage of these rumors to further my cause. They claimed that the reason I had not been found was that the mountain itself had hidden the unjustly treated son of Olaf the Lame.

16

The sea swallowed up the sun, and the white night came. I left my cave and, followed by Trold, made my way to Eirik's hall. By now, during the darkest part of the night, the fainter of the stars were visible.

Hiding behind a bush, I watched the hall. All was still—an owl hooted, and I trembled. A strange bird, the owl, with its huge eyes, neckless body, and great fear of the sunlight. We had few owls on Rogen, and some of the old people were fond of finding omens in their nightly cry. Many believed that if an owl sat on a house, someone within must die before the moon was full. During that year every house on Rogen should have had a dozen owls on its rooftop to hoot their miserable messages. Why are there so many bad omens and so few good ones? Why does man find so much pleasure in foretelling future calamities and so little in his present happiness? Even at a wedding feast, when bride and groom with eyes shining like bright stars sit at table, the guests are ever fond—while sighing from their well-filled stomachs—of speaking of omens of ill will. The bird will sing when hunger's hand is on its throat, but kings, above their golden horns of mead, will speak only of envy, fear, and hate.

I passed Eirik's hall, and made my way toward my uncle's. The owl followed me, hooting its warning to the world. The night was growing whiter, and the eastern sky was red as blood.

The animal in hiding—even the hare whose heart ever beats in fear—has moments when a strange courage takes possession of it and utterly changes its nature. So it was with me. I walked without fear among the buildings, hardly caring whether I was seen or not.

From the pigpen I heard moans. I opened its low doors and looked in. There lay Rark, his wrists and ankles tied together like a sheep that is about to be butchered.

Quickly I cut the ropes that bound him, but they had been pulled so tightly that Rark's feet and hands were numb and useless. He tried to stand up, but he could only with difficulty get to his knees. I dragged him outside; his face was swollen from a beating my uncle had given him, and he had had nothing to eat for three days. I laid him on the ground by that wall of the pigpen that was farthest from the hall, and went in search of a horse.

My father's old mare was grazing in the meadow, and I ran up to her, hoping that she would play no tricks on me. She was liable to let one chase her for a long time before she would consent to be caught. As if she understood the seriousness of the situation, she stood perfectly still when I came up to her, only turning her head to stare with her big brown eyes at my face. I slipped the halter, which I had found in the stable, over her head and rode her back to where Rark was lying.

In my haste I had not taken a saddle, and it was difficult to get Rark up on the mare's back, but at last I succeeded. Skirting the buildings, I led the horse across the meadow; then I gave the halter to Rark and told him to ride on. He was much too weak and confused to protest. He only nodded his head to tell me that he had understood.

I returned to the buildings. Everything was still and deserted. I sneaked into the hen house and grabbed one of the sleeping hens. Before it had time to make any noise, I killed it; two more I slew in the same manner, but the fourth flew out of my hands. I ran out of the hen house, expecting that the clucking of the hens would awaken one of the men.

Fortunately for me, during the past few days great schools of fish had been sighted near Rogen, and the men had been almost continuously at sea. Now they were tired, and they slept on. From the women I had nothing to fear. It was rare that any of them would rouse herself to investigate a noise. On the whole, they worked longer and harder than the men and would not take on a task which was not normally held to be theirs.

I followed the edge of the forest and ran south, grinning to myself at the thought of my uncle's expression—some hours hence—when he would discover that his prisoner had escaped, and that the cock in his henyard was missing a few of his wives.

I caught up with Rark a little southwest of Eirik's hall, and slinging the hens, whose legs I had tied together, over the mare's back, I took the bridle lead. As we came nearer the Mountain of the Sun, it became increasingly difficult for the mare to find foothold among the boulders. Finally we had to give up. Rark lowered himself down from her back and found that his legs—though weak—could support him. I jumped on the mare's back and rode it to where the boulders stopped. There I took off the bridle, gave the mare a slap on her flanks, and watched her trot homeward.

When I returned to Rark, he was sitting rubbing his ankles. Looking up at me, he said, "Thank you." It embarrasses a fool to give thanks and a wise man to receive them. Though Rark was no fool, I was not wise, so I basked in the fact of having saved my friend's life, like a seal sunning himself on a rock.

With great difficulty and much pain, Rark made his way to the small cave. I threw wood on the fire, and while I plucked one of the hens, Rark told me news of home.

"The day after Harold and I visited you, I was locked in the little storehouse. Your uncle knows very well that I hate him, and he suspects that I might be plotting against him, but his greed prevented him from killing me. Each time he looked at me, he saw not only me but the pile of silver a slave is worth—alive! Several people visited me. Erik the Poet came and sat on the floor in silence, his brow furrowed in concentration over the work of forming his thoughts into words. I really thought that he would never speak, and I was not surprised when he rose—as if he were about to go—without having said anything. But at the door he turned and remarked haltingly, 'I am for Hakon.' Funny man, Erik. He is not stupid, but language is a tool he cannot use."

I had finished plucking the hen. Now I cut it open and removed the entrails, which I gave to Trold. I was very pleased that Erik the Poet was on my side. As a child I had often played tricks on him—not all of them kind or innocent.

"Erik Longbeard came, too. He is a good man to have join us, but I wish he were not so vain about that beard of his," Rark continued. "All the time that he and I were talking, he sat combing his beard or pulling gently at it. Olaf the Toothless came. He said he despised both your uncle and Eirik the Fox, and wanted only to see you get your inheritance back."

I had put the hen into the earthen pot, and it was now boiling away over the fire. "Did you believe Olaf the Toothless?" I asked.

Rark laughed. "Believe him? I would never believe anything Olaf said. If I woke from sleep and Olaf said it was night, I would stick my head outside to make certain. But even a liar will tell the truth sometimes. I believe that Olaf was sent by your uncle, but it is possible that he came by himself because he was afraid. Naturally, I told him that I was a miserable slave who had no opinion but my master's, and no master but Sigurd Sigurdson."

Rark inhaled deeply. "That chicken smells like the food of heaven."

I knew that Rark belonged to the new religion. He was fond of placing the people he liked in heaven, and the ones he disliked in Hades. Thora had also believed in the new religion, but she believed that only heaven existed and that Hades was here on earth. Her religion had been an inner part of her. It left her naked and vulnerable and yet protected her. Rark's religion was a coarse piece of clothing that kept him warm, and he offered it only so much attention as he thought necessary. If it was torn, he mended it. When summer came, he put it away and never gave it a thought until the fall storms again began to howl.

"How did you end up in the pigpen?"

Rark was leaning his head close to the pot, breathing the vapors from the chicken soup.

"I had too many visitors in the storehouse."

"And the beating?"

"Don't you think it might be finished—the hen, I mean?"

"Because of me!" I insisted. "Because my uncle wanted to find out from you where I was."

Rark looked at me with embarrassment. "It is three days since I last ate," he muttered.

I took the pot off the fire, stuck my knife into the hen, and lifted it out of the soup.

17

After Rark's escape, would any of our friends be safe? I had made an agreement with Harold the Bowbender that should I think it necessary to call upon him and the other men who were willing to fight for my cause before the dark of the moon (the night we had planned for the attack), I would build a bonfire on the northern slope of the Mountain of the Sun, at a point where it would be visible to the whole island.

The day after Rark's escape we collected wood for the bonfire, and as soon as the sun was low in the horizon, we set it ablaze. The wood was summer-dry, and soon the flames rose thrice a man's height into the sky.

Quickly we returned to the cave to await Harold the Bowbender. A sheep I had stolen that very morning was being roasted over a fire. As I stared into the flames, I asked myself how many would come. Would there be enough warriors to win a battle, or only just enough for a heroic defeat?

A few minutes after midnight the first arrivals came —Erik Longbeard and Erik the Poet and a young man only two years older than myself, Hakon the Black, whose hair was the color of a raven's wing. These men were from my uncle's hall. Erik Longbeard noticed that I was disappointed and assured me that two others were coming—Thor the Lame and Magnus One-Ear, who were out with the sheep. Both of these men were old warriors, but if their age made them of less value in battle, their wisdom in counsel made up for it. Erik Longbeard offered to go and look for them.

While Erik the Poet and Hakon the Black each carved himself a hunk of roasted lamb and started to eat, I walked outside. The night was clear. A gentle breeze blew from the southwest. I decided to attend my bonfire. I didn't want its message to die down like a cry for help strangled by fear. I wanted the flames to shout defiance at my uncle and Eirik the Fox.

Soon it would be decided who was to be master of Rogen. When I was a child, I drank the tales of valor as a babe suckles its mother's milk, but those tales had neither fear nor pain nor death in them. They resembled reality in the same way that the boats we— as children—made of bark resembled the big fifty-oar ships that can brave the northern storms.

The fire had burned down. Low flames flittered across the blackened wood. I collected several dry branches and threw them on the embers. The fire crackled like a thousand twigs being snapped at once, and I felt the heat of the flames as they leaped skyward. I did not think any of the enemy could be near; still it was not wise to stand too close to the flames and make a target of one's self. Each time I put another piece of wood on the fire, I dived quickly back into the shadows. When the fire again was burning brightly, I decided to return to the cave.

I did not see the man coming up the mountain before he was quite near. It was lucky for me that it was a friend, for he approached so close to me that he could have killed me before I had a glimpse of him.

"Shall we call you Hakon the Fearless or Hakon the Fool?" The speaker was Magnus the Fair, a tall, blond man with a sharp tongue, who had often irritated my father.

"An ill-fitting name, Magnus, is as bothersome as an ill-fitting cloak. Have you come to swear allegiance to me?"

"I have come to unswear my allegiance to your uncle. Will that do?" Whenever Magnus spoke, he smiled, in this way making certain that no one ever knew his opinion. Magnus the Fair was a good warrior and honored for his strength as much as he was feared for his tongue.

"The man who swims with the tide is of little use to me." This was not really true, but my feelings were hurt because he had not said that he would swear his allegiance to me.

"And those who swim only against the currents are fools and of no use to anyone."

The smile lurking in the corner of his mouth made me peevishly angry. "How do you know that the tide will turn? How do you know that my uncle won't remain master of Rogen?"

Magnus thought a moment; then with a broad grin he answered. "Your uncle's friends are bound to him not by friendship but by common crimes. That kind of comradeship is a leaky vessel in a storm. Still, they will not give up without a battle, and who knows who will live to swear allegiance to whom? Hakon the Orphan may yet go to his father's hall without ever having sat in his father's seat."

I was annoyed. I gave my trust so willingly—even carelessly—to those whom I loved and who claimed to love me that I had yet to learn that common advantage is a string in the ruler's bow.

While we talked, we had been walking in the direction of the cave. Outside the entrance sat Harold the Bowbender. When he saw me coming, he stood up.

"How many men have you brought me, Harold?" I asked; and fearing the answer, I said to myself, "No less than six! By the gods, no less than six!"

"Eight, including myself."

"Half of Eirik's men! Oh, that fox has a short tail now!" In my happiness I embraced Harold, who good-naturedly laughed at me and stroked my hair.

"You have more than half his men. He has to count on Olaf the Toothless, Sven the Dane, Erling the Swift, Ragnvald Harelip, and Thorstein the Old. We all know what kind of man Olaf the Toothless is. And Sven, Erling, Ragnvald, and Thorstein are the ones who fled from the battle on Thor's Mountain when your father was slain."

484

"If they were cowards then, will they not be cowards again and betray your uncle as they did your father?" Magnus commented softly.

"What if I pardoned them their betrayal of my father? Wouldn't they welcome an excuse not to have to fight?"

Harold the Bowbender answered pensively, "Eirik the Fox has told them that you mean to avenge yourself upon them, and that if you win, you will offer them to Odin."

I shook my head. I could not understand how anyone could believe that I was capable of doing anything so cruel.

"Come," Harold said, "let me present you to my comrades."

Harold's comrades were the very best men on the island—his sons, Nils and Eigil, Erp the Traveler, Giermund the Handsome, Frode the Peaceful, Halfdan the Carver, and Ketil Ragnvaldson. At Ketil I looked long and searchingly, for his father was Ragnvald Harelip, who had chosen to stand by Eirik the Fox. Ketil became uncomfortable under my scrutiny and blushed.

"A son's crime may make white a father's hair, and a father's deeds give red cheeks to his son's face."

I extended my hand to Ketil. "Each man's life is his own, and none but his own deeds shall speak for him. You are welcome, Ketil Ragnvaldson." Ketil grabbed my hand and pressed it.

"Do you all swear allegiance to Hakon Olafson, to help him regain his father's hall and his father's seat as Chieftain of Rogen?"

As Harold the Bowbender spoke, I looked at all the faces that were turned toward me, and momentarily a fear of not being able to speak overcame me.

"By Odin's raven that hears all, by Thor's hammer that no man can escape, I swear it!" Magnus One-Ear proclaimed. He was standing near the fire, and his white beard had turned red in the light from the flames.

"We swear!" the others growled, like angry wolves.

"You have sworn to be loyal to me. Let me swear, as well, that I will be loyal to you." My voice broke at that moment and became a child's voice. I paused to get control of it so that I could speak with deeper tones. "I swear that on Rogen shall rule only justice. That no man shall fear his tongue nor his thought, but each man shall live in peace."

After my speech there was silence, which was finally broken by Magnus the Fair. "I will swear my allegiance to Hakon Olafson, but remember that an oath by Odin and Thor has been broken before. Keep your own promise as a guiding star and you will never need to ask anyone for his loyalty."

The words that Magnus spoke were true, but I wished that they had come from another's mouth—one that was not twisted in a smile. Was it because of vanity that Magnus could never hide his contempt of others? Or was it a kind of wisdom which ever will isolate and make lonely the man who possesses it?

The sun had just risen above the horizon when Harold called for a discussion of plans. Thor and Magnus One-Ear were in favor of staying on the mountain, to give others a chance to join our side. Nils and Eigil Haroldson wanted to attack immediately. Most of the rest were undecided, for Harold the Bowbender had not spoken yet.

Rark stood close by me but could not offer his opinion, for he knew that there were a few of the men who would close their ears to his voice because of their contempt for a slave. He leaned close to me and whispered in a fierce and unhappy tone, "Hakon, we must attack now for Helga's sake. She is in Eirik's house."

I had forgotten my little sister, my playfellow, and I felt guilty, for I knew that I dared not explain to the others my reason for wanting to attack at once. For a slave woman's daughter, freemen could not be asked to go into battle. "We have not food enough here," I argued instead, "nor weapons. Each tiny movement of the sun in the heaven will aid my uncle. Eirik the Fox is fear-ridden now. Let us give him no time to gather courage."

The young men were on my side, but several of the older hoped that if we waited, my uncle might be forced to give up without a battle.

"Hakon is right." At last Harold had spoken, and with a sigh of relief I realized that the old men would not dare to oppose him. "We will visit Eirik the Fox first. Have we a hall to live in and food to eat, our voices will be stronger, and who knows how big a flock Sigurd Sigurdson will have tomorrow. As long as we are like wolves in the forest, only the brave will join us, but once we sit at our own table, men will flock to take their place on our benches."

So it was decided. In a long file Eirik the Fox's uninvited guests left the mountain. Harold the Bowbender and I walked in front. Harold was singing a song, and I was walking beside him, my heart swollen with pride.

18

As we approached Eirik the Fox's hall, we spread out in a half circle. An arrow's shot from the buildings, we halted. A few chickens walked in the cabbage patch, busily examining the earth for food; otherwise the place looked deserted.

"They have gone!" I exclaimed, and stared with dread at the peaceful buildings, for I feared that we would find tragedy inside.

"It could be a trap," Harold muttered. He stuck his spear into the ground, unsheathed his sword, and walked toward the buildings. I started to follow him, but he ordered me to stay behind.

We watched him. Without knowing it, each of us took a step forward as his figure disappeared around the corner of the hall. We waited a few moments, advanced a few steps, and stopped. Each man had an arrow on his bowstring, and our beating hearts gave

489

the lie to the calm hands on our weapons. Harold reappeared. On his face was a wide grin, and he beckoned
us toward him. With cries of joy the men ran forward,
but a fear in my heart for little Helga closed my lips.

The place was deserted. In their joy at so easy a victory, most of the men did not realize that something
was wrong—where were the women and children?
Harold the Bowbender was a widower, and his two
sons unmarried as yet. But both Erp and Giermund
had wives and children, and Halfdan, a mother. That
Ketil's mother had gone with his father, Ragnvald was
not surprised; but where was Frode's little girl, whose
birth had cost his wife's life?

No one understood what had happened. The men
started to search the buildings. In one of the storehouses, we found Freya the Old. She was a woman so
ancient that no one knew her age. Many of the more
foolish among the people of Rogen feared her and said
she was a witch. The truth was that she had reached
that age when memory leaves and takes with it wisdom.

Poor Freya had hidden herself, for she was not yet
so childish that she did not understand the importance
of the message she had been left behind to give us.
Brought out into the daylight and surrounded by the
angry men, fear made her silent. Magnus the Fair, who
knew her best, took her aside and comforted her, drawing
the story of Eirik's departure from her, word by word.

Everyone had taken for granted that in a fight between kinsmen, women and children were left unharmed.
So much had they trusted in this tradition that they

had left their most precious possessions to their enemies. When they now were told that Eirik had taken
their wives and children as hostages, their hatred became so violent that, had Eirik been among them, not
even the god Odin could have saved his life.

It was decided to send Thor the Lame to my uncle
to demand the immediate return of the hostages. Before he left, I asked him to see if Helga was at my
uncle's. I did not dare demand her return, thinking that
for her own sake it would be better to act as if her fate
did not concern me.

At evening Thor the Lame returned; the women were
with him, but not the children. It was a fox-smelling
plot that Thor had to report to us. My uncle offered

me half the island and Eirik's hall if I would acknowledge him and his sons as the rulers of Rogen. I was to take my uncle's old position, and he, my father's seat, and his sons, my birthright. If we did not agree to this, he would kill the children one by one, beginning with the slave girl Helga—"of whom," he had said, "my nephew seems to be so fond."

My uncle had only given us until the next day at noon to reach our decision, so we held counsel at once. Had my uncle not been so clever as to return the women to their husbands, there would have been no discussion. Women care little for honor and much for their children, but only a fool would judge them ill for that.

As the men and women filed into the hall, I lingered outside, wanting a word with Harold the Bowbender. He guessed my intentions and joined me. "Well, Hakon, and what do you say to Sigurd's message?"

I did not know what to answer and stood silent.

"Will you agree?"

"The right to rule Rogen is not so valuable a prize that I would sacrifice a child's life for it," I finally said.

Harold smiled sarcastically, and for a moment his face reminded me of Magnus the Fair's. I realized that Harold did not believe me, and I wished myself back in my cave, alone.

"But one cannot trust my uncle's word." While I spoke, I looked at my feet, thinking all the time, "This will be your excuse."

"So you don't want to give Rogen to Sigurd?"

492

"No!" I shouted with such passion, as though the word had grown in my body and had become bigger than it and therefore needed to escape.

"Good!" Harold touched my shoulder. "Sigurd Sigurdson is not worthy of being the ruler of the gulls on Grass Island."

"But the children!"

"We will give him no time to hurt them. We will attack tonight."

"But will everyone agree?" I nodded toward the hall.

Harold thought for a moment; then he said, "I don't want *everyone.*"

Quickly he told me his plans, and we entered the hall together. Everyone looked at us, trying to guess from our faces what we had decided. I seated myself in Eirik the Fox's big, heavy chair at the head of the table. Harold placed himself at the end of the bench on my right.

"I have decided, for the sake of the children, whose innocent blood I do not want on my hands, to agree to my uncle's demands."

Most of the men were shocked, the women were relieved, and on Thor the Lame's face I thought I saw a sneer.

Eigil Haroldson sprang to his feet and shouted at me, "Hakon the Orphan shall soon be Hakon the Friendless!" And then—since I did not reply—he ran from the hall, banging the door behind him.

I kept my temper and followed Harold the Bow-bender's advice, which was to send Magnus One-Ear and

Thor the Lame to my uncle with the message that we would agree to his terms. Harold wanted both of these men to go, for he trusted neither of them and suspected that they were spies.

For sentries, Harold chose men whom we were sure we could trust. The rest of the warriors were told that they could sleep, though none were allowed to undress, and all had to keep their weapons within reach. Also, I lay down to sleep—this was part of our plan, for we wanted to ensure secrecy.

As I lay waiting for the men to fall asleep, time seemed to stand still, as it does on the night before a feast day. Patience is the gift of age, and I had as yet received none of it. On tiptoe I sneaked from the hall, stopping first by Rark's sleeping place to awaken him. But to my surprise, it was empty.

Down by the boats, the warriors whom Harold the Bowbender had selected were gathered—Ketil Ragnvaldson, Magnus the Fair, Hakon the Black, Erik the Poet, and Eigil Haroldson. Nils and Harold himself were not there, nor did I see Rark.

Eigil grabbed my hand and said, "I am sorry, Hakon, for my words in the hall."

I smiled. "But you didn't know our plan."

"But I should have known that a son of Olaf Sigurdson would not give away his birthright."

I remembered Harold's face when I had said that the right to rule Rogen was not as valuable as a child's life. And I realized that if you give away your gold rings or your best cloak, you will gain fame for your generosity, but if you give up power, you will be rewarded with contempt.

The men were in good spirit. They were sure of victory though they were outnumbered, for none believed that any of Sigurd's men would fight for him.

"Only Eirik the Fox, Sigurd himself, and Sven the Dane will fight. And Eirik will only fight because Rogen is an island and he can't run away," declared Magnus the Fair.

"And why," asked Hakon the Black, "do you think Sven will fight?"

"Sven is a braggart, and his sword is for sale, but he knows that with the blood that is already on it, no man on Rogen but Sigurd will buy it."

I sat down upon the beach and waited for Harold's return. Soon we saw his figure come striding toward us; he carried himself with the agility of a youth, in spite of his forty-two winters.

Harold looked searchingly about him, as though someone were missing. "Where is Rark?" he asked me, and I told him that Rark was not in the hall and that I did not know where he was. "By Thor, I think I know! We'd better hurry."

Quickly he gave orders to the others. Magnus and Hakon the Black were to approach the enemy from the beach; Eigil, Ketil, and Erik the Poet were to bypass the hall and attack from the north; Harold, Nils, and I would come up from the south. Any sentries we came upon were to be wounded, rather than killed—preferably stunned by a blow with the flat of the sword.

"Are you afraid?" Harold asked me, looking into my eyes.

"A little," I answered.

"Good." He laughed. "You will make a chieftain yet. If something should go wrong, remember my sons. They will serve you well if you will serve them."

I nodded my head. "Chieftain," I thought, and then a little bitterly, "who is chieftain here but Harold?"

Looking up at him walking beside me, his body relaxed, his face serene, and yet his eyes sparkling with life, I felt ashamed of myself for having such thoughts.

19

When Harold and I came within sight of my uncle's hall, we halted behind some shrubbery. Until now we had seen no guards, but we soon saw that there could be no thought of taking the place by surprise, for my uncle had posted sentries.

We were waiting for Nils Haroldson, and Harold was obviously worried, for he had been expecting his son to meet us before now. An owl hooted further inland. Harold put his hands to his mouth, and imitating an owl, he hooted three times. Immediately, the other owl repeated the message. We crawled on our bellies in the direction that the hoot of the owl had come from. Behind a small clump of trees we found Nils.

He told us that Sigurd had not posted sentries by the buildings that faced north (perhaps because he wasn't expecting an attack from that direction, and probably he had too few men that he could trust). We decided to send Nils to get Magnus and Hakon the Black, who were hiding near the beach. They came quickly. Then

497

we all made our way to the forest and from there, north. When we were certain that we had walked far enough north to have passed the hall, we turned east toward the coast. Here we joined Erik the Poet, Eigil, and Ketil Ragnvaldson, and together we started toward the hall.

The northern approach offered the further advantage that a series of small hills made excellent hiding places. From the crest of the one nearest the hall we had a good view of all the buildings; Nils was right—there were no sentries on this side.

"I wonder where the children are," I whispered to Harold. He nodded but said nothing. "We ought to know that first, before we attack." Again Harold nodded his head; then he motioned with his hands for us to retreat from the ridge of the hill.

Huddled together at the bottom of the hill, we held counsel. Ketil Ragnvaldson was for attacking right away, but Harold overruled him. Harold had decided that he alone would approach the buildings and try to discover which one housed the children. His plan was that we should take that house first.

Again we crawled to the crest of the hill, and again we ascertained that there were no sentries that might warn my uncle of our coming. Then Harold climbed down the other side of the hill. We watched him. He was crawling on all fours, taking advantage of each rock, little incline, and bush to arrive unseen.

When Harold had reached the first of the buildings, a small hut used for the hens, I could not bear lying still and useless any longer. Turning to Nils, who lay beside me, I said, "Wait here!" and plunged over the top of the hill. I heard Nils whisper, "No," but I paid no attention. With my sword drawn I followed Harold, imitating his approach. I did not look back until I arrived at the hen house. It was only then that I saw that Ketil, Nils, and Eigil had followed me. For better or worse, the attack had started!

Bent over as if a crooked back could make me invisible, I ran round the corner of the house. In front of me, crouching behind a low stone wall that formed the fence of the pigpen, I saw Harold. Silently I made my way to him and crouched by his side. He looked at me with a little smile, but he said nothing. A big sow came close to our hiding place and grunted loudly. Harold took advantage of this to whisper to me, "Are the others coming?"

"Yes."

Harold leaned his head close to my ear and said, "Tell them to wait by the hen house."

I returned to the hen house. Ketil was already there, and soon the last of our band, Erik the Poet, arrived. I gave them Harold's instructions and then ran back to tell him that we were all there. When I regained the wall of the pigsty, Harold was gone. On all fours I made my way around the corner to find him. He was standing by the western wall of the big storehouse, and I was about to join him when I saw another figure approaching from the northern side. It was Eirik the Fox!

When Eirik saw Harold, he drew his sword from his belt. As we had seen no sentries, Harold was not expecting an attack from behind. I did not give my-self time to warn Harold, but rushed with my sword drawn toward Eirik. He was so occupied with the thought of the easy victory he would have over Harold the Bowbender that he did not hear me before I was only a few steps away from him. As he was about to raise his sword, he was pierced by mine. With a loud scream, he fell to the ground.

Harold turned and looked with astonishment at the dying man lying so close to him. I pulled out the sword. The sight of the blood made me sick. Oh, why does man have a lamb's tongue and a wolf's teeth?

At the death cry of Eirik our comrades came running. Seeing my bloody sword and Eirik's dead body, they gave a cry of triumph.

With their yelling, the need for secrecy was gone; now the more noise we made, the better. We rushed first for the hall, hoping to capture my uncle and thus end the battle. But my uncle was not there. The hall was filled with women and children. Seeing them, I called loudly, "Helga! Helga!"

No one answered me. Among the women I saw my aunt, and I ran up to her. She—seeing my bloody sword—believed that I had come to kill her and drew her children close to her and shrieked again and again. Close by her sat Ragnhild, Eirik the Fox's wife. Pointing my sword at her, I shouted, "Where is Helga?"

Staring with fear-filled eyes at my weapon, dirty with her husband's blood, who she did not know was dead, she replied, "Sigurd took her with him." She said no more, but nodded toward the back of the hall where a small door led to the outside. I ran to the door and threw it open.

Sven the Dane with a spear in hand stood guard on the other side. With my sword I hit his spear so hard that the wooden shaft broke in two, and Sven looked with amazement at the little piece of wood in his hand. Then throwing it aside, he fled.

I do not know why I ran toward the beach, for in my state I was not capable of thinking clearly. The cove where the big boats were lying was deserted. I swung my sword in the air and screamed, "Sigurd Sigurdson!" Only a gull answered me, but along the coast, running in the direction of the other hall (the one which my uncle had given to Eirik the Fox and later offered to me) I saw two figures—a tall man with a sword in one hand, who was dragging a child with the other.

"Sigurd!" I screamed, "touch her and you die!"

He was too far away; he could not hear me. I could not understand why he was fleeing in the direction of Eirik's hall until I realized that there were not two but three persons; my uncle had a pursuer. An arrow's shot behind him and gaining fast came Rark!

My uncle stumbled, but then his foot found hold again. Ahead of him was a beach, and beyond that the place where the boats were drawn up—the very place where Harold the Bowbender had first sworn his loyalty to me. With panic I remembered that the smallest boat was usually anchored by a rock in the water. If Sigurd reached that, he might escape, taking little Helga with him.

All of this I thought while I ran as fast as I could to catch up with Rark. Here the coast was not sandy but made of stones that had been worn round by the surf, and many a time I fell. Once I bruised my knee so badly that it bled.

Near the point where the sandy beach began, a cliff jutted out into the sea, and for the moment I lost sight of the others. When I climbed to the top of the cliff, I could see that Rark was but a spear's length behind my uncle.

Sigurd let go of Helga, and she fell face down upon the sand. Rark stopped and reached for the girl, while I screamed with my full force, "Look out, Rark!" For my uncle, instead of continuing to flee, had turned around and was now rushing with raised sword at Rark and Helga.

Rark heard my cry. From his half-reclining position —one knee resting on the sand—he managed with his own sword to deflect the blade of my uncle's, so that it hit not his head—for which it had been aimed—but his left shoulder.

My uncle drew back. Rark was on his feet. I could see the blood rushing from his wound. Then I jumped down from the cliff to the sand beach. As I ran, it felt as if my heart were no longer in my breast but beating in my throat. Before me I saw the two fighting men, and beneath me, the wet sand of the beach. Then all of a sudden I stood still.

The fight was over. I saw my uncle's sword fall from his hand and the ugly gaping wound in his neck. Sigurd's face wore that same look of surprise that I had seen on Bjorn's face when my uncle had slain him.

Rark turned toward Helga, but his legs gave way under him, and he fell. Quickly I ran to his side. His wound was clean and deep. I looked for something to bandage it with. My own clothes were of too rough a wool to be used. My uncle was wearing his fine linen shirt, the one which he had bought a few years before in Tronhjem. It was made from a material that comes from the countries far to the south of Norway. I slit it and tore it from my uncle's body.

Helga stood nearby, frightened and trembling. Forgetting everything she had gone through, I told her sharply to go to Eirik's hall for help. She stared at me unbelievingly and started to cry. Then I realized that she probably didn't know that now she would find only friends at that hall. As hurriedly as I could, I explained to her that she was no longer in peril, but that Rark's life would depend upon her swiftness in getting help. She ran away weeping—whether out of fear or relief from it, I shall never know.

I raised Rark's left arm above his head to stop the flow of blood; then I bandaged his shoulder.

Erik Longbeard and Erp the Traveler, sleep still in their eyes, looked at my uncle, who was lying face down in the sand, and shook their heads.

We carried Rark to the hall. When the blood-soaked bandage was removed, the wound itself shone at us like the flower of the poppy plant that blooms in the spring. With skillful hand Erp, who was known as a healer, explored the wound; then a new bandage was made, and Rark was placed—sitting up—on one of the benches.

He looked strange—his face pale, his left arm lifted above the bandaged shoulder, his hand resting on top of his head. Erp laughed and said, "Three or four days you must sit like this. But then, that is small payment for the gift of being able to brag that you sent Sigurd Sigurdson to Valhalla!"

Rark said nothing, but I could see on his face that the words had not pleased him. Soon we were alone in the hall, Rark, Helga, and myself. The rest had gone to my father's hall. I heard one man say "Hakon's hall."

Rark looked at me and then at Helga. "Never brag of having slain a man, Hakon. Life is holy, and even the foulest of men has once been a child and worthy of love."

Helga was sitting close to me, and my right arm was resting on her shoulder. "I killed Eirik the Fox," I said. To my surprise, the tone of my voice was sad. Helga reached out her hand and touched my forehead, and without knowing why, I thought of my stepmother, Thora.

Rark closed his eyes. The loss of blood was making him sleepy. I took Helga's hand in mine. Suddenly her voice echoed in the deserted hall, "You are master of Rogen, Hakon!"

Impatiently I put my finger to my mouth to remind her that Rark needed rest.

"You have gotten your birthright back!" she whispered, excited, as if—only now—she realized what had happened.

"Birthright," I repeated. But as I thought of Rark's birthright, of Helga's, and of Gunhild's, the word itself seemed to mock me. I will sail Rark back to his own country, and fetch Gunhild from Ulv Hunger's house and give her her freedom. All of a sudden, these thoughts were not wishes—dreams—but certainties, for now I was Hakon of Rogen, as my father had been Olaf of Rogen, a chieftain who could forge out of his dreams deeds that poets would sing of.

"Come!" Eagerly I took Helga's hand, and we walked outside. The sun had risen, and the crest of Thor Mountain was blood red.

Turning toward it, I said, "By Thor, by my father's memory, I promise that I shall bring back to Rogen Gunhild, who suckled me when I was born, and give her her freedom! By Odin, I swear that I shall take Rark back to his home!"

Then searching for words, I added in a tone less defiant, "And to his children."

I looked out over the sea, the path that leads to all adventures; the wind had died and the waters appeared solid like the rock of the mountain. Helga, too, was looking at the sea; she shuddered and pressed my hand. I turned to her and touched her hair, which was short-cropped in the manner of slave women. "You must let your hair grow."

Helga's eyes were filled with tears.

"Why are you crying, Helga?" I exclaimed, for tears in a woman's eyes fill a man with guilt and shame and, therefore, make him angry.

"I am not a slave," Helga said with a slow and wondering voice, and then almost triumphantly she repeated the words: "I am not a slave!"

Suddenly the wind came up. The sea changed; it moved like a giant serpent.

"That is everyone's birthright, his freedom, and the gods have only one message to us, that we must live."

The world turns and the world changes,
But one thing does not change.
In all my years one thing does not change:
The perpetual struggle of Good and Evil.

by T. S. ELIOT

Interpreting the Saga of Hakon

1. Hakon recounts: "Like many weak people's, my uncle's cruelty was dictated by his fears." How is this shown to be true?

2. Why did Sigurd want Hakon to be killed "accidentally"?

3. What did Hakon mean on page 446 when he spoke of his shadow as "the only companion I dared trust . . ."?

4. What likenesses and differences can you find in Sam's experiences in living off the land in *My Side of the Mountain* and those of Hakon in the cave?

5. What incidents brought about the decision to fight for Rogen rather than to try to escape from it?

6. For what reasons did the men of Rogen join Hakon?

7. When Hakon asked if Magnus the Fair had come to swear allegiance to him, Magnus responded that he had come to "unswear his allegiance to Sigurd." Tell what he meant by this statement. Do you think he was justified in this attitude?

8. Though little blood was shed in the retaking of Rogen, it was a decisive victory. What contributed to such a complete victory?

9. Why did Sigurd take Helga with him?

10. How did Hakon feel about winning his birthright?

11. Name people who helped Hakon most, and how they did so. What did Hakon learn from them that would help him become a better leader?

12. One of the outstanding character traits of Hakon was his awareness that he had much to learn. Recall

incidents and statements that show this side of his character.

13. What kind of chieftain do you think Hakon will be? Support your opinion with statements and actions by Hakon that lead you to feel as you do about his future.

14. How did the author make you feel the importance of the sea in the lives of the people of Rogen?

What's in a Name?

Erik Haugaard has chosen names for his characters that denote their personality or some other trait. What can you guess about the following men, using their names as clues?

Harold the Bowbender	Erp the Traveler
Eirik the Fox	Giermund the Handsome
Lief the Lonesome	Frode the Peaceful
Thorkild the Mute	Halfdan the Carver
Erik Longbeard	Ragnvald Harelip
Erik the Poet	Ketil Ragnvaldson
Thor the Lame	Olaf the Toothless
Magnus One-Ear	Erling the Swift
Magnus the Fair	Thorstein the Old

Hakon, as a child growing up under his uncle's rule, was called Hakon the Orphan. Several times during the story he was referred to by other names. What circumstances prompted the following names for him?

Hakon Long-Ears	Hakon Olafson
Hakon the Friendless	Hakon of Rogen

Appreciating an Author's Skill

Hakon's saga offers much to think about, due in part to the author's expressive way of stating observations about human nature. Some of these are given below. Read again the circumstances leading up to each one. Then tell briefly what you think each person meant when he made the observation. The page on which each appears is given in parentheses.

1. Foolborn, they strut around like geese in the farmyard, who think their fate will be better than that of the hens. (page 431)
2. "When you want to catch a wolf, you tie a lamb to a pole and hide nearby." (page 460)
3. Tears are funny guests, as fond of arriving when you are happy as when you are unhappy. (page 466)
4. A man that is governed by his temper is a fool: a piece of driftwood that is at the mercy of the currents and cannot steer its own course. (page 470)
5. It embarrasses a fool to give thanks and a wise man to receive them. (page 478)
6. Rark's religion was a coarse piece of clothing that kept him warm, and he offered it only so much attention as he thought necessary. If it was torn, he mended it. When summer came, he put it away and never gave it a thought until the fall storms again began to howl. (page 480)
7. Oh, why does man have a lamb's tongue and a wolf's teeth? (page 500)

The mythology of the North (Sweden, Denmark, Norway, and Iceland) was recorded in two collections called the Eddas. The Elder Edda is in poetry and dates back almost a thousand years (1056). The Younger Edda is in prose and is over three hundred years old (1640). Quoted below are several passages from the Elder Edda in which the men of the North wonder at their world. The story of Hakon took place at about the same time these men were wondering thus:

before creation . . .

It was Time's morning,
When there nothing was;
Nor sand, nor sea,
Nor cooling billows.
Earth there was not,
Nor heaven above.
The Ginungagap* was,
But grass nowhere.

before order . . .

The sun knew not
Where her hall she had;
The moon knew not
What might he had;
The stars knew not
Their resting-place.

about men . . .

Gates all,
Before in you go,
You must examine well;
For you cannot know
Where enemies sit
In the house before you.

*abyss before the world

More Books to Read

HAUGAARD, ERIK CHRISTIAN. *A Slave's Tale.*
Boston: Houghton Mifflin Company, 1965.

A sequel to the award-winning *Hakon of Rogen's Saga.* This tale is told by Helga, the child of the slave who mothered Hakon when his own mother died. It carries Hakon and Helga into adulthood.

ORMONDROYD, EDWARD. *Time at the Top.*
California: Parnassus Press, 1963.

A piece of science fiction in which Susan takes an elevator to the top floor of her apartment building and finds herself back in the 1880's.

PEARCE, PHILIPPA. *A Dog So Small.*
Philadelphia: J. B. Lippincott Company, 1963.

Ben, a boy of London, dreams day and night of only one thing—a dog of his own. This dream dog becomes so constant a companion that when a real dog comes into his life, Ben is not quite ready for it.

RICH, LOUISE. *The First Book of the Vikings.*
New York: Franklin Watts, Inc., 1962.

An imaginatively written history of the Viking people that includes details about their housing, customs, clothing, education, and laws.

SHARP, MARGERY. *Miss Bianca.*
Boston: Little, Brown and Company, 1962.

Ambassadress of good will from mice to men, Miss Bianca, of *The Rescuers* fame, leads a mission to rescue a little girl who is trapped in the Diamond Palace of the cruel Grand Duchess.

6 7 8 9 10 11 12 13 14 15 16 17 18 19 20 21 22 23 24 25   R   70 69